THE INDEX

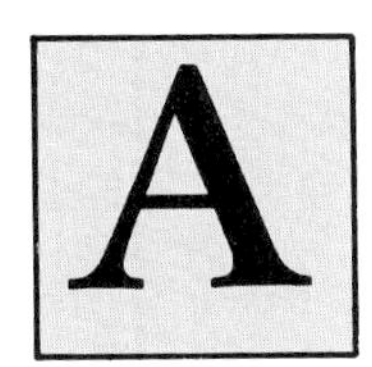

aardvark **5** 298-9; **6** 304, *310*, 311, 316
aardwolf **1** 28; **2** *100-1*, 102, 107
abalones **45** 2674, 2680, *2697*, 2698-9; **46** *2704*
Abbott's booby **17** 993, 994
Abdim's stork **17** 1011, 1012
Abida **47** *2818*
Ablattaria **42** 2472
Abralia **48** 2863
Abraliopsis **48** 2863
  atlantica **48** 2861, 2863
  chuni **48** *2854*
Abraxas grossulariata **44** *2604*, 2609
Abrocoma **5** 289
Abrocomidae **5** 277, 289
Abruzzo chamois **10** *542-3*
Abruzzo National Park **51** 3002, *3012-13*
Aburria pipile **19** 1088
Abyssinian ground hornbill **22** 1278
Abyssinian hyrax **6** 313
Abyssinian roller **22** 1261
Acadian flycatcher **23** 1321
Acantharia **50** 2991
Acanthaster planci **36** 2121, *2132*
Acanthinula aculeata **47** *2818*
Acanthisitta chloris **22** 1316
Acanthiza katharina **24** 1398
Acanthizidae **24** 1398
Acanthobdella peledina **50** 2958
Acanthobdellae **50** 2958
Acanthocephala **49** *2934*
Acanthochitona communis **45** 2684, *2688*
Acanthochitonida **45** 2684, 2686, 2688
Acanthocinus
  aedilis **42** 2506, *2512*
  griseus **42** 2512
acanthodians **31** 1807
Acanthodoris pilosa **47** 2790
Acanthophis antarcticus **28** 1667
Acanthophthalmus kuhlii **32** 1894
Acanthos falcata **40** *2398*
Acanthumus **35** 2067
Acanthuridae **35** 2067
Acanthurus **35** *2065*
Acari **38** 2241; **39** 2293, 2295
accentors **24** 1381-2, 1383
Accipiter **18** 1070
Accipitridae **18** 1057, 1070
Accipitrinae **18** 1070
Acerentomon doderoi **39** *2329*
Achatellinacea **47** 2817, 2818
Achatina
  achatina **47** *2820*
  fulica **47** *2804*, 2817
  maculata **48** *2821-2*, *2829*
Achatinacea **47** 2817, 2818; **48** 2821
Acherontia atropos **44** *2596*, 2624
Achinata fulica **48** *2821*
Achorutes nivicola **39** 2331
Acilius sulcatus **42** *2465*
Acineta **50** *2999*
Acipenser **31** 1856
Acipenseridae **31** 1856
Acipenseriformes **31** 1856
Acleioprocta **47** 2799
Acrocinus longimanus **42** *2510-11*, 2513
Acroloxidae **47** 2806
Acroloxus **47** 2806-7
Acrotelsa collanis **39** *2328*
Acrothoracica **37** 2174, 2177
Acrotrichis thoracica **42** *2465*
Acryllium vulturinum **19** 1101
Acteon **45** 2680
  punctostriatus **47** 2771
  tornatilis **47** *2768*, 2770-1, *2774*
Acteonidae **47** 2767, 2770, *2771*
Actiniaria **49** 2889, 2893
Actinoceratoidea **48** 2853

ABOVE The timid, nocturnal 11-banded armadillo inhabits an underground burrow.

Acmaeidae **45** 2697
Acochlidioidea **47** 2767, 2775
Acochlidium amboinense **47** 2767, 2769-70, 2775
Acoela **49** 2905, 2908
Aconaemys fuscus **5** 289
acorn barnacles **36** 2147, *2156*; **37** 2174, *2177*, *2179*
acorn worms **50** 2965, 2971, *2973*
acouchi **5** 282, 289
Acrania **35** 2090
Acrida mediterranea **40** *2365*
Acridoidea **40** 2369, 2376
Acridoxena hewaniana **40** *2365*
Acris **30** 1795
Acrobates pygmaeus **11** 627
Acrochordidae **28** 1621, 1626
Acrochordis javanicus **28** 1626
Actinophrys **50** *2990-1*
Actinopoda **50** 2991
Actitis hypoleucos **19** 1135
Actophilornis africana **19** 1123
Actornithophilus patellatus **41** 2428
Aculeata **42** 2516; **43** 2529
aculeate wasps **43** 2529
Adacna **48** 2845, 2847
Adalia bipunnata **42** 2472, *2483*
addax **9** *484*, 486, 502
Addax nasomaculatus **9** 502
adders **28** 1669, *1672-3*, 1674-5
Adelie penguin **16** *936*, 938, *940*, *942-5*, *949*
  classification **16** 949
  distribution **16** 944, 948
Adenophorea **49** 2925
Adephaga **41** 2456, 2458; **42** 2461, *2462*
adjutant stork **17** 1011, 1012, 1015
advanced snakes **28** 1640
Aechmophorus occidentalis **16** 960
Aedes **45** 2648-9, 2650
  aegypti **45** *2644*, 2650, 2652
Aegeria vespiformis **44** *2611*
Aegithalidae **24** 1403
Aegithalos caudatus **24** 1403
Aegithina tiphia **23** 1360
Aegolius funereus **20** 1199
Aegotheles cristatus **21** 1214
Aegothelidae **21** 1206, 1214
Aegypinae **18** 1070
Aegyptopithecus **15** 894
Aenides **30** 1750
Aeolidacea **47** 2786, 2799-2800
Aeolidia papillosa **41** 2678, **47** 2800
Aeolidiella sanguinea **47** *2802*
Aeolidiidae **47** 2800
Aeoliodacea **47** 2792
Aeolis papillosa **47** *2774*
Aeoliscus **34** 2000
Aeolosoma **50** 2946-7, 2952
Aeolosomatidae **50** 2952
Aepyceros melampus **9** 532
Aepyprymnus rufescens **11** 642
Aeronautes saxatilis **21** 1218
Aeschna
  cyanea **40** *2355*
  grandis **40** *2353*, 2362
Aesculapian snake **28** 1645, *1660-1*
Aeshnoidea **40** 2351
aestivation process **30** 1753
Aethopyga siparaja **24** 1417
Afghan tortoise **26** 1542, 1544
Afrenulata **50** 2971
Africa, national parks **51** 3002-4, *3015-24*
African...
  armadillo lizard **27** 1565
  armyworm **44** 2591
  ass **6** 340, 341, 344
  banded jewel fish **35** *2050*
  bay owl **20** 1194
  black oystercatcher **19** 1125
  buffalo **6** 307; **8** 463, 467-71
  bulbul **23** 1359
  burrowing frogs **30** 1776
  burrowing snake **27** *1620*
  cichlids **35** *2051*
  civet **2** 85, *97*
  clawed toad **30** 1763, *1764-7*, 1769
  climbing mouse **5** 254, 261
  crested porcupine **5** *272*, 275
  darter **17** *978*, 990
  devil's flower mantid **40** *2398*
  dormouse **5** 270
  driver ants **43** 2559
  dung beetle **42** *2497*
  dwarf crocodile **29** *1684*, 1685,

1691, 1693
dwarf kingfisher **21** 1252
elephant **6** *317-330*
classification **6** 324
extinction threat **6** 330; **51** 3024
epauletted bat **12** *694*
eye worm **49** 2925, 2933
fat mouse **5** *261*
finfoot **19** *1104*, 1114
fish eagle **18** 1070, 1072, *1073*
forest shrew **12** 661, 662
freshwater leech **50** 2956, *2957*
giant snail **47** 2817
golden cat **3** 154; **51** *3021*
golden oriole **25** 1465
grey parrot **20** 1165, 1168, *1169*
ground squirrel **4** 232
harrier-hawk **18** 1070, 1072
hornbill **22** 1275
house gecko **27** 1569
hunting dog **1** 32; **2** 119
jacana **19** 1123
land snail **45** 2677; **48** *2829*
leaf fish **35** 2044
linsang **2** 89
lungfish **31** *1848-9*, 1850-1, *1852*
migratory locust **40** *2377, 2378, 2379*
mole-rat **5** 273, 277, 284, 295
mongoose **13** 740
mud turtle **26** *1524*
open-bill stork **17** 1012-13
panchax **33** *1974*
pitta **22** 1314
porcupine **5** *273-4*
pouched rat **5** 254
pygmy falcon **18** *1055*, 1079, 1080
pygmy goose **18** *1047*, 1052
pygmy kingfisher **21** 1253
pygmy squirrel **4** 222
river martin **23** 1343, 1345
rock hyrax **1** 18
rock python **28** *1632-3*, 1637
rock rat **5** 273, 277, 289
rubber frogs **30** 1786
rufous sparrow **25** 1455
sheet-web spider **38** *2278*, 2279
silverbill **25** 1453
skimmer **20** 1145
skink **27** 1596
spoonbill **17** 1018, 1020
squirrel **1** *15*
swallow-tailed kite **18** 1070
swamp rat **5** 254, 261
termite **41** *2401*
tiger heron **17** 1007
whip sepiolid **48** 2855, 2860
white cheeked otter **1** 55
wild cat **3** 139
wild dog **3** *126*, 132
Afropavo congensis **19** 1096
Agama agama **27** 1585
agamas **27** *1563*, 1565, *1583-5*
agamid lizards **27** 1585
Agamidae **27** 1585
Agamodon anguliceps **27** 1616
Agaonidae **42** 2516
Agaontidae **43** 2521
Agapornis personata **20** 1168
Agathiphagoidea **44** 2595, 2599
Agelaius phoenicus **24** 1440
Agelas oroides **48** *2878*
Agelastes niger **19** 1101
Agelenidae **38** 2263
agile frog **30** 1775, *1776*, 1778
agile gibbon **15** 842, 848
agile mangabey **14** 814-15, 816
Agkistrodon **28** 1669
Aglais urticae **36** *2103*; **44** 2633, *2634*
Agleaactis cupripennis **21** 1228
Aglyptodactylus madagascariensis **30** 1785
Agnatha **31** 1809, *1815-24*
Agopanthia **42** 2512
agouti **5** 277, 282-3, *285*, 289
Agouti **5** 289
Agoutidae **5** 277, 289
Agrias claudia **44** *2634*
Agriocharis ocellata **19** 1101
Agriolimax **48** 2825
reticulatus **47** 2817; **48** *2825*
Agrion puella **40** *2355*
Agrotis segetis **44** 2624
Ahaggar hyrax **6** 313
Ailuridae **1** 28;**2** 67-8
AILURIDS **1** *57-60*; **2** *67-8*
Ailuroedus crassirostris **25** 1476
air-breathing catfish **32** 1911-3
airsac catfish **32** 1912
Aix **18** 1052
Akera bullata **47** *2778, 2779*
Akeridae **47** 2767, 2778
Akis **42** 2490, *2491*
Alabama waterdog **30** 1743, 1745
Alabatidae **33** 1962
Alabes **33** 1962
Alaska blackfish **33** *1922*, 1937-8
Alauda arvensis **23** 1334
Alaudidae **22** 1303; **23** 1334
albacore **34** 2040
albatrosses **16** 908; **17** *962-71*
classification **17** 971
distribution **17** 963
Albert's lyrebird **23** 1325, 1329
Albula vulpes **32** 1872
Albulidae **32** 1872
Alburnus alburnus **32** 1894
Alca torda **20** 1148
Alcae **20** 1148
Alcedininae **21** 1253
Alcedo **21** 1253
Alcelaphini **8** 434; **9** 483-97
Alcelaphus **9** 490
Alces alces **7** 396, 418
Alcidae **20** 1148
Alciopidae **49** 2939; **50** 2942
Alcyonacea **49** 2889, 2900-1
Alcyonaria **47** 2796
Alcyonium
acaule **49** *2900*
digitatum **47** 2796
Aldabra giant tortoise **26** 1544, 1545
alder flycatcher **23** 1321
alderflies **39** 2311; **43** *2566-8*, 2570
Alderia **47** 2777-8
Alectoris rufa **19** 1096
Alectura lathami **19** 1088
Aleochara curtula **42** 2468, *2473*
Aleopcephalidae **33** 1937
Alepisauridae **33** 1946
Alepisaurus ferox **33** 1946
Aleutian ribbed top shell **46** 2703
alewife **31** 1824
Aleyrodidae **41** 2438, 2450
alfonsinos **34** 1988-90
algae **49** 2894-5, 2899
flatworm symbiosis **49** 2908
reef building **49** *2894-5*
algae eaters **32** 1894, 1907
Alianthus moth **44** 2624, *2627*
Alicella gigantea **37** 2203
Alle alle **20** 1148
Allegheny mountain salamander **30** 1751
Allenopithecus nigroviridis **14** 816
Allen's bush baby **13** 748
Allen's swamp monkey **14** 816, 820
Alligator
mississippiensis **29** 1685
sinensis **29** 1685
alligator gar **31** *1808*
alligator lizard **27** 1601-2, 1603
alligator snapping turtle **26** 1533, *1535-6*
Alligatoridae **29** 1685
alligators **1** 11; **29** 1691, 1692, *1693-4*
classification **29** 1685
distribution **29** 1682
origins **29** 1682
allis shad **32** 1889, 1890
Allomyrina dichotomous **42** 2500
Allonais paraguayensis **50** 2946
Alloteuthis
media **48** 2861
subulata **48** 2861, *2867*
Allotopus rosenbergi **42** 2502, 2503
Alopex **3** 127
Alopias **31** 1839
Alopochen aegyptiacus **18** 1044
Alosa **32** 1890
Alouatta **13** 774
alpaca **7** *386*, 387, 388
Alpheus **37** *2211*
alpine accentor **24** *1381-2*, 1383
alpine chamois **10** *541*, 548
alpine chough **25** 1495; **51** 3013
alpine ibex **10** *552*, 555
alpine marmot **4** *220*, 221, *224-5*, 226
alpine newt **29** *1704*, 1729, *1737*, 1738; **30** *1746*
alpine pika **4** *202*, 204, 207
alpine salamander **29** *1725*, 1728, 1729
alpine swift **21** *1216*, *1217*, 1218, 1222-3
altai pika **4** 204
Alutera scripta **35** 2082
Alveolinids **50** *2986*
Alytes obstetricans **30** 1760
amakihi **24** 1435
Amami rabbit **4** 209, 214
Amandava amandava **25** 1453
Amastridae **47** 2819
Amazon ants **43** 2529, *2562*, 2564
Amazon dolphin **10** *585*, 586, 593
Amazon kingfisher **21** 1252, 1259
Amazon leaf fish **35** 2044-5
Amazon parrots **20** 1165, 1168, 1170
Amazona **20** 1168
Amazonian angelfish **35** *2052-3* *2055*
Amazonian manatee **6** 314, 316; **51** 3038
Amazonian umbrellabird **23** 1323
amber snails **47** *2804*, 2817, *2819*, 2820
ambidextrous cricket **40** 2370
Amblipygi **38** 2241, 2252
Amblyceps **32** 1913
Amblycera **41** 2428
Amblycipitidae **32** 1913
Amblyornis **25** 1476
Amblyrhynchus cristatus **27** 1579
Amblysomus hottentotus **11** 655
Ambylopsidae **33** 1948
Ambystoma **29** 1722
Ambystomatidae **29** 1713, 1722
Ameles abjecta **40** 2391, 2400
Amerianna carinata **47** 2807
American...
alligator **29** 1685, *1686*, *1693-4*
army worm moth **39** *2296*
bat star **46** 2715
black oystercatcher **19** 1125
box turtle **26** *1524*
flagfish **33** *1972*, *1975*, 1978
red lynx **3** 139, *142*, 143
red salamander **30** 1751
redstart **24** 1431, *1432*
sheep **10** 563, 566-7, 570
swallow-tailed kite **18** 1073
West Coast limpet **46** 2701
white pelican **17** 980, 983
Americas, national parks **51** *3002-4*, *3033-44*
amethystine python **28** 1633
Amia calva **31** 1856
Amieva amieva **27** 1603
Amiidae **31** 1856
Amiiformes **31** 1856
Amistad Biosphere Reserve **51** 3002, 3004, *3044*
Amitermes meridionalis **41** *2424*
ammocoetes **31** 1818, 1823
Ammodorcas clarkei **9** 529
Ammodytidae **34** 2033
Ammondytes lanceolatus **34** 2033
ammonite molluscs **45** 2670, *2671*
Ammonites **48** 2853-5
Ammonoidea **48** 2853
Ammophila sabulosa **43** *2529*, 2534, *2536*, 2540
Ammotragus lervia **10** 570
Amoeba **50** 2989, 2991
proteus **50** *2977-8*, 2991, *2997*
amoebas **50** *2977*, *2988-9*
classification **50** 2991
Amoebida **50** 2991
amoebocytes **48** 2877
Amorphochilus schnablii **12** 709
Amphiascus **37** *2168*
AMPHIBIANS **26** *1501-3*; **29** *1696-1740*; **30** *1741-1800*; **31** *1806*
blood system **29** 1701
classification **26** *1507*; **29** 1701
evolution/origins **29** 1698-1700
food/enemies **29** 1703-4
reproduction **29** 1704, 1706
senses **29** 1701-2
social life **29** 1706
amphibious clingfish **33** 1962
Amphibola **47** 2806
Amphibolidae **47** 2805, 2806
Amphilonche elongata **50** *2970*
Amphilycus androphorus **36** 2132
Amphipoda **37** 2203
AMPHIPODS **37** 2182, *2188*, *2190-1*, *2203-8*
Amphiprion **34** 2024
percula **34** 2031
Amphisbaena alba **27** 1616
amphisbaenans **26** 1510; **27** 1615, 1616
Amphisbaenidae **27** 1616
Amphitetrus pelagicus **48** *2866*
Amphiuma **30** 1745

amphiumas **29** 1713; **30** *1741-2, 1743*, 1745
Amphiumidae **29** 1713; **30** 1745
Ampulicidae **43** 2524
Amur falcon **19** 1083
Anabantidae **35** 2070
Anabas testudineus **35** 2068, 2070
Anablepidae **33** 1978
Anableps **33** 1978, *1972*
anaconda **27** 1618; **28** *1624*, 1635-6, *1640*
  classification **28** 1637
  distribution **28** 1629
Anacridium aegyptium **40** 2369
Anactinothrips gustaviae **41** 2428
Anadara grandis **48** 2834
Anadoroidea **47** 2786
Anajapygidae **39** 2333
Anamesia **40** *2392-3*
Anamorpha **39** 2307
Anaplasma **50** 2976
Anaplectes melanotis **25** 1459
Anarhichadidae **35** 2056
Anarhichas **35** 2056
Anarhyncus frontalis **19** 1125
Anas
  acuta **18** 1047
  clypeata **18** 1047
  crecca **18** 1047
  penelope **18** 1047
  platyrhynchos **18** 1047
  querquedula **18** 1047
Anaspidea **47** 2767, 2778
Anastomidae **32** 1908
Anastomus lamelligerus **17** 1012
Anathana ellioti **13** 730
Anatidae **18** 1030
Anatini **18** 1030, 1047
Anatis ocellata **42** 2484
Anatolian chamois **10** 548
Anchitherium **6** 333
anchovetta **32** 1890
anchovies **32** 1886, *1889*, 1890, *1940*
ancient murrelet **20** 1148
ancient sand shrimps **36** 2147; **37** 2169
ancient trap-door spiders **39** 2281, 2283
Ancilla glabrata **46** 2755
Ancula gibbosa **47** 2787-90
Ancylastrum sumingianum **47** 2816
Ancylidae **47** 2805, 2816
Ancylocheira octoguttata **42** *2505*
Ancylodoris baicalensis **47** 2785
Ancylostoma duodenale **49** 2925
Ancylus fluviatilis **47** 2816-17
Andean cat **3** *138*
Andean cock-of-the-rock **23** 1322, 1323
Andean condor **18** *1055*, 1056, 1061, 1062, 1064
Andean flamingo **18** 1023, 1024
Andean hillstar **21** *1216*, 1229, 1232
Andean stag-beetle **42** 2503
Andean tapir **6** 351
Anderson's Japanese salamander **29** 1723, 1729
Andigena laminorostris **22** 1290
Andogyrus **42** 2468
Andorhyncus hyacinthus **20** 1168
Andrena cineraria **43** 2539
Andrenidae **43** 2539
Androctonus
  amoureuxi **38** *2249*
  australis **38** *2246*, 2250
Anelytropsis papillosus **27** 1570
anemone fish **34** 2024, *2028-9*, 2031
Anemonia sulcata **49** *2893*
angel sharks **31** 1827, *1838*, 1839, *1840-1*
angelfishes **34** *2018*, 2025; **35** 2048, *2053*, *2064*
  appearance **34** 2027, 2030
  classification **34** *2024*; **35** 2049
anglerfishes **32** 1866; **33** *1957-61*
Angolan black and white colobus **14** *834-5*, 836
Angoumois grain moth **44** 2608-9
Anguidae **27** 1603
anguids **27** 1601, 1602, 1603
Anguilla **32** 1874
Anguillidae **32** 1874
Anguilliformes **31** 1858; **32** *1873-84*
Anguis fragilis **27** 1603
angwantibo **13** 739, 748, *751*, 752
Anhima cornuta **18** 1030
Anhimidae **18** 1030
Anhinga **17** 990
Anhingidae **17** 990
ani **20** 1172, 1175, 1178, 1182
Aniella pulchra **27** 1603
Aniliidae **28** 1621, 1626
Anilius scytale **28** 1626
Anilocra physodes **37** *2202*
animal kingdom **1** 6
anise swallowtail butterfly **39** *2319*
Anisoptera **40** 2350, 2351
Anisozygoptera **40** 2350, 2351
Anna's hummingbird **21** *1216*, 1228, *1237*
Annelida **49** *2935-40*; **50** 2942, 2958
ANNELIDS **36** 2140; **50** 2945, 2948, 2952, 2958, 2966
  classification **50** 2942
  evolution **45** *2670*, 2671
  origins **50** 2950
anoa antelope **6** *306*
anoas **8** *462*, 463, 466, 467
Anobiidae **41** 2456
Anodonta **48** 2833
  anatina **48** *2842*
anoles **27** 1564, 1572, 1579, *1580-1*, 1582
Anolis **27** 1579
Anomala **42** 2498-9
Anomalepidae **28** 1621, 1625
Anomalepsis **28** 1625
Anomalodesmata **48** 2833, 2837, 2848, 2850
Anomalopidae **34** 1990
Anomalops kaptoptron **34** 1989, 1990
Anomaluridae **4** 233
Anomalurus **4** 233
Anomia ephippium **48** 2843
Anomiacea **48** 2837, 2840-1, 2843
Anomiidae **48** 2841, 2842, 2843
Anomma **43** 2529, 2559
Anomura **37** 2213, 2220; **38** 2221, 2223
Anopheles **41** 2444; **45** *2648-50*; **50** *2994-5*
  maculipennis **45** *2649*, 2650, 2652
  stephansii **50** *2995*
anopheline mosquitoes **45** *2644*
Anophylla magnifica **44** *2596*
Aonyx **1** 55
Aotus trivirgatus **13** 774
aoudad **10** 560, 570
Apalis flavida **24** 1394
Apaloderma **21** 1241
Apanteles glomeratus **42** 2516; **43** 2526
Apatosaurus **1** 8
Apatura iris **44** *2634*
ape families **13** 756, 757-9, 760; **14** *837-40*; **15** *841-90*
  classification **13** 728; **14** 839; **15** 842, 852
  primate fatures **12** 718; **13** 722-3, 728; **15** *896-7*
Apeltes quadracus **34** 1993
Apennine chamois **10** *542-3*, 548, 549; **51** *3012-13*
Aphanius iberus **33** 1978
Aphanomyces astaci **37** 2218-19
Aphanopus carbo **35** 2067
Aphidae **41** 2438, 2451
Aphidinae **41** 2451, 2454
aphids **41** *2439*, 2446, *2451*, 2457, *2460*
  classification **41** 2438
  wings **41** *2434*
Aphodhnae **42** 2503
Aphodiina **42** 2503
Aphodius **42** 2492-3
  rufipes **42** 2493, 2503
  subterraneus **42** 2493, 2503
Aphredoderidae **33** 1948
Aphredoderus sayanus **33** 1948
Aphrodite **49** 2937
  aculeata **50** *2941*
Aphroditidae **50** 2942
Aphyosemion **33** 1978
Apicomplexa **50** 2976, 2990-1, 2992, 2993
Apidae **43** *2537*, 2540, 2542-3
Apis **43** 2540, 2543-4
Apistogramma ramirezi **35** 2049
Aplacophora **45** 2674, 2684, *2689*
Aplidium proliferum **35** 2094
Aplocheilidae **33** 1978
Aplocheilus **33** 1978
Aplodinotus grunniens **34** 2033
Aplodontia rufa **4** 233
Aplodontidae **4** 233
Aplotegmentaria **45** 2684, 2689-90
Aplysia **47** 2767, 2769, 2778-9, *2780*
  dactylomela **47** 2779
  depilans **47** 2779
  fasciata **47** 2779
  punctata **47** *2774*, 2779, *2793*
  vaccaria **47** 2779
Aplysiidae **47** 2767, 2778
Anthuridea **37** 2197, 2199
Anthus **23** 1352
Antidorcas marsupialis **9** 529
Antillean ghost-faced bat **12** 716
Antillorbis circumlineatus **47** 2807
Antilocapra americana **8** 432
Antilocaprinae **8** 432, 434
ANTILOCAPRINS **8** 431-4
Antilope cervicapra **9** 529
Antilopinae **9** 529; **10** 569
antilopine kangaroo **51** 3046
Antilopini **8** 434, 444; **9** *517-32*
Antiopella praeclara **47** *2796*
antipa **26** 1553, 1556
Antipatharia **49** 2889
antlers **6** 306-7, *308*
Antrozous pallidus **12** 712
ants **39** 2311, 2326, 2336; **41** 2402; **42** 2516; **43** *2536*, *2551-64*
  classification **43** 2529
  social behaviour **43** *2524-5*, 2554
antshrikes **22** 1313
Anumbius annumbi **22** 1310
Anura **29** 1701; **30** *1755-1800*
Anopla **49** 2920
Anoplura **39** 2311; **41** 2428
Anostraca **36** 2149
Anotopteridae **33** 1946
Anotopterus pharoa **33** 1946
Anourosorex squamipes **12** 662
Anous stolidus **20** 1145
Anser **18** 1044
Anseranas semipalmata **18** 1036
Anseranatini **18** 1030, 1036
Anseriformes **18** *1027-52*
Anserini **18** 1030, 1044
ant lions **39** 2311; **43** *2567*, 2570, *2572*, *2574*
ant mimic jumping spider **38** *2261*
ant-eating spider **38** *2280*
Antarctic cods **35** 2056
Antarctic leopard seal **1** *11*
Antarctic seal **3** 179
Antarctic skua **19** 1140
Antarctic toothfish **35** 2055-6
antbirds **22** 1303, 1313-14
  classification **22** 1303, 1310
  distribution **22** 1308
anteaters **4** *185-9*, *192-3*, 195; **51** 3020
Antechinomys laniger **11** 619
antechinus **11** 619
Antedon
  bifida **36** *2111*; **46** *2720*
  mediterranea **36** 2117
antelope jackrabbit **4** *207*
antelopes **5** 298; **6** 304-5, *306*; **8** *447-60*; **9** *483-540*
  classification **10** 568-9
  national parks **51** *3023*, 3024, 3042
Antennariidae **33** 1961
Antennarius **33** 1960, 1961
Anthipatharia **49** 2899
Anthocoridae **41** 2436, 2438
Anthonomus **42** 2514
  grandis **41** 2456
  pomorum **42** 2506
Anthophoridae **43** *2540*
Anthozoa **49** 2887, 2889, 2893, *2894-5*, *2900*
Anthropoidea **13** 728, 774; **14** 796
Anthropoides virgo **19** 1107
ANTHROPOIDS **13** *755-60*; **15** 897
  classifcation **13** 728
  evolution **13** *727*
Apocrita **42** 2516; **43** 2526, 2529, 2533, 2540
Apoderus coryli **42** *2505*, *2508*
Apodidae **21** 1218
Apodiformes **21** *1215-38*
Aporrhaidae **46** 2720
Aporrhais
  pespelecani **46** *2722*, *2726*
  serresianus **45** *2682*; **46** *2722*
apostlebird **25** 1470-1
Appenine wolf **51** 3012, 3013
apple blossom beetle **41** 2457
apple blossom weevil **42** 2506
apple pygmy moth **44** 2595
apple sawfly **42** 2518
Apseudes spinosus **37** *2196*
Aptenodytes **16** 949
Anurida maritima **39** 2331, *2332*

Apterigidae **16** 925
Apterygiformes **16** 925
Apterygota **39** 2311
Apteryx **16** 925
Apus **21** 1218
aquatic leeches **50** 2958
aquatic moths **44** 2612-13
aquatic oligochaetans **50** 2946
aquatic tenrec **11** 649-51
aquatic warbler **24** *1386*
aquatic worms **50** 2942
Aquila **18** 1070
Ara macao **20** 1168
Arabian camel **7** 381, 388
Arabian gazelle **9** 520, 529
Arabian golden sparrow **25** 1455
Arabian oryx **9** *484*, 490, 499, *501-2*
Arabian ostrich **16** 918-19
Arabian tahr **10** 554, 555, 570
aracaris **22** 1290, 1291
Arachnida **36** 2140; **38** 2241, 2244, 2252, 2255, 2258; **39** 2295
ARACHNIDS **38** *2238-43*, *2670*
Arachnothera juliae **24** 1417
Aramidae **19** 1107, 1117
Aramus guarana **19** 1117
Araneae **38** 2241, 2255, 2258; **39** 2281
Araneomorphae **38** 2258; **39** 2281, 2283
Araneus diadematus **38** *2261*
Araniedae **38** 2258
arapaima **32** *1867-9*
Arapaima gigas **32** 1869
Arapallactus capensis **28** 1645
Arasa borealis **46** 2721
arawana **32** *1868*, 1869
Arbacia lixula **36** 2120
arboreal salamander **30** 1750, *1752*
Arca
  imbicata **48** 2834
  noae **48** 2834, 2835, 2837
  senilis **48** *2835*
  tetragona **48** 2834
  zebra **48** *2832*
Arcacea **48** 2837
Archaeognatha **39** 2311, *2334*, 2335, 2336
Archaeopteryx **19** 1101, 1102
  lithographica **16** *904*, 905
Archaeopulmonata **47** 2801, 2803, 2805
Archbold's bowerbird **25** *1473*, 1474-5
Archeogastropoda **45** 2695, 2697-8, 2700
archeogastropods **46** 2721, 2744
archerfishes **34** 2013, 2025; **35** *2044-5*, *2064*; **51** 3047
Archey's frog **30** 1759
Archidoridae **47** 2795
Archidoris tuberculata **47** 2795
Architectonica
  noblis **46** 2712
  perspectiva **46** *2704*, 2712, 2716
  reevi **46** 2712
Architectonicidae **46** 2712, 2716
Architeuthidae **48** 2861, 2863
Architeuthis dux **48** 2861, 2863
archosaurs **26** 1508, 1509; **29** 1682
Archostemata **41** 2456
Arcidae **48** 2837
Arcocephalus **24** 1394
Arcoida **48** 2835-6, 2837
Arcopecten gibbus **48** 2838-9
Arcos macropthalmus **33** 1962
Arctia caja **44** *2604*, 2624
Arctic char **33** 1924, 1934, *1936*
Arctic cisco **33** 1934
Arctic cod **33** 1950-1
Arctic fox **2** 115, *119-20*; **3** 122, 127, *128*
Arctic hare **4** *202*, 209, 210
Arctic horned octopus **48** 2852
Arctic loon **16** 955
Arctic skua **19** 1139-40; **20** 1142
Arctic tern **20** *1143*, 1145
Arctic walrus **3** *162*
Arctic warbler **24** 1393; **51** 3056
Arctictis **2** 89
Arctiidae **44** 2617, 2624
Arctocebus calabarensis **13** 748
Arctocephalinae **3** 164
Arctocephalus **3** 164
Arctogalidia trivirgata **2** 89
Arctoidae **1** 28
Arctomelon stearnsii **47** 2761
Arctonyx collaris **1** 55
Arcyptera fusca **40** *2365*
Ardea **17** 1007
Ardeidae **17** 999, 1007
Ardeola **17** 1007
Ardeotis kori **19** 1112
Arenaria interpres **19** 1135
Arenariinae **19** 1135
Arenicola marina **49** *2936*; **50** 2942, *2943*
Arenicolidae **50** 2942
argali **10** *561-2*, 563, 566, 570
Argasidae **39** 2295
Argema mittrei **44** *2604*
Argentavis **16** 905
Argentina sphyraena **33** 1937
Argentine pearlfish **33** 1976, 1978
argentines **33** 1923, 1937, 1941
Argentinian snake-necked turtle **26** *1524*, 1531
Argentinian toad **29** 1702
Argentinian vicuna **7** 388
Argentinidae **33** 1937
Argiope bruenninci **38** 2258, *2261*
Argonauta **48** 2870
  argo **48** 2866, 2869, *2870*
  hians **48** 2869
Argonautidae **48** 2868, 2869-70
Argopecten gibbus **48** *2837*
Argulus **37** 2169
argus pheasant **19** 1096, 1097, 1098, *1099*
Argusianus argus **19** 1096
Ariel toucan **22** *1291*
Ariidae **32** 1913
Arion **47** 2817; **48** 2822-3
  ater **47** 2802; **48** *2822*, *2823*, 2824
  rufus **47** *2804*; **48** 2823
  subfuscus **48** 2823
Arionidae **47** 2803; **48** 2822-4
Ariosoma bowersi **32** 1882
Aristotle **32** 1878; **37** 2212
Aristotle's lantern **36** 2125-6
Arixeniidae **40** 2388
Arixeniina **40** 2388
ark shells **48** *2832*, 2834, *2835-7*
Armadillidium **37** 2201
armadillo **4** 194-5, *197*
armadillo girdle-tailed lizard **27** *1597*, 1598
Armina **47** *2797*, 2798
Arminacea **47** 2786, 2798
Arminid sea slugs **47** *2797*, 2798
Arminidae **47** 2798-9
armoured catfish **32** *1906*, 1911, *1912-13*, 1915
armoured shrew **12** 662
army ants **41** 2405; **43** *2557*, *2558*
Aromia moschata **42** 2506-7
Arothron nigropuncatus **35** *2085*
Arrau turtle **26** 1528, *1530*
Arrenurus globator **38** *2242*
arrow squids **48** *2854*, 2867
arrow worms **50** *2970-1*
arrow-head piculet **22** *1293*
Artamidae **25** 1470
Artamus **25** 1470
Artemia salina **36** 2151, *2156*
Arthropoda **36** 2140
ARTHROPODS **36** *2103*, *2138-60*; **50** 2966
  body parts **36** 2140, *2141-4*
  classification **36** 2140
  evolution **36** 2140
  reproduction **36** 2144
Articulata **50** 2966, 2970
Artiodactyla **6** 301
Artogeia rapae **44** 2633
Arvicola **5** 252
Ascalaphidae **43** 2570, 2573
Ascalaphius macaronius **43** *2567*
Ascaphidae **30** 1760
Ascaphus truei **30** 1760
Ascaridida **49** 2925, *2929*
Ascaris lumbricoides **49** 2925, *2929*
Ascension Island frigatebird **17** 994
Ascidiacea **35** 2090
Ascothoracica **37** 2174
Asdemacea **48** 2848, 2849
Asellota **37** 2199
Asellus **37** *2188*, 2200
  aquaticus **37** *2197*
ashy minivet **23** 1357
ashy mouse opossum **11** 614, *615*
ashy wood swallow **25** 1470
ashy-crowned finch lark **23** 1334
Asia, national parks **51** 3002-4, *3026-32*
Asian...
  black bear **2** *70*, 71, 78
  horse gecko **27** 1569
  leaf turtle **26** 1540
  painted frog **30** 1783, *1786*
  tree viper **28** 1669, 1680
  two-horned rhino **6** 357 *1625-7*, 1628
  wild ass **6** 334, 340, *344*, 345-6; **51** 3054, *3055*
  wild dog **3** *129-30*
  wood scorpion **38** 2250
Asiatic file snake **28** 1626
Asiatic shrew-mole **12** 670
Asilidae **45** 2652, 2653
Asilus crabroniformis **45** 2652, 2653-5, *2658*
Asio **20** 1199
asitys **22** 1308, 1315, 1316
asp **28** 1669, *1676-7*
asparagus beetle **41** 2455; **42** 2504, 2506
Aspidites melanocephalus **28** 1637
Aspidontus taeniatus **34** 2019
Aspitrigla cuculus **34** 2007
assassin bugs **41** *2435*, *2437-8*
asses **5** 299; **6** 332, 334, *340-1*, *344-6*; **51** *3054-5*
Astacidea **37** 2212, 2214, 2218, 2219-20
Astacus **37** 2218, 2219
Astartaeca **48** 2845, 2847
Astarte **48** 2845, 2847
Astartidae **48** 2845, 2847
Asterias rubens **36** 2121
Asteroidea **36** 2106, 2107, *2133-7*
Asteronotus cespitosus **47** 2796
Astigmata **39** 2295
Astrapia mayeri **25** 1480
Astronotus ocellatus **35** 2049
Astropecten aurantiacus **36** 2121, *2132*
Ateles **13** 774
Atelopus **30** 1789
Athene noctua **20** 1199
Atherinidae **34** 1982
Atheriniformes **34** 1982
Athyteuthis abyssicola **48** 2854
Atilax paludinosus **2** 98
Atlanta peroni **46** *2735*
Atlantic sand shark **31** 1832
Atlantic square-toothed squid **48** 2861
Atlantic torpedo ray **31** 1841-2
Atlantic warbonnet **35** 2056-7
Atlantidae **46** 2735-6
atlas moths **44** 2597, 2624
Atoracophoridae **48** 2821
Atrax robustus **38** 2277; **39** *2282*
Atrichornis **23** 1328
Atrichornithidae **22** 1303; **23** 1328
Atta **43** 2563
  cephalotta **43** 2529, *2555*
  sexdens **43** 2529, *2555*
Attacus atlas **44** 2624
Attelabinae **42** 2506, 2508, 2514
Attelabius **42** 2506, 2508
Atubaria **50** 2971
Atypidae **39** 2283
Atypus affinis **39** 2283
auger shells **46** 2746; **47** *2762*, *2766*
augur buzzard **18** *1066*; **51** 3017
Augustes scutatus **21** 1228
auks **19** 1135; **20** *1145-8*
Aulacorhynchus caeruleogularis **22** 1290
Aulonogyrus **42** 2468
Aulopiformes **33** 1946
Aulopodidae **33** 1946
Aulopus **33** 1943, 1946
Aulostomidae **34** 2000
Aurelia aurita **49** 2889, *2892*
Auriparus flaviceps **24** 1403
aurochs **8** 463, 468, 475-6
Australasia, national parks **51** 3002-4, *3045-50*
Australasian gannet **17** 994
Australasian treecreepers **24** 1412, 1414-15
Australia, national parks **51** 3002, *3045-9*
Australian...
  channel-bill **20** 1180, 1181
  crested baza **18** 1076
  freshwater crocodile **29** *1687*
  frilled lizard **27** 1565, 1585, *1586*, 1587
  ground parrot **20** 1163
  hopping mouse **5** *255*
  mermaid's pennies **50** 2990-1
  reedy pool damselflies **40** 2351
  sea lion **3** 172
  water rat **5** 254, 262-3
  wild dog **1** 23

Australopithecus **15** 899
Australorbis **47** 2810
Austropotamobius **37** *2192*
pallipes **37** 2218, 2219
Austrorossia mastigaphora **48** 2855, 2860
Autographa gamma **44** *2604, 2624*
avadavats **25** 1452-3
avahi **13** 742, 749
Avahi laniger **13** 742
Aviceda leuphotes **18** 1070
avocets **16** *909, 914*; **19** 1129, *1132-3*, 1137; **51** 3008
Axis **7** 406
axis deer **7** 398-400, 406
axolotl *see* Mexican axolotl
aye-aye **12** *719*, **13** *732*, 733, 735, 750-1; **15** *896*
classification **13** 728, 742
distribution **13** 739
evolution **13** *727*
teeth **13** 734, *745*
Aythya **18** 1047
Aythyini **18** 1030, 1047
Azara's agouti **5** 289
Azara's fox **3** 127
azure butterflies **44** 2632-3
azure damselfly **40** *2355*
azure kingfisher **51** 3049
azure-winged magpie **20** *1178*, 1179; **25** 1489, 1494

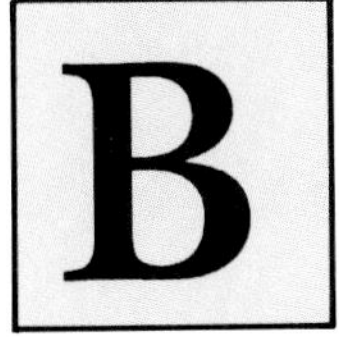

babblers **24** *1389-90*
Babesia **50** 2992, 2993, 2997
babirusa **7** *364*, 366, 370, *371*
extinction threat **7** 372
baboon spider **39** 2281, *2286-7*
baboons **1** *9*; **12** 719; **13** 756; **14** *792*, 793-6, *805-14*, 822
classification **13** 728; **15** *897*
evolution **13** *727*
infant care **13** *722-3*, *760*; **15** 846
national parks **51** 3017
Babylonia **46** 2751
Babyrousa babyrussa **7** 370
back-swimmers **39** 2321-2
Bactrian camel **7** *380-1*, 387, 388
Bactrian deer **7** 405
badger **1** *38-9*, 48, *52-3*
classification **1** 55
diet/eating habits **1** 27, 41
distribution **1** 43, 53
Badkhyzsky State Nature Reserve **51** 3002, *3054-5*
Baetidae **39** 2338; **40** 2343
Baetis **39** 2338, 2339
Bagre marinus **32** 1913
bagrid catfish **32** 1911
bagworm moths **44** 2602, *2605*, 2609
Baikal seal **4** 184; **51** 3053
Baikal-Skay State Nature Reserve **51** 3002, *3052-3*
bailer shells **46** 2760
Baird's tapir **6** 351, 352
Balaena **10** 577
Balaeniceps rex **17** 1011
Balaenicipitidae **17** 999, 1011
Balaenidae **10** 577
Balaenoptera **10** 577
Balaenopteridae **10** 577
Balanglossus **50** 2971
Balanomorpha **37** 2174
Balanophyllia elegans **47** *2792*
Balantidium coli **50** 2999
Balanus **36** *2156*
perforatus **37** *2179*
Balcis devians **46** *2720*, 2721
bald crow **24** 1390
bald eagle **18** 1055, *1070-2*; **51** 3041
Balearica pavonina **19** 1107
baleen whales **10** 576-84, 596; **32** 1886
Balinese banteng **8** 473
Balinese ox **8** 473
Balistes vetula **35** 2082
Balistidae **35** 2082
Balkan chamois **10** 548
ball python **28** *1629*
balloonfish **35** 2082
Baltic herring **32** 1890
Baltic tellin **48** 2847
bamboo rat **5** 243, 254-5, *272*
bamboo viper **28** 1680
banana spider **38** 2272, 2277
bananaquit **24** 1429, *1430*
banded broadbill **22** *1311*
banded chestnut quilled rock pigeon **51** 3047
banded demoiselle **40** *2355*, 2362
banded duiker **8** 440
banded gecko **27** 1567, 1568, 1569
banded helmet sea snail **46** *2741*
banded knifefish **32** 1920
banded palm civet **2** 92
banded pygmy sunfish **34** 2014
banded sunfish **34** 2016
banded tiger heron **17** 1007
banded jewel fish **35** *2050*
banded-winged dragonfly **40** *2355*
bandfish **32** 1920
bandicoot **11** *608*, 612, 620, *621*
bandicoot rat **5** 261
bangweolo **9** 512
bank swallow **23** 1340, 1345
bank vole **5** 252
Bankia bipalmulata **48** 2850
Bannerman's turaco **20** 1174
banteng **8** *462*, 468, *472*, 473-4
bar-headed goose **18** *1040*
bar-tailed godwit **19** 1130
barasingha **7** 406
Barbarus deer **7** 405; **8** 421
Barbary ape **14** 795
Barbary dove **20** *1153*
Barbary macaque **14** *793*, 795, 803; **15** 846
Barbary sheep **9** *534*, 538; **10** *546-7*, *557-9*, 560, 570
Barbary shrike **23** 1367
barbastelle **12** *690*, 714-15
Barbastellus barbastellus **12** 712
barbel catfish **32** *1916-17*
barbels **32** 1893-5, *1898*, 1899
barbets **22** 1281, *1285-8*
classification **22** 1288
distribution **22** 1282
Barbourisia rufa **34** 1990
barbourisid whalefish **34** 1988, 1990
Barbourisiidae **34** 1990
Barbus **32** 1894
bare-cheeked trogon **21** 1241
bare-faced go-away bird **20** 1178
bare-necked umbrella bird **51** 3044
bare-throated go-away bird **20** 1173
bare-throated tiger heron **17** 1007
bare-throated whistler **24** 1400
bark beetles **41** 2456, 2457
barking deer **7** 395, 396
barklice **41** 2432
barn owl **20** *1184*, 1185, *1190*, 1195, *1196*
classification **20** 1194
nesting sites **20** 1185, 1187
barn swallows **23** 1340, 1345
barnacle goose **18** *1041*, 1044
barnacles **37** *2169-78*, *2179*
barracudas **34** *2037*; **35** *2041-3*, 2048; **51** 3032
barracudinas **33** 1945-6
barred antshrike **22** 1310, *1311*
barred buttonquail **19** *1104*, 1114
barred cichlid **35** 2049, *2055*, *2064*
barreleyes **33** 1937, *1941*
barrelhead whale **10** 586,
Barrow's goldeneye **18** *1052*
Basiliscus **27** 1579
basilisks **27** 1564, 1572-3, *1582-3*
classification **27** 1579
basket shells **46** 2746
basket stars **36** 2106
basking shark **31** *1826*, 1829-30, 1839; **32** 1886
Basommatophora **47** 2803, 2805, 2806-7, *2810*, 2815
bass **34** *2014*, *2015*, 2017, 2022; **35** *2064*
classification **34** 2013
egg predator **34** 1981
bassaricyon **1** *58*
Bassogigas profundissimus **33** 1956
bat families **1** *8*, 9; **12** *677-716*; **51** 3046
classification **12** 681, 694, 704, 709, 712, 716
distribution **12** 679, 684
flight **12** 681-3
navigation **12** 679-81, 684-5, *689*, 691
bat fish **33** *1961*; **35** *2083*; *1961*
bat hawk **18** *1054*, 1070, 1077
bat-eared fox **3** 127, 129, *130-1*; **51** 3018
batagur **26** 1539, 1540
Batagur baska **26** 1539
bateleur eagle **18** *1054*, *1057*, 1070, 1071
bath sponge **48** *2879*, 2880
Bathothauma lyromma **48** *2854*, 2861, 2867
Bathyarca glacialis **48** 2834
Bathydorididae **47** 2786
Bathydoris **47** 2786
Bathyergidae **5** 277, 284
Bathylagidae **33** 1937
bathymyrinid eels **32** 1882
Bathynella natans **37** 2192
Bathynomus giganteus **37** 2196
Bathyomphalus contortus **47** 2801
Bathypolypus arcticus **48** 2852
Bathypteris **33** 1946
Bathysciadiidae **45** 2697; **46** 2702
Bathysciadium costulatum **45** 2697; **46** 2702
Bathyteuthis abyssicola **48** 2854
batise **24** 1399
Batocera **42** 2513
Batrachoididae **33** 1958
Batrachoidiformes **33** 1958
Batrachoseps attenuatus **30** 1750
Batrachostomus auritus **21** 1214
Batrachuperus karlschmidti **29** 1716
Bawean deer **7** 406
bay cat **3** 154
bay duiker **51** 3020
bay owl **20** 1185, 1190, 1195
classification **20** 1194
bay-winged cowbird **24** 1436
baya weaver **25** 1460
bazas **18** 1070, 1073, 1076
beach fleas **37** 2205
beach thick-knee **19** 1137
beaconfish **32** 1908, *1909*
beaded lizards **26** *1518*; **27** 1606, *1607*, *1614-15*
beaded sundial **46** 2712, *2717*
beaked coralfish **34** 2024, *2027*
beaked whales **10** 584, 585-6, 593
bean goose **18** 1040, 1044
bean horse mussel **48** 2840
bear family **1** 20, 59; **2** *69-82*
classification **1** 28
national parks **51** 3012-14, *3037*, 3041, *3052*, 3056
teeth **1** *22*
beard worms **50** *2971-2*
bearded barbet **22** 1288
bearded bellbird **23** 1323, *1324*, *1330*
bearded dragon **26** *1503*; **27** 1587, *1588*
bearded horse mussel **48** 2837
bearded mountaineer **21** 1228
bearded pig **7** 365, 366, 370, 372
bearded reedling **24** 1392-3
bearded saki **13** *769*, 772, 774
bearded seal **4** 184
bearded tit **24** *1390-1*, 1392-3
bearded vulture **18** 1070, *1077*; **51** 3017
Beatragus hunteri **9** 490
beautiful squirrel **4** 234
beaver **1** 11; **4** 216, 221, *236-7*, *239-40*; **51** 3036, 3042
beetle host **41** 2454
classification **4** 233
Bechstein's bat **12** 712
bedbugs **41** *2434*, *2436*, 2438
Bedford, Duke of **7** 395, 411
Bedford's takin **10** 550
bee beetle **42** 2495
bee flies **45** 2652, *2655*
bee hummingbird **21** 1227, 1228
bee louse **45** *2658*
bee tiger hawk-moth **44** 2620
bee worm **49** *2930-1*
bee-eaters **21** *1250*, 1251-2; **22** *1264-8*
classification **21** 1253; **22** 1270
distribution **21** 1267
bee-killer wasps **43** 2537, 2540
bees **39** 2311, *2312*, 2318, *2319*, 2326; **42** *2515-16*; **43** *2538-51*
social behaviour **43** *2524-5*
worker bees **43** *2524*
beetle fly **45** *2658*
beetle mites **39** 2295, 2297
beetles **39** 2320, *2325*; **41** *2453-60*; **42** *2461-2514*
body parts **39** 2313, *2315*, 2324
classification **39** 2311; **41** 2456;

42 2472, 2503
larvae **39** *2310*, *2312*
beira **8** *436*, 438, 444, 446
beisa oryx **9** 499, 502
Belemnoidea **48** 2855
Belenopterus chilensis **19** 1125
Belgian hare **4** 205
bell magpies **25** 1470, 1471-2, 1482
bell-moths **44** 2603-5, *2608*
bellbirds **23** 1323, *1324*, *1330*
Bellerophon bicarenus **45** *2694*
Bellerophontaceae **45** 2695
Bellicositermes **41** *2406*
natalensis **41** *2401*, 2406
Belone belone **33** 1965
Belonesox belizanus **33** 1978
Belonidae **33** 1965
Belontiidae **35** 2070
Belostoma foveolam **41** *2443*
Belostomidae **41** 2438, *2442-3*
belted kingfisher **21** *1253*
beluga fish **31** 1854, 1956
beluga whale **10** *586*, *587*, 593
Bembix
rostrata **43** 2535, 2540
variabilis **43** *2530*
Bengal cat **3** *138*
Bengal fox **3** 127
Bengal tiger **51** 3028
Bennett's cassowary **16** 925, 929
Bennett's tree kangaroo **11** *616*
Bensch's monia **19** 1114
Berlese, Antonio **42** 2486
Bermuda petrel **17** 973
Beroe **49** *2901*, 2902
Beroida **49** 2901
berrypeckers **24** 1415
Berthelinia limax **47** *2776*
Berthella **47** 2780
Berycidae **34** 1990
Beryciformes **34** 1990
Beryx **34** 1990
Bethyloidea **43** 2527, 2529
Betrachemys dahli **26** 1530
Betta splendens **35** 2070
bettong **11** 642
Bewick's swan **18** 1039, 1044
bezoar **10** 558, 570; **14** 826
bharal **10** 560-1, 570
Bhutan papilio **44** *2634*
Bhutanitis lidderdalei **44** *2634*
Bialowieza National Park **51** 3002, *3006-7*
Bibio
hortulanus **45** *2644*, 2646
marci **45** 2646, 2647
Bibionidae **45** 2646, 2647
Bibron's toadlet **30** 1799-1800
bichir **31** *1847*, 1848, *1850-3*
Big Bend gambusia **51** 3043
Big Bend National Park **51** 3002, *3042-3*
big-eye fish **34** 2024, *2031*
big-headed turtle **26** *1524*, 1535, 1536
bighorn sheep **6** 308; **9** 538; **10** 561, *564-7*, 570
bighorn sheep, national parks **51** *3036-7*, 3041-2
bigmouth buffalo fish **32** 1904
bigmouth sleeper **35** 2060
bilby **11** 612, 620
billfishes **35** 2041, 2043, 2048
Binneya **48** 2822
binturong **2** *84*, 85
Bioga dendrophila **28** 1645
Biomphalaria **47** 2810; **49** 2913
glabrata **47** 2816
Biorrhiza pallida **42** 2516, 2520
Bipalium kewense **49** *2906-7*
Bipedidae **27** 1616
Bipes biporus **27** 1616
bipinnaria larva **36** 2136
birch mouse **5** *242*, 243, 254; **51** 3006
bird ticks **39** 2295
bird-dung spider **38** *2280*
bird-eating spiders **38** 2258, *2261*, 2279; **39** *2282*, 2283, *2284-5*
BIRDS **16** -**25** *901-1441*
behaviour **16** 914
body parts **16** 907-12
courtship displays **16** *911*
evolution **16** 904-6
feathers/flight **16** *904-9*
feeding/diet **16** 912, 915-16
introduction **16** 902-3
origin/evolution *1507*
reproduction **16** *912-14*
bird's foot shell **46** *2722*
birds of paradise **16** 909; **22** 1303; **25** *1476-83*
birds of prey **18** *1053-80*
Birgus latro **38** 2223
bishops (weavers) **25** *1454*, *1459*, 1460
bison **6** 308; **8** *461*, 463, 467-8, *477-80*; **9** *481-2*
Bison
bison **8** 468
bonasus **8** 468
bison, national parks **51** *3006-7*, 3041
Biston **44** 2609, 2613
Bithynia tentaculata **46** *2712-13*, 2716
biting lice **39** 2311; **41** *2427-29*
Bitis **28** 1669
Bittacidae **43** 2576
bitterling **32** 1894, *1903-4*
bitterns **16** 909; **17** 997, 1007-8, *1009*; **51** 3008, 3050
classification **17** 999, 1007
distribution **17** 1005
Bittium reticulatum **46** *2718*
BIVALVES **45** *2675-7*; **48** 2833
anatomy **36** 2158; **45** *2673*, 2674
evolution **45** *2670*
Bivalvia **45** 2674; **47** 2776-7; **48** *2831-50*
Blaberidae **40** 2391
black...
baza **18** 1070, 1073
bear **51** 3037, 3041, 3056
beetle **40** 2394
buffalo **8** 467
bulbul **23** *1359*
burying beetle **42** 2472, *2474*
caiman **29** *1681*, 1685, *1686*, *1695*
colobus monkey **14** 830-1, 834, 836
corals **49** 2889, 2899
cuckoo-shrike **23** 1357
devil **33** 1959, 1961
dragonfish **33** *1940*, *1943-5*
drongo **25** 1468
geese **18** 1040
grouse **19** 1092, 1093, *1095*, 1096; **51** 3010
guillemot **20** 1146, 1148
guineafowl **19** 1100, 1101
howler monkey **13** 780
kite **18** 1070, *1072*; **51** 3046
leaf beetle **42** 2506, *2507*
lechwe **9** 512
lemur **13** *732-3*, *737-8*, 742, 743
lion tamarin **14** 790
mamba **28** 1661, 1663, 1666, 1667
mangabey **14** 815, 816, *818*
marlin **35** 2041
muntjac **7** 396
nunbird **22** 1284
panther **3** 135, 136
pigeon **51** 3060
porpoise **10** 593
rat **5** 243, 255
rhino **6** *353-6*, 357-9; **7** 361, 362; **51** 3022
right whale **10** 578
scabbard fish **35** 2067
sea urchin **36** *2124*
skimmer **19** *1122*; **20** 1145
spider monkey **13** *762*, 774; **14** 781
stork **17** 1012\
swan **18** *1037*, 1044
swift **21** 1218
tern **20** 1144, 1145
tetra **32** 1908, *1909*
thinhorn sheep **10** 566-7
tufted-ear marmoset **14** 787, 790
uakari **13** 772
vulture **18** 1061, 1062-4
wallaby **11** 642
widow spiders **38** 2257, 2258, 2270, 2277; **39** *2282*, 2283, *2284-5*
wildebeest **9** 490, 492, *495*
woodpecker **22** 1297, *1298*, *1299*, 1300
black-and-gold cotinga **23** 1322
black-and-white colobus monkey **51** 3020
black-and-white dormouse **5** 270
black-and-white warbler **24** *1432*, 1433
black-and-yellow silky flycatcher **23** 1372
black-backed jackal **2** 115, *117-8*
black-backed magpie **25** 1470
black-banded sea krait **28** *1672*
black-banded sunfish **34** 2014, 2016
black-bellied gnateater **22** 1314
black-bellied hamster **5** 245
black-bellied plover **19** 1125
black-bellied salamander **30** 1751
black-bellied sandgrouse **20** 1152
black-billed cuckoo **20** 1178
black-billed magpie **25** 1491
black-breasted puffleg **21** 1238
black-browed albatross **17** 969
bonding displays **17** *970*
black-capped babbler **24** 1390
black-capped bulbul **23** 1359
black-capped capuchin **51** 3038
black-capped chickadee **24** 1403
black-chinned salamander **30** 1751
black-crested sureli **14** 826
black-crowned night heron **17** 999, *1002-3*, 1006, 1007
black-faced coucal **20** *1172*
black-faced dioch **25** 1459, 1460
black-faced sheathbill **19** 1138
black-faced spinetail **22** 1312

ABOVE An Indian fruit bat has large eyes for sharp vision.

black-footed albatross **17** *968*, 971
black-footed ferret **1** 46; **4** 228
black-handed spider monkey **14** *781-2*
black-headed bulbul **23** 1359
black-headed bunting **24** *1426*
black-headed duck **18** 1051, 1052; **20** 1175
black-headed gull **16** *911*; **20** *1141*, 1142
black-headed heron **17** 1000
black-headed python **28** 1633, 1637
black-headed uakari **51** 3038
black-headed weaver **25** 1458
black-legged seriema **19** 1117
black-lined dragonfly **40** *2355*
black-lined rainbowfish **34** 1982
black-mantle tamarin **14** *787*, 790
black-necked cobra **28** 1641
black-necked crane **19** 1106, 1107
black-necked grebe **16** 957, 960; **51** 3014
black-necked screamer **18** *1029*, 1030, 1031
black-necked spitting cobra **28** *1662*, 1663, 1667
black-necked stork **17** 1011, 1012, *1014*; **51** 3027
black-necked swan **18** *1028*, 1037, 1044
black-necked tailorbird **24** 1394
black-rumped waxbill **25** 1453
black-shanked douc **14** 831
black-shouldered kite **18** 1070, 1076
black-shouldered opossum **11** 615
black-tailed deer **7** 415, 418
black-tailed godwit **19** *1128*, 1130, 1135
black-tailed jackrabbit **4** *202*, *206*
black-tailed phascogale **11** *617*
black-tailed prairie dog **4** *217*, *227*
black-throated diver **16** *953*, *954*, 955
black-throated honeyguide **22** *1280*, 1288
black-throated warbler **24** 1432
black-throated weaver **25** 1460
black-tipped shark **31** *1835*
black-veined white butterfly **44** *2639*
black-vented oriole **51** 3043
black-winged kite **18** 1070, *1076*
black-winged stilt **19** *1132*, 1133, 1137; **51** 3008
blackbird **16** 906, *910*; **22** 1304; **24** *1382*, 1388, 1389
blackbuck **8** *451*; **9** 520, 525, *528*, 529
blackcap **24** 1394-5, *1386*
blackfish **33** 1937-8
blackflies **41** 2446, *2451*; **45** 2644, 2651-2
blackhead mites **39** 2295
blackish shrew opossum **11** 624
blackpoll warbler **24** *1431*
blacksmith (barbet) **22** 1286
blacksmith plover **19** *1120*, 1125, 1126
blacktail **32** 1892
bladder snails **47** 2805, *2809-10*
bladderworm **49** *2914*, 2917
Blanford's fox **3** 127
Blanus cinereus **27** 1616
Blaps **42** 2472, 2490
Blastocerus dichotomus **7** 418
Blastophaga psennes **42** 2516; **43** 2521, 2522
Blatella germanica **40** 2391
Blatellidae **40** 2391
Blatta orientalis **40** 2391
Blattidae **40** 2391
Blattodea **39** 2311; **40** *2389-5*
bleak **32** 1890, 1894, *1902-3*
bleeding heart dove **20** *1160*
bleeding heart tetra **32** *1906*
blennies **34** 2019; **35** *2056-9*
Blenniidae **34** 2013; **35** 2059
Blennius **35** 2059
Blennocampus pusilla **42** 2520
blesbok **9** *489*, 490, *491*
blind goby **35** 2060, 2061
blind lizards **27** 1570, 1572
blind mole-rat **5** 254-5
blind salamanders **30** 1750, 1752
blind snakes **28** *1621-3*, *1624*
classification **28** 1621, 1625
distribution **28** 1621, 1628
blister-beetles **40** 2379; **42** 2472, 2486-7, 2488-9
Blitophaga **42** 2472
blood flukes **47** 2810; **49** 2911, *2912*, 2913
blood-sucking leech **50** 2958
bloodsucker **27** 1583, 1585
bloodworms **50** 2947, *2949*, 2952, 2958
bloody-nose beetle **42** 2503-4
blow fish **35** 2082
blow viper **28** *1643*
blowflies **45** 2659, 2663-4
blue...
bird of paradise **25** *1478*, 1479, 1480
bull **8** *456*, 460
butterflies **44** 2595, 2632, *2633*, *2635*
chaffinch **25** 1441, 1442
crane **9** *493*
crowned pigeon **20** 1156
duiker **8** *437*, 440
fairy wren **24** 1398, 1399
goose **18** 1043
gourami **32** *1865*
grouse **19** 1092, 1093
gularis **33** *1972*
helops **42** 2472, 2490
jay **25** 1489, 1490-1, *1492-3*
limpet **46** 2701
marlin **35** 2041, 2043
mockingbird **23** 1380
monkey **14** 816, 819, 836
mountain butterfly **44** *2634*
peacock limpet **45** *2700*
petrel **17** 973
rock thrush **24** *1387*, 1389
shark **31** *1826*, 1835, 1839
sheep **9** *534*; **10** 560-1, 570
skate **31** 1842, 1843
streak wrasse **34** *2019*
tang **34** *2012*
throat pike-blenny **35** 2059
tit **24** 1402-3, *1407*
vanga **23** *1356*, 1368
whale **1** 9; **10** *572*, *574*, *576-7*, 579-80, 583
wildebeest **9** 490, 492, *495*
blue duck **51** 3050
blue heron **51** 3041
blue-backed fairy bluebird **23** 1360
blue-backed manakin **23** 1332-3
blue-banded snapper **31** *1810-11*
blue-bearded bee-eater **22** 1270
blue-breasted bee-eater **16** *901*
blue-capped babbler **24** 1390
blue-cheeked bee-eater **22** *1267*, 1270
blue-crowned hanging parrot **20** *1162*, 1166, 1168
blue-crowned motmot **21** *1250*; **22** *1269*, 1270
blue-faced booby **17** 992, 994
blue-footed booby **17** *989*, 993, 994
blue-grey gnatcatcher **24** 1392
blue-masked leafbird **23** 1360
blue-naped mousebird **21** *1240*, 1246, 1247
blue-ringed octopus **48** *2866*, 2868, 2869
blue-spotted boxfish **35** 2082, *2086*
blue-spotted electric ray **31** 1841-2
blue-spotted sunfish **34** 2014, 2016
blue-striped pipefish **34** 2000
blue-throated motmot **22** 1269
blue-throated toucanet **22** 1290
blue-tongued skink **27** *1592*, 1593, 1598
blueback salmon **33** 1924
bluebirds **24** 1382, *1386*, 1388
bluebottles **45** *2660*, 2664
bluefin tuna **34** 2011, 2013, *2037*, 2039-40
classification **34** 2036
bluefishes **34** 2036
bluegill sunfish **34** 2017
bluehead wrasse **34** 2025
bluethroat thrush **24** 1388
blunt-snouted spiny-eel **32** 1872
blunthead snake **28** 1643-4
Blyth's reed warbler **24** 1395
Boa constrictor **28** *1624*, 1635, 1637, *1639*
boar **1** *12*
boarfishes **34** *1986*, 1989-90
boas **27** 1618; **28** *1624*, 1628-30, 1634, *1635-41*
classification **28** 1621, 1637
distribution **28** 1628
boat-billed heron **17** 1006, 1007
bobak **4** 221
bobcat **3** 139, 142
bobolink **24** 1440
bobwhite quail **19** 1096, 1100
Boelen's python **28** 1634
Bohemian waxwing **23** 1369, *1370-1*, 1372
bohor reedbuck **9** *504*, 510, 515-16
Boidae **28** 1621, 1637
Boinae **28** 1637
Boleophthalmus **35** 2062, *2063*
Bolitaenidae **48** 2868, 2869
boll weevil **41** 2456, 2457
Bolyeria multicarinata **28** 1637
bombardier beetles **41** 2456; **42** 2462
Bombay duck **33** 1946
Bombina **30** 1760
Bombus **49** *2930-1*
agrorum **43** 2542
lapidarius **43** 2542
pratorum **45** 2540, 2542
terrestris **43** *2536*, 2540, 2542
Bombycidae **44** 2624, 2625
Bombycilla **23** 1372
Bombycillidae **23** 1372
Bombycoidea **44** 2624
Bombyliidae **45** 2652, 2655
Bombylius major **45** 2652, 2655
Bombyx mori **44** 2624, 2625
Bonaparte's tinamou **16** 933
Bonasa bonasia **19** 1093
bone dogfish **31** 1837
bonefishes **32** 1872
Bonellia viridis **49** *2936*; **50** *2950-1*, 2958
Bonelli's eagle **18** 1066
bongo **8** 452, 456-7
bonnet macaque **12** *718*; **14** 803, 805, 808
bonnet shells **46** 2740-2
bonneted leaf monkey **14** 826
bonnethead shark **31** *1837*, 1839
bonobo **15** 852, 888
bontebok **9** *484*, 489-92
Bonus petrochenkoi **45** 2697; **46** 2702
bony fishes **31** 1806, 1808-9, 1814, 1858
primitive **31** *1847-56*
teleosts **31** *1857-60*; **32** *1861-6*
bony-tongued fishes **32** *1868-9*
boobies **17** *978-9*, 991-4
booklice **39** 2311; **41** *2431-2*
boomslang **26** 1522; **28** *1642*, 1643, 1645, *1651-2*
booted eagle **51** 3007, 3054
bootlace worms **49** *2920*
boreal ark shell **48** 2834
boreal squid **48** *2867*
boreal venus shell **48** 2849
Boreidae **43** 2576
Boreogadus saida **33** 1951
boring sponge **48** *2880*; **49** 2892, 2895
Bornean bristlehead **23** 1367
Bornean earless lizard **27** *1607*, 1614, 1615
Bornean hillstream loach **32** 1907, 1984
Bornean orang-utan **15** 852, 853
Bornean tree pie **25** 1490
Borneo banteng **8** 473
Borneo fighting fish **35** 2069
Borneo red cat **3** 154
Bos **8** 468
Boselaphini **8** 434, 447-60
Boselaphus tragocamelus **8** 460
Bosellia mimetica **47** *2776*, 2777
Bostrychia carunculata **17** 1018
bo'sunbird **17** 979
bot flies **45** 2659-60
Botaurinae **17** 1007
Botaurus **17** 1007
Bothidae **35** 2075
Bothriurids **38** 2245
Bothrops atrox **28** 1669
Botia macracantha **32** 1894
Botrylius schlosseri **35** 2094
Botswana, game reserve **51** 3002, *3018-19*
bottle-nosed dolphin **10** 588, *589-91*, 593, *594-5*
Boulengerochromis microlepsis **35** 2048
boutu **10** 585
Bovicola ovis **41** 2428
Bovidae **6** 305; **8** 432, 434; **9** 490, 535; **10** 568-9
BOVIDS **6** 304-5; **9** 485; **10** *541-70*
Bovinae **8** 434, 468; **10** 568
Bovini **8** 434, 461-80; **9** 481-2
bowerbirds **16** *910*; **25** *1472-6*, 1482; **51** 3046, *3048-9*
classification **25** 1476

distribution **25** 1482
bowfin **31** 1848, *1852*, *1855-6*, 1858
distribution **31** 1851
bowhead whale **10** 574, 577, *578*
box crabs **38** 2225, *2228*
box turtles **26** *1522*, *1537-8*, 1539
boxfishes **35** *2082-3*, *2085-6*
Brachidontes domingensis **48** 2840
Brachinus **42** 2462
brachiolaria larva **36** *2113*, 2136
Brachiopoda **50** 2966-7, *2970*
Brachiosaurus **26** 1508
Brachycephalidae **30** 1795
Brachycephalus ephippium **30** 1795
Brachycera **45** 2652
Brachygalba goeringi **22** 1284
Brachygobius xanthozona **35** 2060
Brachylophus fasciatus **27** 1579
Brachypteracias squamigera **22** 1261
Brachypteraciidae **21** 1253; **22** 1261
Brachyteles arachnoides **13** 774
Brachyura **38** 2223
bracon flies **42** 2516; **43** 2522
braconid wasp **43** *2526*
Braconidae **42** 2516
Bradfield's hornbill **22** 1278
Bradypodidae **4** 195
Bradyporidae **40** *2369*
Bradypus **4** 195
brahman **8** 476
brahminy duck **51** 3027
brahminy starling **25** 1462
brain coral **49** 2889, *2894*, 2899
bramble sharks **31** 1836-7, 1841
brambling **25** 1441, 1442-3
Braminy blind snake **28** 1622, 1625
Branchiobdella **37** 2219; **50** 2952
branchiobdellids **50** 2952
Branchioica **32** 1913
Branchiopoda **36** *2147-52*
Branchipus stagnalis **36** *2156*
Branchiura **36** 2147; **37** 2168-9
Branchyura sowerbyi **50** 2948, 2952
Branta **18** 1044
Brant's cormorant **17** 984
Braula coeca **45** *2658*
Brazil, national park **51** 3002, 3004, *3038-9*
Brazilian dung beetle **42** 2503
Brazilian free-tailed bats **12** *678*, 685, *715*
classification **12** 716
distribution **12** 679
Brazilian horned toad **30** 1795, 1798
Brazilian merganser **18** 1052
Brazilian skink **27** 1596, 1598
Brazilian syncarid **37** 2189
Brazilian tapir **6** 351, 352
Brazilian wandering spider **39** *2282*, 2284
Brazilian wolf spider **39** *2282*
bream **32** 1895, *1903*
Bregmaceros macclellandi **33** 1951
Bregmacerotidae **33** 1951
Brelich's snub-nosed monkey **14** 827, 831
brent goose **18** 1041, 1044
Brevoortia tyrranus **32** 1890
bright blue starfish **36** *2111*
brill **35** *2075*, 2080
brimstone butterfly **44** 2638
brindled gnu **9** *483*, 490, *492-5*
brindled guillemot **20** 1148
brine shrimps **36** 2147, *2149-52*, *2156*
bristle-thighed curlew **19** *1120*
bristlemouths **33** *1940*, *1942-3*, 1944
bristletails **39** 2311, 2320, *2329*, *2333-6*
bristleworms **49** *2935-40*; **50** 2941-9
British common swallowtail **44** 2636
British earthworm **50** 2952
British periwinkle **46** 2707, 2712
brittle stars **36** *2127-9*, *2132-3*
classification **36** 2106, 2107
defence **36** *2111*, 2119
diet **36** 2114
evolution **36** 2115
feet **36** 2113
larva **36** *2113*
broad-billed roller **22** 1261, 1263
broad-billed tody **21** *1250*
broad-bodied dragonflies **40** 2351, *2355*, 2358, 2359
broad-bodied fairy shrimp **36** *2156*
broad-nosed caiman **29** *1692*, 1695
broad-nosed gentle lemur **13** 742, 743
broadbill fishes **35** 2041
broadbills **22** 1303, *1307*
distribution **22** 1308
brockets **7** *412*, 417, 418
bronze sunbird **24** 1417
bronze tube-nosed bat **12** 712
bronze-tailed plumeleteer **21** *1229*
bronze-winged jacana **19** 1123
bronzed cowbird **24** *1437*
brook char **33** 1924, *1930*, 1934, *1936*
brook lamprey **31** *1815*, *1817*, 1818
brook salamanders **29** *1702*, 1722-3, *1740*; **30** 1752
classification **29** 1713, 1729; **30** 1750
brook trout **33** 1924, *1930*, 1934, *1936*
Brookesia stumpfii **27** 1592
brotulids **33** 1956
brow-antlered deer **7** 404; **8** 421
brown...
bear **2** *70*, 71, *72-5*
booby **17** *978*, 989, 992, 994
brittle star **36** *2132*
brocket **7** 418
bullhead **32** 1913, 1915, *1918-19*
butterflies **44** 2606, 2607, 2633, *2640*
cahalote **22** 1312
capuchin **13** *762*, 773, 774
dipper **23** 1374
fish owl **20** 1198, 1199
hare **4** 207, 209, *210-11*
hawker dragonfly **40** 2362
hyena **2** 107, *108*
jay **25** 1489, 1491
kiwi **16** 925, 931
lacewings **43** 2572
lehchwe **9** 512
lemur **13** 738, *739*, 742
lesser mouse lemur **13** *732*, 742
long-eared bat **12** 712
mongoose **2** 92
noddy **20** 1144, 1145
pelican **17** 979, 980, *981*, 983, *986-7*
rat **4** 216, *218*; **5** 243, *255-8*
sand boa **28** *1635*
shrimp **37** *2211*
skua **16** *945*
thrasher **23** *1356*, 1380
treecreeper **24** 1414
trout **33** 1923, *1930-3*, 1934
brown-browed albatross **17** *964-5*
brown-eared bulbul **23** 1359
brown-headed cowbird **20** 1175; **24** 1437, 1440
brown-headed tchagra **23** 1367
brown-lipped snail **47** 2817; **48** *2830*
brown-tail moth **44** 2595
brown-throated three-toed sloth **4** *185-6*, 187, *193-4*, 195
Bruce's yellow-spotted hyrax **6** 313
Brunnich's guillemot **20** 1148
brush turkey **19** 1088, *1091*
brush-footed butterflies **44** 2633, 2638-9
brush-tailed bettong **11** 634
brush-tailed phascogale **11** 610, 617
brush-tailed rat kangaroo **11** 634
brushtail possums **11** 612, 624-5, *626*; **51** 3048
Bryde's whale **10** 577
bryozoans **50** *2965*, 2966, *2967-8*
bubal hartebeest **9** 485
Bubalornithinae **25** 1459
Bubalus **8** 468
bubble shells **45** 2674, 2680; **47** 2767, *2768-9*, 2770-3, *2774-5*
Bubo **20** 1199
Buccinidae **46** 2746, 2748, 2750-1
Buccinum **46** 2750
undatum **46** 2715, 2746
Bucconidae **22** 1284
Bucephala clangula **18** 1052
Buceros bicornis **22** 1278
Bucerotidae **21** 1253; **22** 1278
Bucovorus leadbeateri **22** 1278
budgerigar **20** 1165-6, 1168
Budorcas taxicolor **10** 550
Buenos Aires tetra **32** 1910
buff-tip moth **44** *2604*, 2616, 2624
buffalo **8** *463-71*; **51** 3019, 3022, 3024
buffalo gnats **45** *2644*, *2651-2*
buffalo trunkfish **35** 2082, 2086
buffalo weavers **25** 1458, 1459
buffy tufted-ear marmoset **14** 787
buffy-headed marmoset **14** 787, 790
Bufo **30** 1789
Bufonidae **30** 1756, 1789
Bugeranus carunculatus **19** 1107
bugs **39** 2311; **41** *2433-52*
bulbuls **23** 1354, *1358-9*
Bulinus **47** 2810
Buliulacea **48** 2822
bull moth helmet shell **47** *2762*
bull sharks **31** *1835*, 1839
bull snake **28** *1659*
Bulla striata **47** 2767
bulldog bats **12** *678*, 681, 697
bullfinch **25** 1442, *1446-7*
bullfrog **30** 1771-3, *1774*, 1778, 1793
bullhead catfish **32** 1913, 1915, *1918-19*
bullhead shark **31** 1828, 1829
bullheads **34** 2007, *2008*, 2010
Bullidae **47** 2767
bullrout **34** 2007-8
Bulweria bulwerii **17** 973
Bulwer's petrel **17** 973, 974
bumble bees **43** *2536-7*, 2540, *2541*, 2542-3
parasite **49** *2930-1*
bumblebee goby **35** *2060-1*
bummalow **33** 1944, 1946
Bunodactis verrucosa **49** *2886*
Bunolagus monticularis **4** 209
buntings **24** *1420-2*, *1426*, *1427*
classification **22** 1303; **24** 1429
distribution **24** 1430
bunyoro rabbit **4** 209
Buphagus africanus **25** 1462
burbot **33** 1951, 1954
Burhinidae **19** 1121, 1137
Burhinus oedicnemus **19** 1137
Burmeister's seriema **19** 1117
Burmese banteng **8** 473
Burmese brow-antlered deer **7** 404
Burmese roofed turtle **26** 1540
burnet moths **44** 2594, *2609-11*
Burnett River salmon **31** 1850
Burnupia **47** 2816
Burramyidae **11** 612, 627
Burramys parvus **11** 627
burrfish **35** 2082, 2085
burrowing asp **28** 1641, 1646-7
burrowing owl **20** *1184*, 1191, *1194*, 1195, 1199
burrowing shrimps **37** 2212
burrowing toad **30** 1765, 1796
Bursa scrobiculator **46** 2743
Bursidae **46** 2737, 2743
Burton's snake lizard **27** *1570-1*
burying beetles **42** 2471, *2473-5*
bush babies **13** *727*, 733, *734*, *744*, *752-3*
classification **13** 728, 742, 748
distribution **13** 739
primates **12** 718, 719; **15** *896*
senses **13** 721, 722, 752
bush corals **51** 3032
bush dog **2** *110*; **3** 129
bush duiker **8** *436-9*
bush frogs **30** 1756, 1782, 1785
bush hyrax **6** 311, 313
bush quail **19** 1098
bush robin **51** 3050
bush shrikes **23** 1362, 1367
bush wren **22** 1316
bush-cricket **40** *2368*, 2369
bush-tail opossum **51** 3050
bushbuck **8** *448*, 450, *452*, 456; **51** 3016, *3017*
bushman hare **4** 209
'bushman's clock' (butcherbird) **25** 1471
'bushman's clock' (kookaburra) **21** 1260
bushmaster snake **28** 1669, *1678*
bushpig **7** *364*, 365, 367, *371*
classification **7** 370
distribution **7** 366
bushtit **22** *1305*; **24** 1403
bushy-tailed opossum **11** 615
bustard **19** *1104*, 1105, 1106, *1107-8*

classification **19** 1107, 1112
distribution **19** 1106
bustard quail **19** 1114
Busycon **46** 2751-4
canaliculatum **46** 2746
Butastur teesa **18** 1070
'butcher bird'(shrike) **23** 1364
butcherbirds **25** 1471, *1472*
Buteo **18** 1070
Buthidae **38** 2247, 2250
Buthids **38** 2245
Buthus occitanus **38** 2250
butterfish **35** 2056-7
BUTTERFLIES **36** *2103*, *2138-9*; **39** *2309*, *2326*; **44** *2585-99*, *2606-7*, *2629-40*
body parts **39** 2313, *2319*; **44** 2586-9
larvae **39** *2310*, 2311-12, 2318, *2320*
migrations **44** *2588*, 2590
national parks **51** 3056
scent **44** *2606-7*
butterfly blenny **35** *2058*, 2059
butterfly fishes **32** *1867-8*, 1869; **34** *2012*, 2027, 2028
classification **34** 2024
defence **34** 2030
distribution **34** 2025
buttonquails **19** *1104*, 1107, *1114*, 1115-6
buzzard-eagles **18** 1070; **51** 3060
buzzards **18** *1065-6*, *1068-9*
classification **18** 1051, 1057, 1061, 1070
courtship **18** *1059*, 1060
distribution **18** 1056
national parks **51** 3010, 3017
Bycanistes bucinator **22** 1278
Byctiscus
betulae **42** *2508-9*
populi **42** *2506*, *2509*
Bynoe's gecko **27** *1568*
Bythitidae **33** 1956

C

Cabassous **4** 197
cabbage white butterfly **43** 2526; **44** 2633, 2636-8
cabbage white fly **41** 2450
Cacajao rubicundus **13** 774
Cacatua galerita **20** 1168
cachalot whale **10** 593
cachalotes **22** 1309, 1310
cacomistle **1** *58*, *59*; **2** 62, 66-7
cactus ground finch **24** *1425*, 1429
cactus wren **23** *1356*, 1376, 1377, *1379*
nest **22** *1305*; **23** 1378
caddisflies **39** 2311, *2321*, 2322; **43** *2577-80*; **44** *2581-4*
Caddo mountain salamander **30** 1750
Cadulus quadridentatus **45** 2692
Caecidae **46** 2712, 2717
Caecilia thompsoni **29** 1710
caecilians **29** 1698, 1701, 1704, 1706, *1707-10*
Caecum glabrum **46** 2712
Caelifera **40** 2364-5, 2369
Caeminidae **48** 2826
Caenolestes **11** 624
Caenolestidae **11** 612, 624
cahow **17** 972-4
Caiman crocodilus **29** 1685
caiman lizard **27** 1601, 1603
caimans **29** *1681*, 1683, 1691, *1692*, *1695*
classification **29** 1685
distribution **29** 1682
Cairina moschata **18** 1052
Cairinini **18** 1030, 1052
Cairngorms National Nature Reserve **51** 3002, *3010-11*
Calabar python **28** 1634-5, *1636*, 1637
Calabaria reinhardti **28** 1637
Calamaria **28** 1645
Calamian deer **7** 406
Calamobius **42** 2512
Calamoichthys calabaricus **31** 1850
calandra lark **23** 1334, 1339, *1340*
Calandrella cinerea **23** 1334
Calandruccio (eel researcher) **32** 1878
calanoid copepods **37** *2163-4*
Calanoida **37** 2163
Calappidae **38** 2225
Calcarea **48** 2880
Calcochloris obtusirostris **11** 655
Calicnemis latreillei **42** 2501
calico scallop **48** *2837*, *2838-9*
Calidrididinae **19** 1135
Calidris **19** 1135
California alligator lizard **27** 1565
California legless lizard **27** 1602, *1603*, *1607*
California newt **29** 1729, *1738*
California slender salamander **30** *1748*
Californian arrow goby **35** 2060-1
Californian cave salamander **30** 1747
Californian condor **18** 1062, 1064
Californian dwarf octopus **48** 2852
Californian flying fish **33** 1965-6
Californian grey whale **10** 579
Californian grunion **34** 1982, *1984*
Californian leaf-nosed bat **12** 703, 709
Californian sea lion **3** *162*, 164, 172; **51** 3035
Californian tiger salamander **29** 1720-1
Californian toad **29** 1702
Californian top shell **46** 2703
Californian venus clam **48** 2849
Caligo prometheus **44** *2596*
caligoids **37** 2166-7
Caligus rapax **37** *2161*
Caliphyllidae **47** 2777
Caliroa, limacina **42** 2516, *2518*
Callaeidae **25** 1470
Callaeus cinerea **25** 1470
Callanaitis disjecta **48** *2844*, 2849
Callicebus moloch **13** 774
Callichthyidae **32** 1913
Callimico goeldii **14** 790
Callinassa australiensis **37** *2219*
Callionymidae **34** 2033
Callionymus lyra **34** 2033
calliope hummingbird **21** 1228, *1233*, 1238
Calliostoma
annulatum **46** 2703
conulus **46** 2703
fascinans **46** 2703
ligatum **46** 2703
monile **46** 2703
zizyphinum **46** 2703, *2704*
Calliphora erythrocephala **45** 2659, 2664
Calliphoridae **45** 2659, 2663-4
Callisaurus draconoides **27** 1579
Callithrix **14** 790
Callitrichidae **14** 790
CALLITRICHIDS **13** 763-4, 768; **14** *782-90*
Callorhinus ursinus **3** 164
Callorhynchidae **31** 1846
Callorhynchus **31** 1846
Callosciurus **4** 234
Calma glaucoides **47** 2768, *2769*, 2800
Calman, W. T. **37** 2192
Calmella cavolinii **47** 2790
Calocalanus pavo **36** *2156*
Calonectris diomedea **17** 973
Calophysus **32** 1913
Caloprymnus campestris **11** 642
Calopterygoidea **40** 2351
Calopteryx splendens **40** *2355*, 2362
Calosoma sycophanta **41** 2456; **42** 2461
Calotes versicolor **27** 1585
calpe moths **44** *2600*
Calpurnus verrucosus **46** 2720, *2726*, 2758
Caluromyinae **11** 612
Caluromysiops irrupta **11** 615
Calypte **21** 1228
Calyptomena viridis **22** 1307
Calyptraeacea **46** 2720, 2724
Calyptraeidae **46** 2720, 2724
Camallanida **49** 2925
Camargue cattle **8** *474*, 476; **51** 3009
Camargue Nature Reserve **51** 3002, *3008-9*
Camarhyncus pallidus **24** 1429
Cambaridae **37** 2220
Cambarus **37** 2220
Camberwell beauty **44** 2633
camel family **7** *379-81*, 387
classification **7** 388; **10** *569*
ungulate features **5** 298; **6** 301, 304
water storage **7** 386
Camelidae **7** 388
CAMELIDS **7** *379-88*
Camelus **7** 388
camouflage defence, reptiles **26** *1519*, 1520, 1522
Campeloma rufum **46** 2713
Campephaga sulphurata **23** 1357
Campephagidae **23** 1357
Campephila imperialis **22** 1297
Campodea
gracilis **39** 2333, 2335
staphylinus **39** *2335*
Campodeidae **39** 2333, 2334, 2335
Camponotus **44** 2632
herculaneus **43** 2529, *2554*
Camptoceras terebra **47** 2807
Campylomormyrus curvirostris **32** 1869, *1870*
Campylorhamphus trochilirostris **22** 1310
Campylorhyncus **23** 1379
Canada, national parks **51** 3002, *3036-7*
Canada goose **18** *1039*, 1040, *1041*, 1044
Canada warbler **24** *1431*

ABOVE A watchful cheetah at rest on the Kenyan plains.

Canadian lynx **3** 139, 140
Canadian otter **1** 41, 48, 52
canary **25** 1442, 1448
canasteros **22** 1309
Cancellaria cancellata **46** 2746
Cancellariacea **46** 2760
Cancellariidae **46** 2746, 2760
cancellated nutmeg shell **46** *2760*
Cancer pagurus **38** *2225*
Cancridae **38** 2225
candiru **32** 1913, 1920
Candona reptans **36** *2160*
cane rat **5** 273, 277, 289, *295-6*
Canidae **1** 28; **2** 117, 118; **3** 127
CANIDS **2** *108-20*; **3** *121-32*
Canis
adustus **2** 118
aureus **2** 118
dingo **2** 117
familiaris **2** 117
latrans **2** 117
lupus **2** 117
mesomelas **2** 118
rufus **2** 117
simensis **2** 118
canoe shells **47** 2767, *2770*
Cantabrian chamois **10** 548, 549
Canthigaster **35** 2082, 2085
canvasback duck **18** 1047
canyon tree frog **30** 1792, 1795
Cape...
barn owl **20** 1194, 1195, *1196*
buffalo **8** *462*, *464-6*, *467-9*
centipede eater **28** 1645, 1647
cobra **28** *1663*
dikkop **19** 1136
eland **8** 452, 457
elephant **6** 324
fox **3** 127
gannet **17** 994
grysbok **8** 444, 446
hare **4** 207, *208*, *209*
hartebeest **9** 486-7
hunting dogs **2** *109-10*, 115, 119; **3** 132
hyrax **6** *309*, 313
longclaw **23** *1352*
mole-rat **5** 284, 296
mountain zebra **6** 334-5, *338*, 340
pangolin **4** 189, *200*
pigeon **17** *973*
porcupine **5** 273-4, 275
red-tailed flat lizard **27** 1597
shelduck **18** 1044
sparrow **25** 1455
sugarbird **24** 1420
white-eye **24** 1417
capelin **33** 1924, 1937
capercaillie **19** 1092, 1093, *1094*, 1095
Caperea marginata **10** 577
Capitonidae **22** 1288
Capniidae **40** 2345
capped leaf monkey **14** 826
Capra **10** 570
Caprella **37** *2188*
Capreolus capreolus **7** 396, 418
Capricornis **10** 550
Caprimulgidae **21** 1206
Caprimulgiformes **21** *201-14*
Caprimulgus **21** 1206
Caprinae **8** 434; **9** 535; **10** 550
Caprini **8** 434; **10** 570
CAPRINS **9** *533-40*; **10** *541-70*
Capritermes **41** 2405
Caproidae **34** 1990
Caprolagus hispidus **4** 209
Capromyidae **5** 277, 289
Capromys **5** 289
Capros aper **34** 1990
capsid bugs **41** 2437, 2438, 2447
capuchin monkeys **12** 719; **13** *762*, 763-4, *773-9*; **51** 3038
classification **13** 728, 774
distribution **13** 768
capuchin-like monkeys **15** *897*
Capulidae **46** 2720, 2724, 2727
Capulus **46** 2727
ungaricus **46** *2726*
capybara **4** *218*; **5** *272*, 279-81, *282*; **51** 3038
classification **5** 277, 289
carabid ground beetle **42** *2465*
Carabidae **41** 2456; **42** 2472
Carabus
auronitens **41** 2456
clathratus **42** 2462
variolosus **42** *2465*
caracal **3** 139, *140*, *142*, 143-4; **51** 3054
caracaras **18** 1079, 1080
Carangidae **34** 2036
Caranx hippos **34** 2036
Carapidae **33** 1956
Carassius auratus **32** 1894
Carcharhinidae **31** 1839
Carcharhinus **31** 1839
Carcharodon
carcharias **31** 1839
megalodon **31** 1827
Carcinus maenas **38** *2224*, 2225-9
Cardiacea **48** 2847
Cardiidae **48** 2846, 2847
cardinal fish **34** *2012*, 2013
cardinal grosbeaks **24** *1423*, *1427*, *1428*, 1429
cardinal tetra **32** *1906*, 1908-9
Cardinalinae **24** 1429
Cardinalis cardinalis **24** 1429
Cardiocranius paradoxus **5** 268
Carditacea **48** 2845, 2847
Cardium
aculeatum **48** *2844*
costatum **48** 2846
echinatum **48** *2846*
edule **48** 2847
Carduelinae **25** 1442
Carduelis **25** 1442
Caretta caretta **26** 1553
Carettochelyidae **26** 1553
Carettochelys insculpta **26** 1553
Cariama cristata **19** 1117
Cariamidae **19** 1107, 1117
Caribbean fire sponge **48** 2880
Caribbean flamingo **18** 1022, 1024
Caribbean monk seal **3** 179, 180; **4** 184
Caribbean pygmy squid **48** 2861, 2862
Caribbean reef squid **48** *2862*
Caribbean tongue-fish **35** 2075
caribou **7** 418; **8** 421, 424; **51** 3036
Carinaria **46** *2735*, 2736
mediterranea **46** *2726*
Carinariidae **46** 2734
Cariophyllia clava **49** *2886*
Carmen white-tailed deer **51** 3042
carmine bee-eater **21** *1250-1*; **22** *1264-6*, 1267, 1268
classification **22** 1270
Carnegiella striata **32** 1908
CARNIVORES **1** *19-36*
carnivorous diving beetles **41** *2455*, 2456; **42** *2463-8*
Carolina dove **20** 1156, *1159*
Carolina duck **18** 1052
Carolina narrow-mouthed frog **30** 1784, 1786
Carolina wren **23** 1377, *1378*, 1379
carp **32** *1891-3*, 1895-7
classification **31** 1858; **32** 1894
distribution **32** 1910
swim bladder/hearing **32** *1861-3*
'carp fleas' **37** 2169
Carpathian chamois **10** 548
carpenter ants **43** 2529, *2554*
carpenter bees **43** *2540*
carpenter moths **44** 2605, 2609
carpet python **26** *1514*; **28** *1633*
carpet sharks **31** *1829*, 1830-1, 1839
Carpodacus erythrinus **25** 1442
Carpus acus **33** 1956
carranchina **26** 1530, 1531
carrier shells **46** 2720, 2724, *2726*, 2727
carrion beetles **42** *2471-3*, 2493-4, 2503
carrion crow **25** 1485, 1489, 1498, *1500*
Carterodon sulcidens **5** 289
cartilaginous fishes **31** 1808-9, 1814, *1824-46*; **32** 1861
evolution **31** 1806
Carychium **47** 2805
Cascade Cavern salamander **30** 1752
cascavel **28** 1644, 1669, 1679-80
Caspian sea cockles **48** 2845, 2847
Caspian seal **4** 184
Caspian striped-neck terrapin **26** *1539*
Caspiomyzon wagneri **31** 1818
casquehead **27** 1596, 1598
Cassida **42** 2504, 2506
Cassidae **46** 2737, 2740
Cassidaria echinophora **46** 2740, *2742*
Cassin's finch **25** *1447*
Cassin's honeyguide **22** 1288
Cassis tuberosa **46** *2740-2*
cassowaries **16** 918, *925*, *928*, 929
Castor **4** 233
castor bean tick **38** *2242*
Castoridae **4** 233
Casuaridae **16** 925
Casuariformes **16** 925
Casuarius **16** 925
cat family **3** *133-60*
classification **3** 139, 144, 154, 158
distribution **3** 135-6, 140
eyes and teeth **1** 21
national parks **51** 3013, *3016*, *3021*, *3038-40*, *3044*, 3054, *3056-7*
predators **1** 29, 34
cat flea **45** 2665, *2666*, 2667
cat sharks **31** 1834, 1839
cat snake **28** *1642*, 1645, *1651*, 1652
Catablyrhyncinae **24** 1429
Catagonus wagneri **7** 370
catalufas **34** 2024
Catamblyrhyncus diadema **24** 1429
catarrhine monkey **14** 793
Catastomus **32** 1894
catbirds (bowerbirds) **25** 1474, 1476
catbirds (mockingbirds) **23** 1378, 1379, *1380*
caterpillars **39** *2311-12*, 2318
catfishes **32** *1906*, *1912-20*
classification **31** 1858; **32** 1913; **35** 2056
communication **32** 1891-2
distribution **32** 1911
Catharacta **20** 1142
Cathartes **18** 1064
Cathartidae **18** 1057, 1064
Catocala **44** 2617
nupta **44** 2624, *2596*
Catoprion **32** 1908
Catostomidae **32** 1894
cattle **1** 16; **5** 298; **6** 301, 304-5, 308; **8** 463, 475
cattle egret **17** 1004, 1007; **51** 3008
cattle horsefly **45** *2652-3*
cattle tyrant flycatcher **22** 1317, 1320
Caucasian bison **9** 482
Caucasian chamois **10** 548
Caucasian salamander **29** 1730
Caudata **29** 1713
cave cricket **40** 2368, 2369, *2376*
cave salamanders **30** 1745, 1747, 1750
cave swallow **22** *1305*
cavefish **33** 1948-9
caviare **31** 1851
cavies **4** 218
Caviidae **5** 277, 278
Caviomorpha **4** 233; **5** 277
CAVIOMORPHS **5** *271-96*
Cavolinia **47** 2782, 2786
tridentata **47** *2774*
Cavoliniidae **47** 2782, 2786
cavy family **5** *271-96*
Cebidae **13** 774
CEBIDS **13** *761-80*; **14** *781-2*
Cebuella pygmaea **14** 790
Cebus **13** 774
Cecidomyia veronica **45** 2645
Cecidomyiidae **45** 2645, 2647
cedar waxwing **23** 1369, *1371*, 1372
Celebes coucal **20** 1178
Celebes macaque **14** *792*, 803, *804*, 805, 808
Celebes rainbow fish **34** 1982, *1984*
Celebes wild pig **7** 365, 370
Celyphus **45** *2658*
Cenocrinus asteria **36** *2117*
centipede-eater **28** 1645, 1646-7
centipedes **36** 2103, 2140; **39** *2301-3*, *2306-8*
Central American cacomistle **2** 66-7
Central American coati **1** *21*
Central American river turtle **26** 1535
Central Kalahari Game Reserve **51** 3002, *3018-19*
centralian carpet python **28** 1633
Centrarchidae **34** 2014
Centriscidae **34** 2000
Centriscus **34** 2000
Centroberyx **34** 1990
Centrocercus urophasianus **19** 1093
Centrolenella vireovittata **30** 1799
Centrolenidae **30** 1799
Centropus **20** 1178
Centrotus cornutus **41** 2439

Centrotypus amplicornis **41** *2439*
Centruroides **38** 2247, 2250
gracilis **38** *2246*
Centrurus noxius **38** 2250
Centurio senex **12** 709
Cepaea
hortensis **47** *2804*
nemoralis **47** 2817; **48** *2830*
Cephalaspidea **47** 2767, 2770
Cephalaspidomorphi **31** 1809, 1818
Cephalobaena tetrapoda **50** *2964*
Cephalocarida **36** 2147; **37** 2169
cephalocarids **36** 2147
CEPHALOCORDATES **35** 2090-2, *2100*
Cephalodiscus **50** 2971
Cephalophinae **8** 434, 439, 440
CEPHALOPHINS **8** *436-8*, 440
Cephalophus **8** 440
Cephalopoda **45** *2676*; **48** 2855, 2861, 2868, 2869
CEPHALOPODS **48** *2851-71*
classification **45** 2674, 2681
evolution **45** *2670*
shell **45** *2673*, 2681
Cephalopterus ornatus **23** 1322
Cepphus grylle **20** 1148
Ceram Island bandicoot **11** 620
Cerambycidae **41** 2456-7; **42** 2504, 2506
Cerambyx cerdo **41** 2456
Ceratias holboelli **33** *1959-61*
Ceratitis capitata **45** *2657-8*, 2659
Ceratodontidae **31** 1850
Ceratodontiformes **31** 1850
Ceratophrys 1795
Ceratophylloidea **45** 2665
Ceratotherium simum **7** 361
cercarian **49** *2911*, *2912*
Cercocebus **14** 816
Cercodobo granulifera **50** *2970*
Cercomys cunicularis **5** 289
Cercopidae **41** 2438, 2448-9
Cercopithecidae **14** 796-836; **15** *897*
CERCOPITHECIDS **14** *791-836*
Cercopithecus
aethiops **14** 816
cephus **14** 816
diana **14** 816
hamlyni **14** 816
mitis **14** 816
mona **14** 816
neglectus **14** 816
petuarista **14** 816
Cercopithicinae **14** 796, 803, 811, 816
Ceresa bubalus **41** *2448*
Cerianthus
filiformis **49** *2886*
membranaceus **49** *2897*
Cerithiacea **46** 2712, *2717*, 2718, *2727-8*
Cerithiidae **46** *2718*
Cerithiopsidae **46** 2718
Cerithiopsis
barleei **46** *2719*
tubercolaris **46** 2719
Cerithium **46** 2718
Certhia **24** 1412
Certhiidae **24** 1412
Cerura vinala **44** *2596*, 2624
Cervidae **7** 396, 406, 418
CERVIDS **7** *389-91*, *393-420*; **8** *421-4*
Cervinae **7** 396, 406
Cervus
albirostris **7** 406
canadensis **7** 406
duvauceli **7** 406
elaphus **7** 396, 406
eldi **7** 406
nippon **7** 396, 406
timorensis **7** 406
unicolor **7** 406
Ceryle **21** 1253
Cerylinae **21** 1253
Cestida **49** 2901, 2902
Cestoda **49** 2911, 2915
Cestoidea **49** 2905
Cestus veneris **49** 2901
Cetacea **10** 577, 593
CETACEANS **10** *571-96*
Cetomimidae **34** 1990
Cetonia **42** 2498
aurata **42** 2493, 2495
Cetoniinae **42** 2495, 2503
Cetorhinus maximus **31** 1839
Cetti's warbler **24** *1394*
Ceylon elephant **6** 324, 326
Ceyx pictus **21** 1253
chachalacas **19** 1088, 1092, 1098
chacma baboon **14** 811
Chacoan peccary **7** 370-1
Chactidae **38** 2251
Chactids **38** 2245
Chad hartebeest **9** 486
Chaenichthyidae **35** 2056
Chaenophryne parvonicus **33** *1960-1*
Chaenopsidae **35** 2059
Chaenopsis ocellata **35** 2059
chaetae **49** 2939
Chaetocnema tibalis **42** 2503, 2506
chaetoderms **45** 2684
Chaetodontidae **34** 2024
Chaetogaster **50** 2947, *2948*, 2952
Chaetognatha **50** *2970-1*
Chaetomys subspinosus **5** 283
Chaetonotina **49** 2923
Chaetophractus **4** 197
Chaetopteridae **50** 2942
Chaetopterus variopedatus **49** *2936*; **50** 2942
Chaetosoma **49** 2925
Chaetura pelagica **21** 1218
chafer beetle **41** *2453*
chafers **42** 2491-2, 2494-5, *2498-9*, *2501*, *2505*
chaffinch **16** 909; **25** *1441*, 1442
chain pickerel **33** 1937-8
chalcid wasps **42** *2519*; **43** *2521*
Chalcides **27** 1598
Chalcidoidea **42** 2516; **43** 2521
Chalcophaps indica **20** 1156
Chalcosoma **42** 2493
atlas **42** 2500
Chalicodoma muraria **43** 2540, 2541
Chamaeleo
chamaeleon **27** 1592
hoehnelii **27** 1592
jacksonii **27** 1592
melleri **27** 1592
oustaleti **27** 1592
zeylanicus **27** 1592
Chamaeleontidae **27** 1592
Chamaesaura **27** 1598
chameleon dragon **27** 1587
chameleon nerite **46** 2705
chameleons **26** *1513*, 1517; **27** 1564, *1587-92*
classification **27** 1592
distribution **27** 1565
chamois **8** 434; **9** *533*, 535, 538, *540*; **10** *541-4*, 548-9
chamois, national parks **51** *3012-13*
Chanidae **32** 1892
Channa
africanus **35** 2071-2
asiatica **35** 2072
micropeltes **35** 2071
channel bass **34** 2032
channel-billed toucan **22** *1291*
channelled whelk **46** 2746, 2754
Channidae **35** 2072
Chanos chanos **32** 1892
Chapman's zebra **6** *338*, *339*, 340
Characidae **32** 1908
Characiformes **32** 1907-8
CHARACINS **32** 1892, 1907-9, *1910-11*
Charadrii **19** 1121
Charadriidae **19** 1121, 1125
Charadriiformes **19** *1119-40*; **20** *1141-8*
Charadriinae **19** 1125
Charadrius **19** 1125
Charaxes **44** 2640
jasius **44** 2633, 2640
Charaxiinae **44** 2633
Charina bottae **28** 1637
Charonia **46** 2743
tritonis **46** 2737
chars **33** 1924, *1930-1*, 1934, *1936*
Chathamiidae **43** 2580; **44** 2584
chats **24** 1382, 1387-8
Chauliodontidae **33** 1944
Chauliodus sloanei **33** 1944
Chauna **18** 1030
Cheat mountain salamander **30** 1750
'checkerspot' moth **44** *2602*
cheese mites **39** 2295
cheetah **1** 11, 23, 27, *29*, 36; **3** *134*, *156-7*, *159-60*
distribution **3** 140, 154
national parks **51** 3018, *3019*, 3023, 3054
Cheilinus undulatus **34** 2023
Cheirodon axelrodi **32** 1908
Cheirogaleidae **13** 742
Cheirogaleus medius **13** 742
Cheiromeles torquatus **12** 716
Chelicerata **36** 2140; **38** 2241, 2234, 2244
CHELICERATES **38** *2233-80*
body parts **38** 2235-6
evolution **38** 2234-5
reproduction **38** 2236
Chelictinia riocourii **18** 1070
Chelidae **26** 1530
Chelidoptera tenebrosa **22** 1284
Chelifer cancroides **38** *2242*
Chelmon rostratus **34** 2024
Chelodina longicollis **26** 1530
Chelonia **26** 1510, 1523-56
Chelonia **26** 1553
Cheloniidae **26** 1553
Chelorrhana savagei **42** 2495
Chelus fimbriatus **26** 1530
Chelydra serpentina **26** 1535
Chelydridae **26** 1535
Chermesinae **41** 2451, 2452, 2454
Chersydrus granulatus **28** 1626
chestnut jacamar **22** 1284
chestnut quail-thrush **24** 1390
chestnut-bellied heron **17** 1005
chestnut-bellied sandgrouse **20** 1152
chestnut-eared aracari **22** *1289*
chestnut-eared bulbul **23** 1359
chestnut-sided shrike-vireo **24** 1435
chevrotains **5** 298; **7** 389-91, 392, 414; **10** *569*
Chiasognathus grantii **42** 2502-3
chickadee **24** 1403
chicken lice **41** 2428
chicken red mites **39** 2295
chiffchaff **24** 1394, 1398
chigger mites **39** 2297
chigoe flea **45** 2665-7
Chihuahuan shiner **51** 3043
children's python **28** *1634*, 1637
Chilean cave lizard **27** *1594*
Chilean flamingo **18** *1023*, 1024
Chilean huemul **7** 417, 418; **8** 424
Chilean lapwing **19** 1125
Chilean plantcutter **23** 1325
Chilean shrew opossum **11** 624
Chilean woodstar **21** 1238
Chilia melanura **22** 1310
Chilina fluctuosa **47** 2806
Chilinoidea **47** 2806
Chilocorus **42** *2487*
bipustulatus **42** 2472, 2483
Chiloglanis **32** 1913
Chilognatha **39** 2303, 2304
Chilomastix mesnili **50** 2976
Chilomycterus schoepfi **35** 2082
Chilopoda **39** 2302, 2303, 2307
Chimaera monstrosa **31** 1846
chimaeras **31** 1827-8, *1838*, *1846*; **35** 2066
Chimaeridae **31** 1846
chimney swift **21** 1217, *1218*
chimpanzees **14** 838; **15** *847*, *849*, 859, 863, *866-90*
classification **13** 728; **14** 839; **15** 852
distribution **15** 848
facial expressions **13** *759*
national parks **51** 3020, 3024
physical shape **12** *719*, 720; **15** *843*, *900*
primate features **12** 717; **13** *722-3*, *727*, 756
tool use **1** 14; **15** 852, *874-8*
China, national parks **51** 3002, 3051, *3058-9*
chinchilla **5** *272*, 283-5, *286*
classification **5** 277, 289
Chinchilla laniger **5** 289
chinchilla rat **5** 277, 289, 295
Chinchillidae **5** 277, 289
Chinese...
alligator **29** 1685, 1692, 1694
dormouse **5** 262
giant salamander **29** 1716, *1717*
goose **18** 1040
little bittern **17** 1008
mitten crab **38** 2231
monal pheasant **51** 3059
muntjac **7** 396
paddlefish **31** 1854-6
pangolin **4** *198*, 200
roe deer **7** 413
silk moth **44** 2606
snub-nosed monkey **14** 827
water-deer **7** 396, 411
xenosaur **27** *1607*, 1609
Chinese-shrew mole **12** 670
chinkara **9** 529
chinook salmon **33** 1924, *1925*

chinstrap penguin **16** 938, *940, 942, 943*
classification **16** 949
distribution **16** 948
Chioglossa iusitanica **29** 1729
Chione californiensis **48** 2849
Chionididae **19** 1121, 1137
Chionis alba **19** 1137
chipmunk **4** *217*, 222, 229, *230-1*
classification **4** 233
Chirocentridae **32** 1890
Chirocentrus dorab **32** 1890
Chirolophis ascanii **35** 2056
Chiromantis xerampelina **30** 1785
Chironectes minimus **11** 615
Chironitis **42** 2495
Chironomidae **45** 2650, 2652
Chironomus plumosum **45** 2650-2
Chiropotes satanus **13** 774
Chiroptera **12** 681
CHIROPTERANS **12** *677-716*
Chiroteuthidae **48** 2867
Chiroteuthis
picteti **48** *2854*, 2867
veranyi **48** 2867
Chiroxiphia caudata **23** 1331
chiru **8** 434; **9** *534*, 535-6, 538
chisel-teeth lizards **27** 1564, 1582-3, *1585-8*
chital **7** *395*, 398-400, *410*
classification **7** 406
Chiton
barnesi **45** 2686
olivaceus **45** 2684, 2688
tuberculatus **45** 2684, *2686-8*
viviparus **45** 2686
Chitonidae **45** 2684, 2686
CHITONS **45** 2672, 2674, 2676, 2679-80, *2683-9*
Chitra indica **26** 1553
Chlaenius vestitus **42** *2465*
Chlamydera nuchalis **25** 1476
Chlamydosaurus kingii **27** 1585
Chlamydoselachidae **31** 1828
Chlamydoselachus auguineus **31** 1828
Chlamydotis undulata **19** 1112
Chlamyphorus **4** 197
Chlamys
opercularis **48** *2831-2*, 2834, 2837
tigerina **48** 2837
Chlidonias niger **20** 1145
Chloebia gouldiae **25** 1453
Chloephaga picta **18** 1044
Chloroceryle americana **21** 1253
Chlorocharis emiliae **24** 1417
Chlorophthalmidae **33** 1946
Chloropsis **23** 1360
Choeradodis laticollis **40** *2398*
Choeropsis liberiensis **7** 378
Choloepus **4** 195
chomatophores **35** 2074
Chondracanthus zei **37** *2168*
Chondrichthyes **31** 1809, *1825-46*
Chondropomidae **46** 2706
Chondropython viridis **28** 1637
Chondrostoma nasus **32** 1894
chordates **35** 2090
Chordeiles minor **21** 1206
Chorisochismus dentex **33** 1962
chough **25** 1489, *1495*; **51** 3013
choz choz **5** 289, 294
Christmas Island frigatebird **17** 994
Christmas tree worm **50** 2942, *2946*
Chromadoria **49** 2925
Chromodorididae **47** 2794
Chromodoris **47** 2794
quadricolor **47** *2774*
valencies **47** *2791*
Chrotogale owstoni **2** 92
Chryosochloridae **11** 651, 655
chrysidid wasps **43** 2527, 2529
Chrysididae **43** 2529
Chrysiridia ripheus **44** *2604*
Chrysis ignita **43** 2527, 2529
Chrysocloa **42** 2504
Chrysodoa **42** 2504
Chrysolophus pictus **19** 1096
Chrysomela **42** 2504
populi **42** 2506
sanguinolenta **42** *2507*
chrysomelid beetle **42** *2465*
Chrysomelidae **42** 2506
Chrysopa vulgaris **43** *2567*, 2570
Chrysopalax trevelyani **11** 655
Chrysopelea ornata **28** 1645
Chrysopidae **43** 2570, 2571
Chrysopogon alba **45** *2654*
chub **32** 1894, *1900-1*
Chuck Will's widow **21** 1207
chuckwalla **26** *1518*; **27** *1578*, 1579
chukar **51** 3054
chum salmon **33** 1924
Chunga burmeisteri **19** 1117
churchyard beetle **42** 2472, 2490
cicadas **39** 2326; **40** *2364*; **41** 2434, 2438, *2447-8*
Cicadella viridis **41** 2449
Cicadellidae **41** 2449
Cicadetta montana **41** 2447
Cicadidae **41** 2438
Cichlasoma **35** 2049
Cichlidae **34** 2013; **35** 2049
cichlids **31** 1814; **35** *2048-56, 2064*
classification **34** 2013; **35** 2049
distribution **34** 2026-7
evolution **35** 2049-50
Cicindela **41** 2456, 2460
Cicinnurus regius **25** 1480
Ciconia **17** 1012
Ciconiidae **17** 999, 1012
Ciconiiformes **17** *995-1020*
cigar shark **31** 1841
cilia **49** 2887
Ciliata mustela **33** 1951
ciliates **50** *2977, 2996-7, 3000*
Ciliophora **50** 2971, 2976, 2992, 2997
Cimex **41** 2436-7
columbarius **41** 2436
lectularius **41** 2436, 2438
pipistrelli **41** 2436
rotundatus **41** 2436
Cimicidae **41** 2436, 2438
Cinclidae **23** 1374
cinclodes **22** 1309, 1310, 1312
Cinclosoma castanotum **24** 1390
Cinclus **23** 1374
cinereous vulture **18** *1078*
Ciniflo similis **39** 2289
cinnabar moth **44** 2593
Ciona intestinalis **35** *2091*
Cionellidae **47** 2819
Circaetinae **18** 1070
Circaetus **18** 1070
Circinae **18** 1070
Circus
aeruginosus **18** 1070
cyaneus **18** 1070
macrourus **18** 1070
melanoleucus **18** 1070
Cirrata **48** 2868, 2869
Cirratulicae **50** 2942
Cirrepedia **36** 2147; **37** 2169, 2174
Cirrothauma murrayi **48** 2868-9
cisco **33** 1924, 1934
Cissa chinensis **25** 1489
Cisticola juncidis **24** 1394
Cistothorus palustris **23** 1379
Cites **7** 401, 405; **15** 890
Citharinidae **32** 1908
citrine wagtail **23** 1353
civets **1** 59; **2** 84, 85, *87*, 93, *96-7*; **51** 3030
classification **1** 28; **2** 89, 92
distribution **2** 86
Cladocera **36** 2152, *2160*
Cladognathus giraffa **42** 2502-3
clam shrimps **36** 2151-2, *2156*, 2158
Clamator glandarius **20** 1178
clams **45** 2670, 2673-4, 2680; **48** 2833, 2837
bitterling host **32** 1903
Clangula hyemalis **18** 1052
Clarias batrachus **32** 1913
Clariidae **32** 1913
Clarke's gazelle **9** 529
Clark's nutcracker **25** *1488*, 1489, 1498; **51** 3037
Clathrina **48** *2875*, 2876, 2880
Clathrus **46** *2719*, 2721, 2729
Claudius angustatus **26** 1535
Clausilia dubia **47** *2818*
Clausiliidae **47** 2819
Clavagella aperta **48** 2848
Clavagellacea **48** 2848, 2850
Clavelina **35** *2093, 2096-7*, 2098
lepadiformis **35** 2094
clawed toads **30** 1763-5, *1766-7*
classification **30** 1769
distribution **30** 1768
clawless otter **1** 55
cleaner fishes **32** 1894, *1907*
cleaner wrasse **34** *2018-19*, 2023
clearwing moths **44** 2608, 2609, *2611*
Cleioprocta **47** 2799-2800
Clelia clelia **28** 1645
Cleopatra's asp **28** 1662-3
Clevelandia ios **35** 2060
click beetle **42** *2505*
Clifden nonpareil moth **44** *2622*
cliff frog **51** 3043
cliff swallow **22** *1305*; **23** 1343, 1345, *1346-7*
Climacteridae **24** 1412
Climacteris picumnus **24** 14
climbing gouramis **35** 2070
climbing mouse **5** 261
climbing perches **34** 2026-7; **35** *2064, 2067-8*, 2070
climbing salamanders **30** 1750
climbing sea cucumber **36** *2117*
clingfishes **33** *1962*
Clinidae **35** 2059
Clinius testudinariius **35** 2059
Cliona **49** 2882, 2895
celata **48** *2880*
Clione limacina **47** *2774*, 2784, *2785*
Clionidae **47** 2784, 2786
Cliopsidae **47** 2784
Cliopsis **47** *2784*
Clitellata **50** 2958
cloak anemone **49** 2897
clothes moths **44** 2600-2, 2609
clouded leopard **3** *134*, 141, 158; **51** 3058-9
clouded yellow butterfly **44** *2588*, 2633, *2637*, 2638
clown loach **32** 1894, *1907*
clownfish **34** *2011*, 2012-13
classification **34** 2024
reproduction **34** 2028-9, 2031
club-spined sea urchin **36** *2117, 2127*
club-tailed dragonfly **40** *2355*, 2359
Clubionidae **38** 2263
Clupea **32** 1890
Clupeidae **32** 1890
Clupeiformes **31** 1858; **32** *1885-90*; **33** *1922, 1940*
Clytra **42** 2504
Clytus **42** 2513
Cnemidiphorus **27** 1603
Cnidaria **49** 2884, 2889
coal tit **24** 1403, 1406
coanoflagellates **50** *3000*
coati **1** *21, 58*; **2** *61-2*
cobia **34** 2036
Cobiculidae **48** 2847
Cobitidae **32** 1894
Cobitis taenia **32** 1894
cobras **26** *1509, 1522*; **28** 1640-1, *1661-5, 1668*; **51** 3054
classification **28** 1667
distribution **28** 1644, 1661-2
mongoose attack **2** *88*
Coccidae **41** 2438, 2452, 2454; **42** 2483
Coccidia **50** 2991, 2992-3
Coccidula rifa **42** 2482
Coccinella septempunctata **42** 2472, 2483
Coccinellidae **41** 2456; **42** 2472, 2482
Coccosthraustes coccosthraustes **25** 1442
Cocculinacea **45** 2700
Coccyzeus erythrophthalamus **20** 1178
cochineal insect **41** 2438
Cochlearius cochlearius **17** 1007
cockatoos **20** *1162*, 1163-4, *1167*, 1168
cockchafers **42** 2491, 2498, *2500-1*, 2503
cockles **45** 2676; **48** 2845, 2846-7
cockroaches **39** 2311, 2313, 2318, 2326; **40** *2389-95*
termite comparison **41** 2403
cocks-of-the-rock **23** *1321*, 1322-3, 1324, *1330*
coconut crab **38** 2223, *2224*
Cocos finch **24** 1429
cod icefishes **35** 2055-6
codlets **33** 1951
Codonosiga botrytis **50** *3000*
cods **31** 1814, 1858-9; **32** 1866; **33** *1948*; **34** *1996*
classification **33** *1950-1*
courtship **33** *1949*
coelacanth **31** *1806*, 1808-9, 1848, *1850, 1852*
Coelacantha ornata **50** *2970*
Coelacanthiformes **31** 1850
Coelenterata **49** *2883-2902*
Coeloplana mesnili **49** 2901, *2902*
coelurosaurs **16** 904
Coenagrionoidea **40** 2351
Coendou prehensilis **5** 283
Coereba flaveola **24** 1429
coho salmon **33** 1924

Coke's hartebeest **9** *487*, 488, 490
Coleoidea **48** 2855, 2857, 2861, 2869
Coleoids **48** 2857-71
Coleonyx variegatus **27** 1569
Coleoptera **39** 2311, 2320; **41** *2453-60*; **42** *2461-2513*;
coley **33** 1952
Colias **44** 2633, 2638
colies **21** 1247
Coliiformes **21** 1241, *1245-8*
colima warbler **51** 3042
Colinus virginianus **19** 1096
Colisa lalia **35** 2070
Colius **21** 1247
collared anteater **4** *187*, 188, 195
collared aracari **22** *1280*, 1290
collared dove **20** 1156, *1159-60*
collared flycatcher **24** 1400
collared lizard **27** 1572, *1573*, 1579
collared mangabey **14** 816
collared peccary **7** *364*, 366, 370-2; **51** *3042*
collared pika **4** 209
collared pratincole **19** 1137; **51** 3008
collared puffbird **22** *1280*
collared redstart **24** 1431, 1433
collared sunbird **24** *1416*
collared trogon **21** 1241, *1242*
Collembola **39** 2303, 2320, 2329, 2333
Colletes canicularis **43** 2539, 2540
Colletidae **43** 2539
Colliidae **21** 1247
Collocalia fuciphaga **21** 1218
Collosum **50** 2990
Collozoum **50** 2991
Colluricincla megarhynca **24** 1400
Colobinae **14** 796, 826, 836
colobine monkeys **14** 796, *822-36*
Colobus **14** 836
colobus monkeys **13** *755*, *757*; **14** 793, 822, 830-1, *834-5*
  classification **14** 796, 836; **15** *897*
  distribution **14** 794
  national parks **51** 3017, 3020
Colombian shrew opossum **11** 624
colonial hydra **49** 2889
colonial sea squirts **35** 2093, *2098*
Colorado beetle **41** *2455*, 2456, **42** 2504, *2506*
colpeo fox **3** 127, 129
Coluber viridiflavus **28** 1645
colubrid snakes **28** 1621, *1640-61*
  classification **28** 1621, 1645
  distribution **28** 1644
Colubridae **28** 1621, 1645
colugos **12** *673-6*, 679
Columba **20** 1156
Columbariidae **46** 2746, 2748
Columbellidae **46** 2746, 2751
Columbidae **20** 1156
Columbiformes **20** *1148-1160*
comatulids **36** 2116
comb duck **18** 1052
comb jellies **49** *2901-2*
comb-footed spiders **38** 2257, 2258, *2259*, *2278*; **39** 2283
combtooth blennies **34** 2013; **35** 2058-9
comet (starfish) **36** *2111*
comma butterfly **44** *2600*, 2633
Commerson's dolphin **10** *592*
"common" entries *see under* main name
compass jellyfish **49** *2891*
compass termites **41** *2422*, *2424*
Conacea **46** 2746; **47** 2765
Concentricycloidea **36** 2106, 2107, 2137
conchostraca **36** 2151
conchs **45** 2676; **46** 2720, 2722-4, *2726*, *2732-3*
concolor gibbon **15** 842, 846
condors **18** *1055*, 1056, 1060, 1062, 1064
Condylartha **10** 573
Condylura cristatus **12** 670
cone shells **45** 2678; **46** *2715*, 2758-9; **47** *2762*, *2763-5*
  classification **45** 2676
  distribution **47** 2766
cone-headed grasshopper **40** *2365*, 2382
Conepatus **1** 55
Conger conger **32** 1874
conger eels **32** 1874, 1880, *1882-3*
Congo eels **30** 1741-2, *1743*
Congo peacock **19** 1098
Congo peafowl **19** *1086*, 1096, 1098
Congo serpent eagle **18** 1071
Congridae **32** 1874
Conidae **46** 2746
Coniopterygidae **43** 2570
Connochaetes **9** 490
Conolophus subcristatus **27** 1579
Conopophaga **22** 1314
Conopophagidae **22** 1314
Conops quadrifasciatus **45** *2658*
Conraua goliath **30** 1778
conures **20** *1162*, 1163
Conus
  arenatus **46** 2746; **47** 2764
  californicus **47** 2766
  daucus **47** 2766
  geographus **47** 2766
  gloria maris **47** 2766
  marmoreus **46** 2746; **47** *2762*, 2764-5
  mediterraneus **46** 2746; **47** 2764, 2766
  mercator **47** *2764*
  planorbis **47** 2764
  striatus **46** 2714-15
  tinianus **47** 2766
Convoluta roscoffensis **49** 2905, 2908-9
convolvulus hawk-moth **44** 2524, *2588*, *2590*, 2622
coolie loach **32** 1894, 1906
Cooloola propator **40** 2369
coots **19** 1108, 1112, *1113*, 1114
Copeina arnoldi **32** 1908
Copepoda **36** 2147; **37** 2163
COPEPODS **36** 2147, 2152, *2156*; **37** *2161*, *2162-9*, *2191*
  parasites **49** 2933
Cope's giant salamander **29** 1722
Cophotis ceylanica **27** 1585
copperhead snake **28** 1669, 1680
coppersmith **22** 1286, 1287, 1288
Copris **42** 2492, 2495
  lunaris **42** *2498*, 2503
Coquerel's mouse lemur **13** 745
coquina shell **48** 2847, *2848*
Coracias
  caudata **22** 1261
  garrulus **22** 1261
Coraciformes **22** *1261-78*
Coraciidae **21** 1253; **22** 1261
Coraciiformes **21** *1249-60*
Coracina novaehollandiae **23** 1357
Coragyps atratus **18** 1064
coral pipesnake **28** 1626
coral snake **28** 1658, 1661, *1666-7*, *1668*
coral trout **34** *2019*
coral-billed nuthatch **23** 1368
coral-feeding snails **46** 2746, 2748
coralfish **34** 2024, *2027*, 2030
coralline sponges **48** 2880
Coralliophila lamellosa **46** 2748
Coralliophilidae **46** 2746, 2748, *2749*
Corallus caninus **28** 1637
corals **36** 2103; **48** *2872-4*; **49** *2884-7*, 2889, 2893, *2897-2901*, **51** *3032*
  reef building **49** *2894-5*
Corambidae **47** 2786
Corbicula **48** 2845, 2847
Corbiculidae **48** 2845
Corbulidae **48** 2848-9
Corcoracidae **25** 1470
Corcorax melanorhamphos **25** 1470
Corculum cordissa **48** 2846
Cordulai aenea **40** *2350*
Cordulegasteroidea **40** 2351
Cordylidae **27** 1598
Cordylus **27** 1598
Coregonus **33** 1924
Corinaria **46** 2737
Coris julis **34** 2023
Corixidae **39** 2321; **41** 2438, 2444
cormorants **17** *978*, 979, *984-90*
  classification **17** 980, 990
  distribution **17** 984
  feathers **16** *911*
  national parks **51** 3014, 3035, 3046
corn snake **28** *1642*
corncrake **19** 1112, 1114
cornetfishes **34** *1999*, 2000
Cornucia zebrata **27** 1598
Coronella austriaca **28** 1645
Corophium scutum **37** *2205*
corsac **2** 119; **3** 127, *128*
Corsican brook salamander **29** 1740; **30** *1741*, *1746*
Corsican ox **8** 476
coruros 5 289, 294
Corvidae **22** 1303; **25** 1489
CORVIDS **25** *1484-1500*
Corvus **25** 1489
Corydalidae **43** 2570
Corydon sumatranus **22** 1307
Corydorus **32** 1913
Corymbites cupreus **42** *2505*
Corynopoma riisei **32** 1908
Coryphaena **34** 2036
Coryphaenidae **34** 2036
Coryphella
  iodenia **47** *2800*
  verrucosa **47** *2774*, 2799
Coryphellidae **47** 2799
Cory's shearwater **17** 973
Corythaeola cristata **20** 1178
Corythaixoides personata **20** 1178
Coscinasterias tenius **36** *2111*
Coscoroba coscoroba **18** 1044
coscoroba swan **18** *1030*, 1036, 1044
Cossidae **44** 2605
Cossoidea **44** 2605, 2609
Cossus cossus **44** 2609
Cossyphus **42** 2490
Costa Rica, biosphere reserve **51** 3002, 3004, *3044*
Costa's hummingbird **21** *1215*, 1228, *1237*
cotingas **22** 1303; **23** *1322-4*, *1330*
Cotingidae **22** 1303; **23** 1322
Cottidae **34** 2007-8
cotton bollworm **44** 2609
cotton-headed tamarin **14** 782
cotton-top tamarin **13** *758*, 768; **14** 782, *783*, *790*
cottonmouth snake **28** 1669, *1670-1*, 1680
cottontail **4** 202, 207, 209, *212-13*
cottony cushion beetle **42** 2486
Cottus **34** 2007
Coturnix **19** 1096
Coua cursor **20** 1178
couas **20** 1178, 1181
coucals **20** *1171-2*, 1175, 1178, *1181-2*
cougar **3** 139; **51** 3036-7
Count Raggi's bird of paradise **25** 1480
courol **22** 1261
coursers **19** 1121, 1136, 1137, 1138
cow sharks **31** 1828-9
cowbirds **16** 914; **24** *1436-7*, 1440
cowfishes **35** 2082, 2085-6
cowries **45** 2678, 2693, 2694; **46** *2714-15*, *2725-31*, *2734-5*, 2758
  classification **46** 2720
  distribution **46** 2736
coyote **1** *23*; **2** *115-16*, 117; **3** *128*
coypu **5** 273, 277, 288, *290-3*
  distribution **5** 275
crab louse **41** 2428, *2431*
crab parasites **36** 2147
crab plover **19** *1120*, 1121, *1134*, 1137
crab scorpions **38** 2234
crab spiders **36** *2143*; **38** 2257, *2258*, *2261*, 2270, 2280; **39** 2289
crab-eating macaque **14** *792*, *803*, 808
crab-eating raccoon **1** *23*, *58*; **2** 62
crabeater seal **3** 179; **4** 181, 184
crabs **36** *2102*, *2153-5*; **37** *2179-82*, 2212, 2220; **38** *2221-32*
  classification **36** 2140, 2147
  courtship **37** *2190-1*
  crustacean features **36** *2145-6*
  evolution **38** 2223, 2232
  origins/evolution **36** 2140
  parasites **37** 2177-8
  Sacculina infection **37** *2180*
Cracidae **19** 1088
Cracticidae **25** 1470
Cracticus louisadensis **25** 1470
crag chilia **22** 1309, 1310
crag martin **23** 1345, 1346, 1347
crakes **19** 1108, 1114
Cranchiidae **48** 2861, 2867
cranchiids **48** 2867
crane flies **45** *2641*, *2643-5*, 2647
crane hawk **18** 1070, 1072
cranes **19** *1103*, *1105-7*, *1110-1*, 1115
Craseonycteridae **12** 681, 704
Craseonycteris thonglongyai **12** 704
Craspedacusta sowerby **49** *2889*
Craspedosomidae **39** 2304
Crassostrea **48** 2842, 2843
Craveri's murrelet **20** 1148
crawfish **37** *2214*

crawling water beetle **41** *2455*
Crax rubra **19** 1088
crayfish **36** *2146*; **37** 2178, 2182, *2191-2*, *2211-13*, 2218-19
cream-coloured courser **19** 1136, 1137
cream-spot tiger-moth **44** *2620*
Creatophora cinerea **25** 1462
Crematogaster scutellaris **43** 2529, *2556*
Crenella faba **48** 2840
Crenicichla **35** 2048
creodonts **1** 25
Creophilus maxillosus **42** *2473*
Crepidula, fornicata **46** *2714*, 2720, *2724*
crest-tailed marsupial rat **11** 610
crested...
auklet **20** *1146*
bell-bird **24** 1400
berrypecker **24** 1416
eagle **51** 3044
gibbon **15** 842
hawk **18** 1076
honey buzzard **51** 3052
lark **23** 1334, *1339*
mangabey **14** 816
mantid **40** *2395*, *2398*
murrelet **20** 1148
porcupine **5** 273, 275
rat **5** 249, 254
screamer **18** *1029*, 1030-1
seriema **19** *1104*, *1117*
serpent eagle **18** *1054*, 1070
shrike-jay **25** 1489-90
swifts **21** 1218, 1224, *1225*, 1227
tit **24** *1403*; **51** 3010
tree swift **21** *1216*, 1224, *1225*, 1227
wood partridge **19** 1096
crevalle jack **34** *2012*, 2036
Crex crex **19** 1112
Cribochalina vasculum **48** 2880
cricket frog **30** 1795
crickets **39** 2311, 2323, 2324, 2326; **40** *2363-82*
Criconemoides **49** *2928*
Cricosaura typica **27** 1570
Crimora papillata **47** 2790
crimson rosella **20** *1162*, 1166, 1168
crimson-collared tanager **24** *1426*
crimson-winged woodpecker **22** *1298*
Crinifer piscator **20** 1178
Crinoidea **36** 2106, 2107, 2115-6
crinoids **36** 2110, 2115
Crioceris duodecimpunctata **42** 2506
Cristatella **50** 2968
Cro-Magnon Man **15** *900*
croaker **34** 2031-3
Crocidura **12** 662
crocodile bird **19** 1137
crocodile icefishes **35** 2055-6
crocodile lizards **27** 1602, 1609
crocodile newt **29** 1723
crocodiles **1** 11; **26** *1511*; **29** *1688-93*
classification **29** 1685
distribution **29** 1682
national parks **51** 3027, 3028, 3032, 3047
origin **26** *1504-5*
CROCODILIANS **26** *1507*, 1508-9, 1510; **29** *1681-95*
Crocodilydae **29** 1685
crocodylia **29** *1681-95*
Crocodylus
acutus **29** 1685
cataphractus **29** 1685
niloticus **29** 1685
palustris **29** 1685
porosus **29** 1685
rhombifer **29** 1685
siamensis **29** 1685
Crocothemis erithraea **40** 2355
Cromeria **32** 1892
cross-breasted turtles **26** 1533, 1535
Crossarchus obscurus **2** 98
Crossaster papposus **36** 2121, *2132*
crossbills **25** 1441, 1442, *1446*, 1447; **51** 3010
Crotalinae **28** 1669
Crotalus **28** 1669
Crotaphytus collaris **27** 1579
Crotophaga sulcirostris **20** 1178
crown conchs **46** 2746, 2751
crown-of-thorns starfish **36** 2114, 2130, *2131*, *2132*
crowned crane **19** *1103*, 1106, 1107
crowned hawk eagle **18** 1066
crowned lemur **13** 742
crowned pigeons **20** 1156
crows **22** *1304*, 1305; **25** 1484, *1485*, 1498 1500; **51** 3013
classification **22** 1303; **25** 1489
distribution **25** 1482
Crustacea **36** 2140, 2147
CRUSTACEANS **1** 40, 41-2; **36** 2103, *2146-60*; **37** *2161-2219*; **38** *2221-32*
body parts **36** 2141, *2146-7*
classification **36** 2140, 2147
courtship rituals **37** *2190-1*
evolution **37** 2208, **45** *2670*
reproduction **36** 2147
Crypsirina culcullata **25** 1489
Cryptobranchidae **29** 1713, 1716
Cryptobranchus alleganiensis **29** 1716
Cryptocellus **39** 2290
Cryptocephalus **42** 2504
Cryptocercidae **40** 2391
Cryptocheiilus comparatus **43** 2538, 2540
Cryptochiton stelleri **45** 2684, *2685*
Cryptodira **26** 1530, 1535
Cryptodonta **48** 2833-5, 2837
Cryptoplax **45** 2689
larvaeformis **45** 2684, 2688-9
Cryptoprocta ferox **2** 89
Cryptoproctinae **2** 89
Cryptops **39** 2307
Cryptostiginata **39** 2295
Cryptotermes **41** 2405
Crypturellus variegatus **16** 933
crystal goby **35** 2060, 2065
Crystallogobius linearis **35** 2060
Crystallophrisson indicum **45** *2690*
Ctaenochaetus striatus **35** 2065
Ctenidae **39** 2289
Ctenizidae **38** 2258; **39** 2281
Ctenocephalides felis **45** 2665
Ctenodactylidae **5** 277, 286
Ctenodactylus
gundi **5** 289
vali **5** 286
Ctenolabrus rupestris **34** 2023
Ctenomyidae **5** 277, 289
Ctenophora **49** 2901-2
Ctenophora festiva **45** *2644*
Ctenopoma ansorgi **35** *2067*, 2070
Ctenus ferus **39** *2282*
Cuban boa **28** 1639
Cuban brown scorpion **38** *2246*
Cuban crocodile **29** 1685, 1692
Cuban hutia **5** 287, 289
Cuban night lizard **27** 1570, 1571-2
Cuban snail **47** *2804*
Cuban solenodon **11** 651
Cuban tody **22** 1270
Cuban trogon **21** *1240*
Cubitermes sp. **41** *2424*
cuchia **34** *2006*
cuckoo falcons **18** 1073
cuckoo gurnard **34** 2007
cuckoo ray **31** 1838, 1842
cuckoo weevil **42** 2509
cuckoo wrasse **34** 2023, 2025
cuckoo-roller **21** 1253; **22** 1261, 1263, 1266
cuckoo-shrikes **23** 1354, 1355, *1357*, 1358
cuckoos **20** *1172*, 1173, 1174-5, *1174-82*; **51** 3050
classification **20** 1178
parasitism **16** 914; **20** *1175-80*; **24** *1381*
Cuculidae **20** 1178
Cuculiformes **20** *1171-82*
Cuculus canorus **20** 1178
Cucumaria planci **36** *2117*
Cucumaricola notabilis **37** *2168*
Culex
fatigans **45** 2650, 2652
pipiens **45** 2649, 2650, 2652
Culicidae **45** 2647, 2652
culicine mosquitoes **45** *2644*
Cumacea **37** 2194
cumaceans **37** *2188*, 2194-5, *2196*
cuon **2** *110*, 111, 114-15
Cuora flavomarginata **26** 1539
cup coral polyps **49** *2886*
curassows **19** 1088, 1092, 1098
Curculio elephas **42** 2506, *2514*
Curculionidae **41** 2456; **42** 2506, 2513
Curimatidae **32** 1908
curl-crested aracari **22** 1290
curlew quill louse **41** 2428
curlews **16** 909; **19** 1126, *1128*, *1127*, 1129, 1135sx **51** 3046
currawongs **25** 1471, 1472
Cursorius cursor **19** 1137
cuscus **11** 612, 616, *624-5*, 626; **51** 3048
cushion star **36** *2131*, 2136
cusk eels **33** 1948, 1956
Cuspidaria **48** 2848
cuspidata **48** *2844*
rostrata **48** 2848
Cuspidariidae **48** 2848
cut-throat trout **33** 1931
cutlassfishes **35** 2066-7
cutthroat eels **32** 1874, 1884
cuttlefishes **45** 2674-5, 2678, 2681; **48** *2851-2*, *2854-5*, *2858*, *2860-1*
Cuvier's beaked whale **10** 593
Cuvier's gazelle **9** 529
Cuvier's toucan **22** 1290
Cyamidae **37** 2207
Cyanerpes cyaneus **24** 1429
Cyanocitta cristata **25** 1489
Cyanopica cyana **25** 1489
Cyclanorbis senegalensis **26** 1553
Cyclarhis gujanensis **24** 1435
Cyclina sinensis **48** 2849
Cycloderma frenatum **26** 1553
Cyclope neritea **46** 2751
Cyclopes didactylus **4** 195
cyclopoid copepods **37** *2162*, *2163*, *2165-6*, *2167*
Cyclopoida **37** 2163
Cyclopteridae **34** 2007
Cyclopterus lumpus **34** 2007, 2010
Cyclorrhapha **45** 2655, 2659
Cyclostomata **31** 1818
Cyclothone **33** 1944
Cyclura cornuta **27** 1579
Cydippida **49** 2901
Cygnus **18** 1044
cylinder millipedes **39** 2303, *2304*
Cylindrachetoidea **40** 2369
cylindrical skinks **27** *1595-6*
Cymatiidae **46** 2737, 2742-3
Cymatium parthenopaeum **46** 2743; **47** *2762*
Cymatoceps nasutus **34** 2033
Cymbiola imperialis **47** 2761
Cymbiolacca peristicta **47** 2761
Cymbium cymbium **47** 2761
Cymbulia **47** 2782-3
peroni **47** *2774*, *2784*
Cymbuliidae **47** 2782
Cynipidae **42** 2516, *2520*
Cynocephalidae **12** 676
CYNOCEPHALIDS **12** *673-6*
Cynocephalus **12** 676
cynodonts **1** 11
Cynofelidae **1** 28
Cynogale bennetti **2** 92
Cynoglossidae **35** 2075
Cynoglossus senegalensis **35** 2075
Cynolebias bellotti **33** 1978
Cynomys **4** 233
Cynopterus sphinx **12** 694
Cynthia cardui **44** 2633
Cyphoma gibbosum **46** 2729-30
Cypraea
albuginosa **46** 2736
cervus **46** 2734, 2736
citrina **46** 2736
cribraria **46** *2726*
midwayensis **46** 2734
moneta **46** 2720, 2734
piperita **46** 2736
spurca **46** 2736
sulcidentata **46** *2731*
talpa **46** 2734
tigris **46** 2720, *2725*, 2730, 2736
zonarie **46** *2734*
Cypraeacea **46** 2720, 2727
Cypraecassis rufa **46** *2741*
Cypraeidae **46** 2720, 2730
Cypreacassis rufa **47** *2762*
Cyprina islandica **48** 2845, 2847
Cyprinacea **48** 2847
Cyprinidae **32** 1894
Cypriniformes **31** 1858; **32** *1891-1920*
Cyprinodon diabolus **33** 1978
Cyprinodontidae **33** 1978
Cyprinodontiformes **33** *1963-80*; **34** 1981-4, *1996*
Cyprinus carpio **32** 1894
Cypris **37** 2171
Cypselurus
californicus **33** 1965
cyanopterus **33** 1965
heterurus **33** 1965

rondeleti **33** 1965, 1968
Cypsiurus parvus **21** 1218
Cyrtopleura costata **48** *2844*
Cyrtus gibbus **45** *2658*
Cystophora cristata **4** 184
Cystophorinae **3** 179
Cythere **36** *2160*

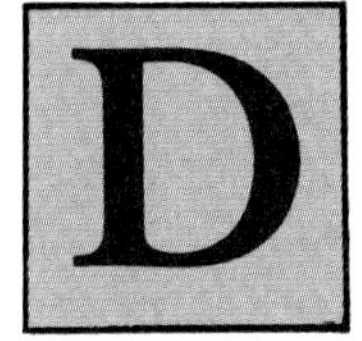

dab **35** 2075, *2078-9*
dabbling ducks **18** 1030, 1031, 1044-7
dabchick **16** *915*, *956*, 960
dace **32** *1862*, 1894, 1901
Dacelo novaeguineae **21** 1253
Daceloninae **21** 1253
Dachnonypha **44** 2595, 2599
Dactylopius coccus **41** 2438, 2452
Dactylopteridae **34** 2004
Dactylopteriformes **34** 2004
Dactyloscopidae **35** 2059
Dactyplopterus volitans **34** 2004
Dacus oleae **45** 2657, 2659
daddy-longlegs **39** *2290*; **45** *2641*, *2643-5*, 2647
daggertooth fish **33** 1945-6
Daird's blind snake **28** 1623
dalgyte **11** 620
Dallia pectoralis **33** 1937
Dall's porpoise **10** 588, 593
Dall's sheep **10** 561, *563*, 566-7, 570
Dalmatian pelican **17** *977*, 980, 982; **51** 3014
Dama
dama **7** 396, 406
mesopotamica **7** 406
dama gazelle **9** *518-19*, 520, 529
dama wallaby **11** *637*, 642
Damaliscus **9** 490
damp-wood termites **41** 2403, 2405
Dampierosa daruma **34** 2007
damselfishes **34** 2013, 2024, *2028-31*
damselflies **39** 2311; **40** *2349-62*
Danaus **44** *2607*
Danio malabaricus **32** 1894
Daphnia **36** *2156*, *2159*
Daphnis nerii **44** 2624
Daption capense **17** 973
Dardanus arrosor **38** *2224*
dark chanting goshawk **18** 1064-5
dark green racer **28** 1660
dark-eyed junco **24** 1429
dark-rumped petrel **17** 973
dark-sided salamander **30** 1752
dark-winged trumpeter **19** 1117
darkling beetles **41** 2456; **42** 2472, *2490-2*
D'Arnaud's barbet **22** *1285*, *1286*, 1288
darters **17** *978*, 980, 984, *990-1*
Darwin, Charles **15** 892-3; **27** 1574; **37** 2169; **51** 3034
Darwin's finches **24** 1423, *1424-5*; **51** 3035
Darwin's frog **30** 1798-9

ABOVE A mature red deer stag roars to ward off rivals.

Darwin's rhea **16** *923-4*, *926-7*
classification **16** 925
Darwin's termite **41** 2403, 2405, 2407
Dascylius **34** 2024
dassies **6** 312
Dasyatidae **31** 1844
Dasyatis pastinaca **31** 1844
Dasyoprocta azarae **5** 289
Dasypeltis scabra **28** 1645
Dasypoda plumipes **43** *2538*, 2539
Dasypodidae **4** 197
Dasyproctidae **5** 277, 289
Dasypus novemcinctus **4** 197
Dasyuridae **11** 612, 619
Dasyuroides byrnei **11** 619
Daubentonia madagascariensis **13** 742
Daubentoniidae **13** 742
Daudebardia **48** 2824
David, Père Armand **2** 68
Davis mountain kingsnakes **51** 3042
dawn blind snakes **28** 1621, 1625
day heron **17** 1000
De Brazza's monkey **14** *795*, 816, *818*, 819
dead men's fingers **49** 2889, 2901
Dead Sea sparrow **25** 1455
dead-leaf butterfly **44** 2597
dealfishes **34** 1987-8
death adder **28** 1667, *1668*, *1669*
death's head hawk-moth **44** *2596*, 2620-1, 2624
death's head monkey **13** 773
deathwatch beetle **41** 2456, 2457
Decapoda **37** 2182, 2208, *2211-20*; **38** 2223
decorator crab **38** *2230*
deep sea Arctic ark shell **48** 2834
deep sea squid **48** *2854*
deep-sea angler fishes **32** 1866; **33** *1958-61*
deep-sea hatchetfish **33** *1940*, *1942-4*
deep-snouted pipefish **34** *1996*, 2000, *2002*
deep-water eyeless octopus **48** 2868, 2869
deer, national parks **51** *3010-11*, 3013
deer cowrie **46** 2734, 2736
deer families **1** 26; **7** *389-420*; **8** *421-4*; **10** 569
endangered species **8** 421, 424
rut behaviour **8** 421-2
ungulate features **5** 298; **6** 301, 304-8
deer fly **45** *2653*
deer mouse **5** *243*, 244
defassa waterbuck **9** *503*, 505, *509*, *510*; **51** 3024
degu **5** 277, *288*, 289, 294
Deinacrida heteracantha **40** 2369
Delichon urbica **23** 1345
Delima itala **47** *2804*
Delphacidae **41** 2438, 2447
Delphinapterus leucas **10** 593
Delphinidae **10** 593
Delphinus delphis **10** 593
Demodicidae **39** 2295
demoiselle crane **19** 1106, 1107
demoiselles **40** 2351, *2355*
Demospongiae **48** *2875-6*, 2880
Dendragapus obscurus **19** 1093
Dendrobates pumilio **30** 1785
Dendrobatidae **30** 1756, 1785
Dendrobranchiata **37** 2212
Dendrocincla fuliginosa **22** 1310
Dendrocolaptidae **22** 1303, 1310
Dendrocopos **22** 1297
Dendrocygna **18** 1036
Dendrocygnini **18** 1030, 1036
Dendrodorididae **47** 2796
Dendrohyrax **6** 313
Dendroica **24** 1431
Dendromurinae **5** 261
Dendronanthus indicus **23** 1352
Dendrone phthya **49** *2898*
Dendronotacea **47** 2786, 2796, 2797
Dendronotus
arborescens **47** *2774*
frondosus **47** *2795*, *2796*, 2797
Dendrospis **28** 1667
Dentaliidae **45** 2692
Dentalium **45** *2692*
dentalis **45** 2692
inaequicostatum **45** 2692
rossati **45** 2692
senegalensis **45** *2691*, 2692
stenoschizum **45** 2691
texasianum **45** 2692
vulgare **45** 2692
Dentex dentex **34** 2033
Denticeps clupeoides **32** 1890
Denticipitidae **32** 1890
denticle herring **32** 1890
Dermanyssidae **39** 2295
Dermaptera **39** 2311; **40** 2387, 2388
Dermatemydidae **26** 1535
Dermatemys mawei **26** 1535
Dermestes lardarius **42** *2473*
Dermochelyidae **26** 1553
Dermochelys coriacea **26** 1553
Dermogenes pusillus **33** 1965, *1967*
Dermophis mexicanus **29** 1710
Dermoptera **12** 674, 676
dero **9** 529
Deroceras **48** 2825, *2826*
Derocheilocaris notabilis **37** *2169*
Des Murs' wiretail **22** 1310
desert...
beetle **42** *2491*
choughs **25** 1494
cottontail **4** 209, *212*
dormouse **5** *242*, 248, 254
gundi **5** 286
hedgehog **11** *646*, 655, *656*
horned lizard **27** 1573
isopod **37** *2198*, 2199
jerboa **5** *242*, 268, 270
lark **51** 3054
locust **40** *2363*, *2365*, 2369, 2376-9
monitor **27** 1609
night lizard **27** 1570, 1571
pupfish **33** 1973
rat kangaroo 11 642
scorpion **38** *2246*
shovelfoot **30** 1799, 1800
sparrow **25** 1455
tortoise **26** *1518*, *1524*
Desmana moschata **12** 670
desmans **11** 647-9; **12** 670, *672*
Desmodontidae **12** 681, 709
Desmodus rotundus **12** 709
desmognaths **30** 1751
Desmognathus **30** 1750
Desmopteridae **47** 2782-3
deuterostomes **50** 2966-7, *2970-3*
Deuterostomia **45** 2670
devil rays **31** 1844-6
devilfish **10** 577
devil's coach-horse beetle **41** *2454*; **42** 2472, *2476*
Devil's Hole pupfish **33** 1973, 1978
dhaman **28** 1661
dhole **3** *129-30*
Diactor bilineatus **41** *2439*
Diadacna **48** 2847

diadem monkey **14** 816
diadem sifaka **13** 742, 748-9
Diadema setosum **36** 2120
Diaemus youngi **12** 709
diamond fish **35** *2046*
diamond-birds **24** 1416, 1417
diamondback rattlesnakes **28** *1668*, 1669, *1679*
diamondback terrapin **26** *1538*
diana monkey **14** *795*, 816, *818-9*; **51** 3020
Diapis pengagona **42** 2486
diapsids **26** 1558
Diard's trogon **21** 1241, *1243*
Diaspis pentagona **43** *2521*
Diastylis
  lucifera **37** *2196*
  rathkei **37** *2188*
  tumida **37** *2196*
Diatryma **16** 905
Diazona violacea **35** 2094
Dibamidae **27** 1570
Dibamus **27** 1570
dibatag **9** *518*, 529, 530-1
Dibranchiata **48** 2855
Dicaeidae **24** 1417
Dicaeum **24** 1417
Dicamptodon **29** 1722
Dicamptodontidae **29** 1713, 1722
dice snake **28** *1655*
Dicentrarchus labrax **34** 2023
Dicerorhinus sumatrensis **7** 361
Diceros bicornis **7** 361
Dicranocephalus bourgoini **42** 2495
Dicrocoelium denditicum **47** 2819
Dicruridae **25** 1465
Dicrurus **25** 1465
Dictynidae **39** 2289
Dictyophara europaea **41** *2446*
Dictyoptera **40** 2391
Dicyemida **48** *2874*
Didelphidae **11** 612, 615
Didelphis virginiana **11** 615
Didemnum molle **35** *2088-9*, 2090
Didinium **50** *2977*, 2979, 2992, 2998
Didunculus strigirostris **20** 1156
digger wasp **40** 2397
digitigrade species **1** 21
Digonota **49** 2923
dik-diks **8** *436*, *439-41*, 444
dikkops **19** 1136
Dinarda dentata **42** 2478
Dinemellia dinemelli **25** 1459
dingo **1** 23, 36; **2** *114*, 115, 117; **51** *3046*
dingy skipper **44** 2633
Dinoflagellata **50** 2976, 2985
Dinoflagellida **50** 2976
Dinomyidae **5** 277, 289
Dinomys branicki **5** 289
Dinopidae **39** 2290
Dinoptera gigantea **43** 2536
dinosaurs **1** 8, 10, 11; **26** *1507*, 1508-9; **29** 1682
Diodon **35** 2082
Diodontidae **35** 2082
Diodora **45** 2699
  apertura **45** *2699*
  aspera **45** 2700
  dysoni **45** 2697
  graeca **45** 2697, 2699
Diomedeidae **17** 971
Diomedia **17** 971
Diphylla ecaudata **12** 709
Diphyllodes magnificus **25** 1480
Diplogale hosie **2** 92
Diplogasteria **49** 2925
Diplolepis rosae **42** 2516, *2519-20*
Diplopoda **39** *2302-4*
Diploptera punctata **40** 2391
Diplotaxodon **35** 2050
Diplura **39** 2303, *2332*, 2333, 2334
diplurans **39** 2311, 2328, 2329, *2333-5*
Dipluridae **38** 2258; **39** 2283
dipnoi **31** 1808
Dipodidae **5** 254, 268
Dipodomys **4** 233
dippers **22** 1304, 1305; **23** 1373-4, *1375-6*
Diprion pini **42** *2516*, *2519-20*
Diprionidae **42** 2520
Diprotodonta **11** 612
Dipsas indica **28** 1645
Diptera **39** 2311, 2323; **45** *2641-64*
  classification **45** 2647, 2652, 2659
Dirofilaria immitis **49** 2925
disc-tongued toads **30** *1760-3*
disc-winged bat **12** 681, 708, 709
Discartemon sangkarensis **48** 2822
Disceus **31** 1844
Discoglossidae **30** 1760
Discoglossus pictus **30** 1760
Discordorididae **47** 2795
Discosoma **34** 2031
discus **35** 2049, *2054-5*, *2064*
dish backed tree frog **30** *1764*, *1793*, 1795
Disoclyna **50** *2986*
Dispholidus typus **28** 1645
Dissotictus mawsoni **35** 2056
Distaplia rosa **35** 2094
Distoechurus pennatus **11** 627
Distomum macrostomum **47** 2820
Distomus variolosus **35** *2094*
Ditrysia **44** 2595, 2599, 2600, 2609, 2624, 2633
divers **16** *952-5*
  classification **16** 954
  distribution **16** 957
diving beetles **41** *2455*, 2456; **42** *2462-8*
diving ducks **18** 1030, 1047-8
diving petrels **17** 962, 971
  classification **17** 976
  distribution **17** 963, 974
  nesting **17** 976
dobson flies **39** 2311; **43** 2566, 2568, 2570
Dobsonia moluccensis **12** 694
Docimodus johnstoni **35** 2051
Dociostaurus maroccanus **42** 2488
Dodecaceria **49** 2939; **50** 2942
dog cockles **45** 2675; **48** 2836, 2837
dog flea **45** 2666-7
dog louse **41** 2428
dog salmon **33** 1924
dog tapeworm **49** 2911, *2916*, 2917
dog whelks **45** *2679*; **46** *2727-8*, 2746, *2747-8*, *2751-3*, 2759
dogfishes **31** *1831*, 1834, 1839
dogs **1** 14, 34
  canid family **2** *108-20*; **3** *121-32*
  classification **1** 28; **2** 117-18; **3** 127
  distribution **2** 115-16, 119
  domestic **2** 111, 117
  eyes **1** 21
  national parks **51** 3018, 3023, 3026
  predator **1** *23*, 29, 36
  teeth **1** *22*
Dolabella **47** 2779
Dolhinow, Phyllis Jay **14** 834
Dolichonyx orizivorous **24** 1440
Doliolids **35** 2100
dollar bird **22** 1261, 1263
Dolly Varden trout **33** 1934
Dolomedes fimbriatus **38** *2271*
dolphin fish **34** *2012*, 2036, 2038-9
dolphins **1** *10*; **10** 572, 574, 584-5, *588-96*; **51** 3035
Dolycoris baccarum **41** *2440*
domestic cat **3** 136, 139
domestic cockroaches **40** 2394
domestic goat **10** 558-60, 570
domestic guinea-pig **5** *272*
domestic sheep **10** 559-60, 567, 570
Donacia **42** 2504
  crassipes **42** *2465*
Donacidae **48** 2847
Donax **48** 2847, *2848*
donkey **6** 340
dor beetles **42** 2492, *2497*, 2503
dorcas gazelle **9** 520, 524, *525*, 529
Dorcatragus megalotis **8** 444
Doria's goshawk **18** 1065
dorid sea slugs **45** 2678
Doridacea **47** *2785-90*, 2792, 2794-7
Doridoxa ingolfiana **47** 2786
Doridoxidae **47** 2785-6
dories **34** *1987*, 1989-90
Doris verrucosa **47** *2787*
dormancy **2** 71; **30** 1753
dormouse **5** *242*, 243, *263*, 266-8
Dorylinae **43** 2559
Doryrhampus melanopleura **34** 2000
Doto fragilis **47** 2797
Dotoidae **47** 2797
dotterel **19** 1125; **51** 3011
double-crested cormorant **17** *978*, 990
double-toothed barbet **22** *1285*, 1287, 1288
douc monkeys **14** 822, *824*, *827*, 831
douroucouli **13** *763*, 764-5, 774; **51** 3038
dove shells **46** 2746, 2751
Dover sole **35** *2074*, 2075, *2083*
doves **20** *1152-3*, 1156, *1158-60*
  see also pigeons
dowitchers **19** 1135
downy emerald dragonfly **40** *2350*
Dracaena guianensis **27** 1603
Draco volans **27** 1585
DRACONEMATIDS **49** 2925, *2926*
Dracunculus medinensis **49** 2925, 2929, 2933
dragon lizards **27** 1582
dragonets **34** *2033* -4
dragonfishes **33** *1940*, 1943
dragonflies **36** 2143, 2144; **39** 2311, 2318, 2322, *2324*; **40** *2349-62*; **43** 2573
Dreissensia **48** 2847
Dreissensiacea **48** 2845, 2847
Dreissensidae **48** 2845, 2847
Drepanididae **24** 1435
Drepanophorus **49** *2919*, 2920
drill **13** 723; **14** *792*, 808, 811, 813-14
drilling acorn barnacles **37** 2177
driver ants **43** 2529, 2559-62
Dromadidae **19** 1121, 1137
Dromaiidae **16** 925
Dromaius novaehollandiae **16** 925
Dromas ardeola **19** 1137
dromedary **7** *379*, 381, 386-7, 388
Dromiciops australis **11** 624
dromiid crab **38** *2224*
Dromiidae **38** 2223-5
droneflies **39** 2321; **45** *2656-7*, 2659
drongos **25** *1454*, 1465, *1468*
Drosophila melanogaster **45** 2659
Drosophilidae **45** 2659
drums **32** 1863; **34** 2033
dry-wood termites **41** 2403, 2405
Dryocopus martius **22** 1297
Dryophis nasuta **28** 1645
dryopid beetles **42** *2465*, 2481-2
Dryopidae **42** 2472, 2481-2
Dryopithecus **15** 894-5
Dryops auriculatus **42** *2465*
Dryptus moritzianus **48** 2822
Dublin Bay prawn **37** *2214*, 2218
Dubois, Eugene **15** 894, 899
duck mussel **48** 2842
duck-billed platypus **1** 15; **11** *604-6*
ducks **18** *1028-34*, 1036, 1041, *1044-52*
  classification **18** 1030, 1036, 1044
  distribution **18** 1031
  national parks **51** 3008, 3027, 3050
Ducula aenea **20** 1156
dugong **5** 298; **6** *313-14*, 315-16
Dugong dugon **6** 314
duikers **8** 434, *436-8*, 440; **10** *568*; **51** 3016, 3020
Dulidae **23** 1374
Dulus dominicus **23** 1374
Dumetella carolinensis **23** 1380
dune mole-rat **5** 284, 295
dung beetles **41** 2456, 2457, 2458; **42** 2492-4, *2496-7*, *2498*, 2503
  classification **42** 2503
  distribution **42** 2495
Dungeness crabs **38** 2225
dunlin **19** 1127, *1130*, 1135
dunnart **11** 619
dunnock **20** 1176; **24** *1381*, 1383
Dusicyon **3** 127
dusky broadbill **22** 1307
dusky cockroach **40** 2391, *2394*, 2395
dusky leaf monkey **14** *825*, 826
dusky perch **34** *2012*
dusky purpletuft **23** 1322
dusky salamander **30** 1750, 1751
dusky titi monkey **13** *764-5*, 768, 774
dusky-footed woodrat **5** 244
dusty wings **43** 2570
Duvaucelia odhneri **47** 2770
dwarf...
  anteater **4** 195
  antelopes **8** 434, 435-6, 438-46; **10** *569*
  bee **43** 2540
  brocket **7** 417-18
  bush baby **13** 748, 752
  caiman **29** 1685, *1695*
  crocodile **29** *1684*, 1685, *1691*, 1693
  goby **31** 1809
  gourami **35** *2067*, 2070

lemurs **13** 733, 735, 745; **15** *896*
classification **13** 728, 742
mongoose **2** *96*
seahorse **34** 2000
shark **31** 1827, 1839
siren **30** 1754
snake **28** 1644, 1645
sperm whale **10** 593
topminnow **33** 1978, 1980
tree mantis **40** 2391
waterdog **30** 1743
Dynastes **42** 2493, 2500, 2503
Dynastinae **42** 2503
dytiscid beetles **42** *2465*
Dytiscidae **41** 2456; **42** 2468
Dytiscus **41** 2456; **42** *2465*, 2468

eagle owl **20** *1185*, *1192-3*, 1196, 1199; **51** *3006*, 3007, 3013
eagle rays **31** *1827*, *1838*, *1844-5*
eagles **16** 906, 907; **18** *1053-5*, 1063-4, 1066-7, *1071*
classification **18** 1057, 1061, 1070
courtship **18** *1059*, 1060
distribution **18** 1056
national parks **51** 3007, *3010-11*, 3013-14, 3017, 3027, 3044
predator **18** 1057-8
ear-shelled water snail **47** *2708*
eared grebe **16** 957
eared nightjar **21** 1207
eared seals **3** 164, 167
earless lizard **27** 1572
earless seal **3** 164, 167, 176, 180
earthcreepers **22** 1309, 1310, 1312
earthworms **29** 1708; **49** 2937; **50** 2942, 2946, 2948-50, *2952-3*, 2956
earwigs **39** 2311; **40** *2387* -9
East Caucasian tur **10** 570
eastern...
blue-tongued skink **27** *1592*
bluebird **24** 1382, *1386*, 1388
box turtle **26** *1537*
broad-billed roller **21** *1250*; **22** 1261, 1263
brown snake **28** 1641
coral snake **28** *1667*, *1668*
cottontail **4** *202*, 207, 209, 212-13
diamondback rattlesnake **28** *1679*
double-collared sunbird **24** *1413*
fence lizard **27** 1573
grass owl **20** 1195
grey kangaroo **11** *609*, *616*, 642, 644
hognosed snake **28** *1643*
kingbird **22** *1318-9*, 1320
lowland gorilla **15** 852, 856, 890
newt **29** 1729, *1739*, 1740
pocket gopher **4** 233
ringtail possum **11** *632*
tarsier **13** 748
tree hyrax **6** 312, 313
turtle dove **20** 1159
water dragon **27** 1585, 1587
Eastern American trap-door spider **38** *2261*
Eatoniellidae **46** 2706
Ecdyonuridae **40** 2343
Echeneididae **34** 2013; **35** 2046
Echeneis naucrates **35** 2046-7
echidna **10** *597-60*; **11** *601-4*, 606
Echidna **32** 1874, *1880*
Echimyidae **5** 277, 289
Echinarachnius parma **36** *2117*
Echinococcus granulosus **49** 2911, 2917
Echinocridium cordatum **36** 2120
Echinodermata **36** 2106, 2107
ECHINODERMS **36** 2102, *2104-37*; **50** 2966
classification **36** 2107
distribution **36** 2120-1
evolution **36** *2115*
locomotion **36** 2109
regeneration **36** *2110-11*
reproduction **36** *2112-14*
Echinoidea **36** 2107, *2124-7*
Echinometra locunter **36** *2126*
Echinophthiridae **41** 2428
echinopluteus (larvae) **36** *2112*
Echinoprocta rufescens **5** 283
Echinops telfairi **11** 651
Echinorhinus **31** 1841
Echinosorex gymnurus **11** 655
Echinus
esculentus **36** *2101-2*
melo **36** *2117*, *2125*
Echiura **50** 2950, 2958
echiuran worms **49** *2936*; **50** *2950-1*, 2958
Eciton **43** 2529, *2558*
eclectus parrot **16** *905*
ecological equivalents **1** 27
Ectobius **40** 2391, 2395
Ecuador, national park **51** 3002, *3034-5*
Ecuadorean shrew opossum **11** 624
EDENTATES **4** *185-200*
Edentulina affinis **48** 2822
edge-snouted worm-lizards **27** *1607*, *1616*
edible crab **38** *2225*
edible dormouse **5** 266-7
edible frog **29** *1696-7*; **30** *1771*, 1778
edible nest swiftlet **21** 1218, *1223*
edible scallop **48** *2840*
edible snail **45** *2675*; **47** *2804*, *2812*, 2817; **48** *2827-8*
edmi **9** 529
Edriolynchnus schimnidti **33** *1960*
eel-skippers **35** 2060, 2062-3
eelpouts **35** *2056*, 2057
eels **31** *1858-9*; **32** *1863*, *1873-84*
see also electric eels; spiny-eels
classification **32** 1874
distribution **32** 1876
eeltail catfish **32** 1911, *1913*, 1920
egg-eating snakes **28** 1641, *1642*, 1644, *1645-7*
eggar moths **44** 2591, 2626
egrets **17** 997, *998*, 1000, 1007; **51** 3008, 3046
Egretta **17** 1007
Egyptian...

ABOVE The common earwig feeds on a wide variety of plant matter.

cobra **28** 1644, 1662-3, 1667
goose **16** *902-3*; **18** *1044-6*
grasshopper **40** *2382*
locust **40** 2369, 2382
mongoose **2** *96*
mosquito **45** *2644*
nightjar **21** 1206
plover **19** *1136*, 1137
pygmy shrew **12** 662
rousette **12** 693, 694, *697*, *701*
slit-faced bat **12** 699
spiny-tailed lizard **27** 1585-6
tomb bat **12** 697, 704
tortoise **26** 1542
vulture **16** 916; **18** 1070, *1076*, 1077, 1078
eider ducks **18** *1049*, 1050, 1052
Eidolon helvum **12** 694
Eimeria zurnii **50** 2992
Eingana (Rainbow Snake) **28** 1632
Eisenia foetida **50** *2953*, *2955*
Elamis maugetii **42** 2472
eland **8** *448*, 450, *453*, 457, 460
classification **8** 452
Elaninae **18** 1070
Elanus **18** 1070
Elaphe longissima **28** 1645
Elaphodus cephalophus **7** 396
Elaphurus davidiensis **7** 406
elapid snakes **28** 1640
Elapidae **28** 1621, 1667
Elapinae **28** 1667
Elasmobranchi **31** 1827
Elasmucha grisea **41** *2433*
Elassoma **34** 2014
Elater sanguineus **42** *2505*
Elateridae **41** 2456; **42** 2472, 2478
Eld's deer **7** *399*, 404, 406, *410*; **8** 421
electric catfish **32** 1911, 1913
electric eels **32** 1869, *1870-1*, *1906*, *1920*
electric rays **31** *1841-2*
Electrona rissoi **33** *1942*
Electrophoridae **32** 1920
Electrophorus electricus **32** 1920
Eledone moschata **48** 2869
Eledonella pygmaea **48** *2866*, 2869
elegant cuttlefish **48** 2855
elegant trogon **21** 1244
elegant-crested tinamou **16** *932*, 933
Eleodes **42** 2462
Eleonora's falcon **18** *1074-5*, 1080; **19** 1083
Eleotrididae **35** 2060
elephant hawk-moth **44** 2595
elephant louse **41** 2428
elephant seal **3** *161*, 163, 167, *176-7*; **4** 181, *182*, 183
elephant snout fishes **32** 1869, *1870-1*
elephant-shrews **11** *646*, *657*, *660*
classification **11** 660
distribution **11** 647
elephant-trunk fish **35** 2072
Elephantalus **11** 660
Elephantidae **6** 324
elephants **1** 12; **5** 298; **6** 304, *317-30*
national parks **51** 3020, 3022, *3030-1*
elephant's trunk snake **28** 1626
Elephas maximus **6** 324
Eleutherodactylus jasperi **30** 1795
elf owl **20** 1195, 1199, *1200*
Elgaria multicarinatus **27** 1603
elk **7** 393-4, 396, *414-19*
national parks **51** 3006, 3036, 3041, 3056
Ellesmeroceratidae **48** 2853
Ellobiacea **47** 2805
Ellobiidae **47** 2801, 2803, 2805
elm bark beetle **41** 2456-7; **42** *2505*

elmid beetle **42** *2465*
Elmis **42** *2465, 2472, 2481*
Elopidae **32** 1872
Elopiformes **32** 1872; **33** *1940*
Elops saurus **32** 1872
elvers **32** 1874, *1877, 1879*
Elysia viridis **47** 2770, 2778
Elysiidae **47** 2767, 2778
elytra **41** 2458
Emarginula **45** *2698*, 2699
Emballonuridae **12** 681, 704
Emberiza **24** 1429
Emberizidae **22** 1303; **24** 1429
Embiidae **39** 2338
Embioptera **39** 2311, 2338; **40** 2347-8
emerald cuckoo **20** *1172*, 1180-1
emerald damselflies **40** 2351, 2359
emerald dove **20** 1156, *1160*
emerald hummingbird **21** *1238*
emerald tree boa **28** 1636, 1637
Emerita talpoida **37** 2220
emperor bird of paradise **25** *1477, 1478*, 1479, 1480
emperor dragonfly **40** 2352
Emperor of Germany bird of paradise **25** 1479
emperor goose **18** *1027*
emperor moths **39** *2318*; **44** 2624, 2625, *2626, 2630-1*
emperor penguin **16** 913, *936*, 937-8, 940-3, *945-7*
  classification **16** 949
  distribution **16** 944, 948
emperor tamarin **14** *783, 787*, 790
Empusa pennata **40** *2398*
emu **16** 918, 925, *929-30*
emu-wren **24** 1399
Emus hirtus **42** *2473*, 2477
Emydidae **26** 1539
Enchytraeidae **50** 2948, 2952
endangered species **1** 14; **7** 401, 405
  Arabian oryx **9** 501
  Arabian tahr **10** 555
  argali **10** 566
  badger **1** 53
  Cape hunting dog **2** 119
  cat family **3** 159; **51** 3018, 3028, *3038-9*, 3044, 3056
  cheetah **1** 36; **51** 3018
  cranes **19** 1105
  crocodilians **29** 1692
  deer **8** 421, 424
  desmans **12** 672
  elephants **6** 330; **51** 3024, 3030
  giant panda **2** 68; **51** 3058
  great apes **15** 890
  grey bat **12** 688
  guenons **14** 819
  hares **4** 214
  hippopotamuses **7** 378
  hummingbirds **21** 1238
  ibex **10** 553, 555
  leaf monkeys **14** 825
  lemurs **13** 745
  lorises **13** 754
  markhor **10** 557, 558
  mouflon **10** 560
  mountain gorilla **1** 18
  Nilgiri tahr **10** 554
  otter **1** 51
  parrots **20** 1170
  polar bear **2** *77*
  pygmy hog **7** 372
  rabbits **4** 214
  rhinoceros **6** 358; **51** 3032
  sea otter **1** 56
  snow leopard **1** 35
  Spanish goat **10** 553, 557
  Taiwanese serow **10** 541
  tarsiers **13** 754
  urial **10** 563
  whales **10** 576, 578
Enderoceratoidea **48** 2853
Endochironomus tendens **45** *2644*
Endodontacea **48** 2822
Endodontidae **48** 2822
Endontacea **47** 2817, 2818
English glow-worm **42** *2478-9*
English White Park cattle **8** 476
Engraulidae **32** 1890
Engraulis **32** 1890
Enhydra lutris **1** 55
Enidae **47** 2819
Enneacanthus gloriosus **34** 2014
Enoplia **49** 2920, 2925
Enoploteuthidae **48** 2861, 2863
Ensatina **30** 1750
Ensifera **40** 2364-6, 2369
Ensifera ensifera **21** 1228
Ensis
  directus **48** 2848, 2849
  ensis **48** *2844*, 2848-9
  siliqua **48** *2848-50*
Entamoeba **50** *2989*, 2991
entellus langur **14** 826
Entelurus aequoreus **34** 2000
Enterobius vermicularis **49** 2929
Enteropneusta **50** 2971, *2973*
Entoconcha **45** 2678
Entoconchidae **46** 2721
Entovalva **48** 2845-7
Entroprocta **49** *2919-20*
Eobania vermiculata **47** *2813*
epauletted bats **12** *690, 694, 698*
Ephelota **59** 2981
Ephemera
  danica **40** 2344, **39** *2337*, 2338
  ignita **40** *2342*
  vulgata **40** 2344
Ephemeridae **39** 2338, *2339*
Ephemeroptera **39** 2311, 2321, 2338; **40** 2341
Ephestia kuehniella **44** *2604*
Ephiophlebia **40** 2351, 2362
Ephippiorhynchus senegalensis **17** 1012
Ephthianura tricolor **24** 1398
Epicaridea **37** 2202
Epicrates **28** 1637
Epimorpha **39** 2307
Epinephelus lanceolatus **34** 2023
Episcopal mitre **47** 2761
Epitoniacea **46** 2712, 2719
Epitoniidae **46** 2712, 2719, 2720
Epitonium **46** 2721
  scalare **46** 2712, *2726*
Epomophorus gambianus **12** 694
Eptatretus **31** 1818
Eptesicus serotinus **12** 712
Equidae **6** 340
EQUIDS **6** *331-48*
Equus **6** 333
  africanus **6** 340
  burchelli **6** 340
  caballus **6** 340
  grevyi **6** 340
  hemionus **6** 340
  przewalskii **6** 340
  zebra **6** 340
Erato **46** 2720, 2729
  voluta **46** *2728*
erect-crested penguin **16** 949
Eremitalpa granti **11** 655
Eremophila alpestris **23** 1334
Eremopterix grisea **23** 1334
Eresus niger **39** 2289
Erethizon dorsatum **5** 283
Erethizontidae **5** 277, 283
Eretmochelys imbricata **26** 1553
Erignathus barbatus **4** 184
Erinaceidae **11** 651, 655
Erinaceus **11** 655
Erinna **47** 2806
Eriochier **38** 2231
Eriophyidae **39** 2295
Eriosomatinae **41** 2451-2, 2454
Erisidae **39** 2289
Erisoma **41** 2450, 2452
Eristalis tenax **45** 2656-7, 2659
Erithacus rubecula **24** 1388
ermine moth **44** 2603, *2608*, 2609
Erosa erosa **34** 2007
Erpeton tentaculatum **28** 1645
Errantia **49** 2937; **50** 2941-2
Ersus niger **38** 2267, *2268-9*
Erycinacea **48** 2845, 2847
Erynnis tages **44** 2633
Erythrocebus patas **14** 816
Esacus magnirostris **19** 1137
Eschrichtidae **10** 577
Eschrichtius robustus **10** 577
escolars **35** 2067
Esocidae **33** 1937
Esolus angustatus **42** 2472, 2481
Esox **33** 1937
Estrilda melanotis **25** 1453
estrildid finches **25** *1448-9*
  classification **25** 1453
  distribution **25** 1452
Estrildidae **25** 1453
estuarine crocodile **29** 1685, *1690*, 1693; **51** 3028, 3032, 3047
Ethiopia, national park **51** *3016-17*
Ethiopian hedgehog **11** 655
Ethiopian umbrella termite **41** *2424*
Etroplus **35** 2048
Euarminiacea **47** 2798
Euborlasia quinquestria **49** *2919*
Eucarida **37** 2182, 2189, 2208
Eucera longicornis **43** *2542*
Euchroreus purpuratus **43** *2536*
Eucidarius tribuloides **36** *2117*
Euciroa teramachi **48** *2844*
Euconolus fulvus **48** 2823-4
Eudicella grallii **42** 2495
Eudocimus ruber **17** 1018
Eudora truncatula **37** *2196*
Eudoridacea **47** 2794
Eudromia elegans **16** 933
Eudromias morinellus **19** 1125
Eudyptes **16** 949
Eudyptula minor **16** 949
Euglena **50** 2976, 2979, *2984*
Eulimacea **46** 2721
Eulimidae **46** *2720-2*
Euliphyra **44** 2635
Eumalacostraca **37** 2182, 2189
Eumeces obsoletus **27** 1598
Eumenes
  arbustorum **43** 2527, 2529, *2532*
  coarctata **43** *2536*
  coarctatus **43** 2528
Eumenidae **43** 2527, 2529
Eumetopias jubatus **3** 172
Eunectes murinus **28** 1637
Eungella National Park **51** 3048, 3049
Eunicacea **49** 2939; **50** 2942
Eunice viridis **49** *2936*
Eunicella cavolini **49** *2886*
Euodice cantans **25** 1453
Euparypha pisana **48** 2827
Euphagus carolinus **24** 1440
Eupharyngidae **32** 1874
Euphausiacea **37** 2182, 2208, *2188*
Euphractus sexcinctus **4** 197
Euplectes **25** 1459
Eupleres goudoti **2** 92
Euproctes platycephalus **29** 1729
Eurasian bittern **17** 1007-8
Eurasian catfish **32** 1913, 1914
Eurasian cuckoo **20** 1175, *1176-7*, 1178, *1179*
Eurasian curlew **19** *1127*, 1129, 1135
Eurasian deer **8** 421
Eurasian eagle owl **20** 1199
Eurasian golden plover **19** 1125, *1126*
Eurasian kingfisher **21** *1249*, 1252, 1253, *1256, 1257*
Eurasian sheep **10** 561-3, 566, 567, 570
Eurasian slow-worm **27** 1601, 1603, *1605*, 1606, *1607*
Eurasian water shrew **12** 662
Eurasian woodcock **19** 1131
Eurasian worm snake **28** 1622-3, *1624*, 1625, 1628
Eurasian wren **23** *1377*, 1378, 1379
Europe, national parks **51** 3002, 3004, *3005-14*
European...
  adder **28** 1669, 1672, 1674, *1675*
  badger **1** *52*, 55
  barracuda **35** 2041-3
  beaver **4** 221, 233, 239
  bee-eater **22** *1263*, 1267, 1268, 1270
  bison **8** 469, *478-9*, 480; **9** 482; **51** 3006, *3007*
  black vulture **18** 1078
  black widow spider **39** *2284*
  brown trout **33** *1930*
  bubble shell **47** *2774*
  catfish **32** 1913, 1915
  cockchafers **42** *2501*, 2503
  coot **19** 1112, 1113, 1114
  corn borer moth **44** 2609, 2612
  dragonet **34** 2033-4
  earwig **40** *2387*, 2388
  eels, distribution **32** 1876
  flat oyster **48** 2843, *2845*
  free-tailed bat **12** 716
  freshwater eel **32** 1874, *1875-9*
  frog **30** *1758, 1771, 1775*
  glass lizard **27** 1602, *1603*
  glow-worm **42** 2472
  grass snake **28** 1645, *1654-5*
  grayling **33** 1935
  guitarfish **31** 1842, 1843
  hare **4** *201-2*, 203, *207-11*
  hedgehog **11** 645, *650*, 655-6, *658-9*; **12** *664-5*
  hookworm **49** 2925, 2928
  kestrel **19** *1082*
  lantern fly **41** *2446*
  leaf-toed gecko **27** 1569
  limpet **45** 2697, 2701
  lobster **36** *2148*; **37** *2192*, 2214, *2218*, 2219
  lugworm **50** *2943*
  lynx **3** 140

manta ray **31** 1844
mink **1** 40, 47
mole **1** 18; **11** *646-7*; **12** *668-71*
monkfish **31** *1840*, 1841
mudminnow **33** 1937
nightjar **21** *1201*, *1202*, 1204, *1205*, 1206
polecat **1** *37*
pond turtle **26** 1526, *1536*, *1538*
praying mantis **40** 2391, *2396*, 2397, *2398*
pygmy shrew **12** 662
rat flea **45** 2665
roe deer **7** 412-13
roller **22** 1261
sand-smelts **34** 1982-3
sandhopper **37** *2205*
scorpions **38** *2246*
sea bass **34** 2017, 2023
sea eagle **18** 1070, 1072
sea-lily **46** 2720
shore crab **38** *2224*
short-winged grasshopper **40** *2365*
shrew **11** 646; **12** *661*, 662, *666-7*
signature spider **38** 2258, *2261*
smelt **33** 1924, 1937
sole **35** 2075
spadefoot **30** 1768, *1769*, *1771*
spiny lobster **37** *2192*, 2213
spoonbill **17** 1020
squirrel **51** 3013
starfish **36** *2134*
stargazer **34** 2035
starling **25** 1461-2, *1463*
stone curlew **19** 1137
storm petrel **17** 976
stripeless tree frog **30** *1755*
sun starfish **36** *2132*, *2135*
swallowtail **44** 2633, *2636*
syncarid **37** *2193*
toad **29** *1699*; **30** *1771*, *1787*, *1788*, 1789
tree frog **30** 1791-2, 1795, *1796-7*
water shrew **12** *663*, *668*
wels **32** 1913, *1914-15*, 1892-3
whip snake **28** 1660
wild cat **3** *136*, *141*
wild rabbit **4** *202*, 206, 207, *212-13*
classification **4** 209
worm lizard **27** *1615*, 1616
yellow cowrie **46** 2736
Euroreutes naso **5** 268
Eurycantha calcarata **40** 2385
Eurycea **30** 1750
Eurylaimi **22** 1303
Eurylaimidae **22** 1303, 1307
Eurypharynx pelecanoides **32** 1874
Eurypterida **38** 2234, 2237-8, 2241
Eurypyga helias **19** 1117
Eurypygidae **19** 1107, 1117
Eurystomus orientalis **22** 1261
Eurytrachelus titan **42** 2502
Euryzygomatomys spinosus **5** 289
Euscorpius **38** 2244
flavicaudus **38** *2246*, 2251
italicus **38** *2246*
Eustheniidae **39** 2338; **40** 2345
Euthecosomata **47** 2781, 2782, 2786
Eutoxeres aquila **21** 1228
Evania appendigaster **42** *2519*
Evastacus armatus **37** *2211*
evening grosbeak **25** 1448
Everglades kite **18** *1054*, 1055, 1070, 1072
Everglades pygmy sunfish **34** 2014
Evermannichthys metzelaari **35** 2060
evolution **1** 6
amphibians **29** *1698-1700*
arthropods **36** 2140-1
birds **16** 904-6
cephalopods **48** 2853
echinoderms **36** 2115
fishes **31** *1806*, 1807-9
fossils **50** *2986-7*
horse family **6** 333
invertebrates *2670*
mammals **1** 8-11, 17-18; **26** 1506-8
man **15** *895*, *899-900*
mustelids **1** 41
natural selection **15** 892-3
primates **12** 719-20; **13** *727*
reptiles **26** 1506-9
ungulates **6** 319
Exocoetidae **33** 1965
Exocoetus volitans **33** 1965
Exoporia **44** 2595, 2599
Extatasoma tiaratum **40** 2385
eye worm **49** 2925, 2933
eyed ladybird **42** 2484
eyed sea cucumber **36** 2106
eyed-silkmoth **39** *2318*
Eyra barbara **1** 46-7
Eyrean grass wren **24** 1399

F

Fabre, Jean-Henri **44** 2606
Facelina **47** *2802*
fairy armadillo **4** *186*, 196-7
fairy bluebirds **23** *1356*, 1360, *1361-2*; **51** *3030*
fairy hummingbird **21** 1228, 1236
fairy penguin **16** 948
fairy pitta **22** 1314, 1315
fairy prion **17** 973
fairy shrimps **36** 2146, 2147, 2149, 2150, *2156*
fairy wrens **24** *1386*, 1398, 1399
Falco **18** 1080
Falconer's goat **10** 557-8
falconets **18** 1056, 1079, 1080
Falconidae **18** 1057, 1080
Falconiformes **18** *1053-80*; **19** *1081-4*
falcons **18** *1054*, 1060, 1079-80; **19** 1081; **51** 3014, 3017
classification **18** 1057, 1061, 1080
predators **18** 1055-6, 1057, 1085
Falculea palliata **23** 1368
fallow deer **7** *394*, 396-8, 406; **8** 421
false chameleon **27** 1579
false coral snake **28** *1624*, 1626, 1627, 1628
false featherback **32** *1868*, 1869
false gharial **29** *1684*, 1685, *1692*
false killer whale **10** 588, 593
false mole crickets **40** 2369
false paca **5** 281, 289
false ringlet butterfly **51** 3007
false scorpion **38** 2241, *2242*
false sunbirds **22** *1311*, 1315-16
classification **22** 1316
distribution **22** 1308
false trumpets **46** 2751
false vampires **12** *678*, 679, 688, 699, 705
classification **12** 681, 704, 709
fan mussel **48** *2832*
body parts **36** 2107, 2108, 2109
classification **36** 2107, 2115
diet **36** 2114
feather-duster worm **49** *2936*
feather-tailed copepod **36** *2156*
featherback fishes **32** *1868-9*, 1871
feathers **16** 904, *907-9*, 910
feathertail glider **11** 627, *630-1*
feathertail possum **11** 627
Felidae **1** 28; **3** 139, 144, 154, 158
FELIDS **3** *133-60*
Felinae **3** 139
Felis **3** 139
aurata **3** 154
badia **3** 154

ABOVE A red fox hides in the grass watching for prey.

fan worms **49** *2935*, *2936*, 2937, *2938*, 2939; **50** 2942, *2946*
fan-footed gecko **27** *1568*
fan-tailed warbler **24** 1394
fanaloka **2** 92, *96*
fantail **51** 3050
fantail flycatcher **24** 1399, 1400
fantail pigeon **20** 1158
Fasciola hepatica **47** 2809; **49** *2911*, *2912*
Fasciolaria tulipa **46** 2754
fat dormouse **5** *261-2*, 266
fat fly **45** *2658*
fat-tailed dwarf lemur **13** *735*, 742
fat-tailed jerboa **5** 268
fat-tailed scorpion **38** *2246*, 2247, *2249*, 2250
faucet snail **46** 2712, 2713, 2716
Favoriniae **47** 2800
Favorinus **47** 2800
fawn-breasted bowerbird **25** 1476
Fea's muntjac **7** 396
feather fleas **36** 2146
feather louse **41** *2431*
feather midge **45** 2650-2
feather stars **36** 2106, *2110-11*, *2115*, 2116, 2020-1
bengalensis **3** 154
caracal **3** 139
colocolo **3** 158
concolor **3** 139
geoffroyi **3** 158
guigna **3** 158
iriomotensis **3** 154
jacobita **3** 158
jaguarundi **2** 89
lynx **3** 139
manul **3** 154
marmorata **3** 154
pardalis **3** 158
planiceps **3** 154
rubiginosus **3** 154
rufus **3** 139
silvestris **3** 139
temmincki **3** 154
tigrinus **3** 158
viverrina **3** 154
wiedi **3** 158
yaguaroundi **3** 158
Felou gundi **5** 286
Felovia vae **5** 286
fence lizard **27** 1573
fennec **2** *110*, 119; **3** *122*, *123*, 126, 127

fer-de-lance **28** 1644, *1668*, 1675, *1678*
feral goat **10** 560
Ferminia cerverai **23** 1379
ferret **1** *38*, 46
ferret-badger **1** 55
Ferrissia **47** 2816
Ficedula **24** 1400
Ficidae **46** 2737, 2744
Ficus **46** 2744
- *communis* **46** 2737
- *filosa* **47** *2762*

fiddler crabs **36** 2102; **38** *2226-7*
field cricket **40** *2365*, *2374*, 2369
field vole **5** *250*
fieldfare **24** *1386*, 1388
fiery capped manakin **23** 1332
fiery-breasted bush shrike **23** 1367, *1368*
fifteen-spined stickleback **34** 1992-3, *1996-7*
fig insects **43** 2521-2
fig shell **47** *2762*
fig shells **46** 2737, 2744
fig wasps **42** 2516
figbirds **25** 1465
fighting fishes **35** 2069-70
Fiji banded iguana **27** 1579
Fiji petrel **17** 976
filarial nematodes **49** 2929, 2933
Filariida **49** 2925
file shells **45** 2675; **48** 2841, 2843
filefishes **35** 2087
fin whale **10** 577, 579, 580-1
- migratory route **10** *572*
- spout **10** *573*

finches **16** *909*; **22** 1304, 1305; **24** *1426*; **25** *1441-53*
- classification **22** 1303; **24** 1429; **25** 1442, 1453
- Darwin's **24** 1423, *1424-5*
- distribution **24** 1430; **25** 1441-2

finfoots **19** *1104*, 1106, 1107, 1114, 1116
fingerfish **34** 2022
finless porpoise **10** 593
Fiona **47** 2799, 2800
Fionidae **47** 2799
Fiordland crested penguin **51** *3050*
Fiordland National Park **51** 3002, 3004, *3050*
fiordland penguin **16** 948, 949
fire bugs **41** 2438, 2441
fire corals **49** *2887*, 2889
fire salamanders **29** 1703, *1713*, 1722-3, *1724-8*; **30** *1746*
- classification **29** 1713, 1729

fire trogons **21** 1241
fire worm **49** *2936*
fire-bellied toads **29** 1703; **30** 1760, 1761-2
fire-birds **17** 972
firebrats **39** 2311, *2328*, 2335
firecrest **24** 1398
fireflies **39** 2324, 2326; **42** 2472, 2478, 2481
firewood gatherer **22** 1310, 1312
fiscal shrike **23** 1366, *1367*
Fischer's chameleon **27** *1563*
Fischer's greenbul **23** *1359*
Fischer's lovebird **51** 3023
fish crow **25** 1498, 1500
fish lice **36** 2147; **37** *2168-9*
fish-eating rat **5** 243
fish-leeches **50** 2958
fisher (marten) **5** 277
fisherman bat **12** 697, 704
FISHES **31-5** *1801-2087*
- classification **31** 1809
- distribution **31** 1809
- evolution/origins **31** 1806-9
- fishing practices **31** 1814
- freshwater **32** *1891-1920*
- introduction **31** 1802-3
- mouthbrooders **31** 1814; **35** 2048-9, *2051*, 2054-6, 2069
- osmoregulation **31** 1858
- reproduction **31** 1814
- swim bladder **31** 1858; **32** *1861-3*

fishing cat **3** *142*, *149*, 154; **51** 3028
fishing eagles **18** 1070
fishing owl **20** *1196-8*, 1199
fishing snake **28** 1648-9
fishing spider **38** *2271*
Fissipedes **1** 28
Fissurella **45** *2694*, 2699
Fissurellacea **45** 2697, 2699
Fissurellidae **45** 2680, 2699
Fistularia **34** 2000
Fistulariidae **34** 2000
five-bearded rockling **33** 1951, *1953*, 1954
five-lined skink **27** 1565
flabby whalefishes **34** 1988, 1990
Flabellifera **37** 2197
Flabellina affinis **47** *2774*, *2798*, 2799
Flabellinidae **47** 2799
flag cichlid **35** *2055*
flagellates **50** 2976, *2980-3000*
flamingos **16** *902-3*, *907*, 912; **17** 997; **18** *1021-6*
- classification **17** 999; **18** 1024
- national parks **51** *3008*, 3009

flapshell turtle **26** 1556
flashlight fish **34** *1988*, 1990
flat lizards **27** 1597
flat oyster **48** 2841, *2845*
flat-backed millipedes **39** 2303
flat-headed cat **3** 154
flat-tailed horned lizard **27** 1573
flatback turtle **26** 1553
flatfishes **31** 1858, 1860; **32** 1862; **35** *2073-80*
flathead fishes **34** 2007
flatworms **36** 2103; **49** *2903-18*
flea beetles **41** 2455; **42** 2503, 2506, *2507*
fleas **39** 2311; **40** *2364*; **45** *2664-7*
flesh-fly **45** 2659, *2662-3*, 2664
flies **39** *2317*, 2318, *2319*; **45** *2641-64*
- compound eye **45** *2642*

flight
- birds **16** *904-8*
- flying fishes **33** *1967-8*
- hatchetfish **32** 1910-11

flittermouse **12** *712*
Florida gopher tortoise **26** *1545*
Florida Keys white-tailed deer **7** 414; **8** 424
Florida pipefish **34** 2000, 2003
Florida worm-lizard **27** 1616
flounders **35** 2073-5, *2078*
flower bat **12** 703
flower bugs **41** 2436, 2438
flower-eating beetles **42** 2492, 2493
flowerpeckers **24** 1415-16, 1417
flowerpiercers **24** 1429-30
flowerpot snake **28** 1622, 1625
flukes **49** 2911, *2912-5*
- pond snail parasite **47** 2809, 2810, 2820

flutemouth **34** *1999*, 2000
Fly River turtle **26** 1553, *1555-6*
fly-hunting wasps **43** 2540
flycatchers **22** 1304; **24** 1399-1400
flying dragon **27** 1564, *1583*, 1585
flying fish **33** 1964-5, *1966-9*; **34** *1996*
- flight mechanism **33** *1967-8*

flying fox (carp) **32** *1861*
flying foxes (bats) **12** *677-8*, *686-7*, 692-5, *696-702*
- *see also* fruit bats
- classification **12** 681
- distribution **12** 679
- non-hibernators **12** 689-90
- wings *680*, 683

flying frogs **30** 1779-82, 1785
flying gecko **27** 1564, *1566*, 1568, 1569
flying gurnards **34** *2004*, *2037*
flying lemur **12** *673-6*, 679
flying mouse **11** 627
flying snake **28** 1645, *1649*, 1651
flying squids **48** 2861, 2867
flying squirrels **4** 223, 226, 233, *234-5*; **12** *674*, 679
flying steamer duck **18** 1044
foliage-gleaners **22** 1309, 1312
follicle mites **39** 2293, 2295, 2297
Foraminifera **50** *2980*
foraminiferans **50** *2986-9*, 2990-1
Foraminiferida **50** 2989, 2991, 2989
forbes squid **48** 2861
forceps fish **34** 2024, 2027
Forcipiger longirostris **34** 2024
forest buffalo **8** 467, 468
forest duikers **8** 437-8, 440; **51** 3020
forest elephant **6** 324
forest falcon **18** 1079
forest ground thrush **51** 3024
forest heron **17** 1007
forest kingfishers **21** *1252*, 1253, 1260
forest rabbit **4** 207
forest wagtail **23** 1352
forest wallaby **11** 642
Forficula auricularia **40** 2388
Forficulidae **40** 2388
Forficulina **40** 2388
fork-crowned dwarf lemur **13** *732*, 742
fork-tailed drongo **25** *1468*
fork-tailed flycatcher **22** *1311*
fork-tailed swift **21** 1223
Formica **42** 2478
- *fusca* **43** *2562*, 2564
- *rufa* **43** 2529, 2563-4

Formicariidae **22** 1303, 1310
Formicidae **43** 2529, 2551
Formicinae **43** 2563-4
Formosan mouse opossum **11** 609
Formosan rock macaque **14** 805
Formosan sika **7** 404
fossa **2** 84-5, 87, 89
Fossa fossa **2** 92
fossils **50** *2986-7*
four-bearded rockling **33** 1954
four-eyed fishes **33** 1964, *1972*, 1978; **34** *1981-3*
four-eyed toad **30** 1795
four-horned antelope **8** 434, *448-50*, *457*, 460; **10** *568*
four-spined stickleback **34** 1992-3
four-spotted ladybird **42** 2472, 2483
four-toed elephant-shrew **11** 660
four-toed hedgehog **11** 655
four-winged flying fishes **33** 1966-7
fox kestrel **19** 1084
fox shark **31** 1834
fox squirrel **4** *219*, 221
fox-like opossum **51** 3050
foxes **1** *30-1*, 35; **2** *110*, *119-20*; **3** *121-31*
- classification **3** 127
- distribution **3** 115, 119
- national parks **51** 3017, 3018
- predator **1** 26, 29; **3** 121
- senses **1** 21, 27; **3** 123
- suburban survival **3** 121, *124-5*

foxface fish **35** 2066-7
France, nature reserve **51** 3002, *3008-9*
franciscana **10** 593
francolins **19** 1096, 1099
Francolinus jacksoni **19** 1096
Fratercula **20** 1148
freckled duck **18** 1030, 1044
freckled nightjar **21** 1206
free-tailed bats **12** *678*, 683, 685, *690*, *715*
- classification **12** 681, 716
- distribution **12** 679

Fregata **17** 994
Fregatidae **17** 994
Frenulata **50** 2971
freshwater...
- angelfish **35** *2064*
- bass **34** 2014, 2022
- bloodworms **50** 2948, *2949*
- crabs **38** 2229
- crayfish **36** *2146*; **37** 2212-13, 2219-20
- eels **32** *1874-7*
- fishes **32** *1891-1920*
- green hydra **49** *2886*
- grunt **34** 2033
- jellyfish **49** *2889*
- limpets **47** 2805, 2816
- mites **39** 2295, 2297
- mussel **48** *2842*
- snail **46** *2704*
- sponge **48** *2879*, 2880
- worms **50** 2952

frigatebirds **16** *911*; **17** *978*, *991*, *992-4*; **18** 1058; **35** *2041*
- classification **17** 980, 994
- distribution **17** 992

frilled shark **31** *1826*, 1828-9
fringe-eared oryx **9** 499, 502
fringe-finned fish **31** 1848-9
fringe-lipped bat **12** 685
fringe-toed lizard **27** 1576
Fringilla **25** 1442
Fringillidae **22** 1303; **25** 1442
Fringillinae **25** 1442
Fritillarids **35** 2098
Fritziana goeldii **30** 1795
frog shells **46** 2737, 2743
frog-hoppers **41** 2438, *2448-9*
frogfishes **33** *1960*, *1961*
frogmouths **21** 1203, 1204, 1206, *1210-11*, *1212-14*
frogs **29** *1696-8*, *1701*, 1703, 1704; **30** *1755-1800*
- classification **29** 1701; **30** 1756
- distribution **30** 1768, 1774, 1790
- senses **29** *1700*, 1702, *1706*

Fromia ghardaqana **36** *2132*

front-fanged snakes **28** 1621, 1640-1, 1644, *1661-67*
fruit bats **12** 680, *684*, *686-8*, 692-5, *696-9*
see also flying foxes
fruit flies **39** 2326; **45** 2642, *2657-9*
fruit pigeons **20** 1153, 1156
Fucus **46** 2714
Fuji-Hakone-Izu National Park **51** 3002, *3060*
Fulgoridae **41** 2438, *2446-7*
Fulica **19** 1112
fulmars **16** *909*; **17** *961-2*, *968*, 971, 973
classification **17** 973
distribution **17** 963
spitting defence **17** *969*, 971
Fulmarus **17** 973
fulvous leaf-nosed bat **12** 702-3, 704
fulvous whistling duck **18** 1036
Fundulus heteroclitus **33** 1978
fungus feeder **42** *2505*
fungus gnat **45** *2644*
fungus-growing termite **41** *2403*, 2405
funnel-eared bat **12** 708, 709, 681
funnel-web spider **38** 2258, *2262*, 2263, 2272, 2277; **39** *2281*, *2282*, 2283, 2285
fur seal **3** *162*, 168-9, 172-4; **51** 3035
classification **3** 164
Furipteridae **12** 681, 709
Furnariidae **22** 1303, 1310
Furnarius rufus **22** 1310
furniture cockroach **40** *2391*, 2395
Fusilinids **50** *2986*
Fusinus **46** 2754

Gaboon viper **28** 1641, *1668*, 1669, 1672-3
gadfly-petrels **17** 972, 973, 976
Gadidae **33** 1951
Gadiformes **31** 1858; **33** *1947-56*; **34** *1996*
Gadus morhua **33** 1951
gafftopsail catfish **32** 1913-14
Galaginae **13** 748
Galago **13** 748
galagos **13** 748
Galapagos dove **51** 3035
Galapagos flightless cormorant **17** *990*
Galapagos giant tortoise **26** *1508*, *1542-4*, *1547-9*; **51** 3034
Galapagos land iguana **27** *1577*, 1578, 1579
Galapagos National Park **51** 3002, *3034-5*
Galapagos penguin **16** *936*, 948, 949, 950
Galapagos sea lion **3** 172; **51** 3035
Galathea **37** *2220*
Galaxias **33** 1924, *1942*
galaxiid **33** 1924, *1942*
Galaxiidae **33** 1924
Galba **47** 2806
Galbalcyrhyncus leucotis **22** 1284
Galbula ruficauda **22** 1284
Galbulidae **22** 1284
Galemys pyrenaicus **12** 670
Galeocerdo cuvier **31** 1839
Galeodes **38** 2253
arabs **38** 2242
Galeorhinus **31** 1839
Galerida cristata **23** 1334
Galerucella luteola **42** 2504
Galidia **2** 92
Galidictis **2** 92
Galidiinae **2** 89, 92
Galiteuthis suhmi **48** *2854*
gall midges **45** 2645-6, 2647

ABOVE A red-legged grasshopper feeding in a lowland forest.

gall mites **39** *2295*, 2298
gall wasps **42** 2516, *2520*
Galleria mellonella **44** 2609
Galliformes **19** *1084-1102*
Gallinagininae **19** 1135
Gallinago gallinago **19** 1135
Gallinula chloropus **19** 1112
galliwasp **27** *1607*
Gallotia symonyi **27** 1603
Gallus gallus **19** 1096
Gambian epauletted fruit bat **12** 693, 694, *699*
Gambusia affinis **33** 1978
gamebirds **19** *1087-1102*
Gammaridea **37** *2204-6*
Gammarus **37** 2203
marinus **37** *2204*
pulex **37** *2188*
Ganges bull shark **31** 1835
Ganges dolphin **10** *584*, 586, 593; **51** 3027
Ganges susu **10** 593
gannets **16** *911*; **17** *988-9*, 991-2, 994
classification **17** 980, 994
distribution **17** 992
gaping file shell **48** *2832*, *2841*, 2843
garden chafers **42** 2498-9, 2503, *2505*
garden dormouse **5** *267*, 268-9
garden eel **32** *1873-5*, *1882-3*
garden pebble moth **44** 2612
garden slug **47** 2802
garden snail **45** 2676; **47** 2802; **48** 2828, 2830
garden spider **38** *2261*
garden tiger-moth **44** *2604*, 2617, 2624
garden warbler **24** *1393*, 1395
garfish (needlefish) **33** 1964, 1965
garganey **18** *1046*, 1047
garibaldi fish **34** 2024, 2030
garlic snail **45** 2678
garpike **31** 1855, 1856
Garrulax leucolophus **24** 1390
Garrulus glandarius **25** 1489
gars **31** *1806*, *1852*, *1855*, 1858
classification **31** 1809, 1856
distribution **31** 1851
non-teleosts **31** 1848
garter snakes **28** 1645, 1653-4, *1655*, 1658
Gasteracantha **38** *2257*
Gasteropelecidae **32** 1908
Gasteropelecus levis **32** 1908
Gasterophilidae **45** 2659
Gasterosteidae **34** 1993
Gasterosteiformes **334** *1991-2004*
Gasterosteus aculeatus **34** 1993
Gastotricha **49** *2921-34*
Gastromyzon borneensis **32** 1894
Gastropacha quercifolia **44** 2624
Gastropoda **45** 2671, *2693-2700*; **47** *2761-2820*; **48** *2828*
body parts **45** *2672-4*, *2682*
classification **45** 2674, 2680
evolution **45** *2670*, 2680
general features **45** *2675-8*
GASTROPODS **36** 2103; **46-47** *2701-80*; **48** *2821-30*
Gastropteridae **47** 2767
Gastrotheca marsupiata **30** 1795
gaur **8** 451, 467-8, *470-1*, 472-3
national parks **51** 3004, 3026, 3030
Gavia **16** 954
'gavial' **29** 1695
Gavialidae **29** 1685
Gavialis gangeticus **29** 1685
Gaviidae **16** 954, 957
Gaviiformes **16** *952-5*
gayal **8** *462-3*, 473
Gazella **9** 529
gazelles **6** 308; **8** 434; **9** *517-32*; **10** *569*; **51** 3022-3
Gecarcinidae **38** 2231
geckos **26** *1511*, *1512*, *1519*; **27** 1564, *1566-9*
classification **26** 1562, 1569
distribution **26** 1565
geese **16** *906-7*; **18** *1027-36*, *1039-44*, *1046-9*; **51** 3027
classification **18** 1030, 1036, 1044
distribution **18** 1031
Gekko gecko **27** 1569
Gekkonidae **27** 1562, 1569
gelada baboon **14** *792*, 795, 811, *814*; **51** 3017
Gelechioidea **44** 2608-9
Gempylidae **35** 2067
gemsbok **9** *499*, *500*, 502; **51** 3018
genets **2** *83-6*, 89, *94-5*; **5** *267*
Genetta **2** 89
Genevieve azure butterfly **44** 2632-3
gentle lemur **13** 736-7, 742, 743
gentoo penguin **16** *936*, *941*, 943, *945*, 949
distribution **16** 944, 948
Genyochromis mento **35** *2051*
Genypterus capensis **33** 1956
Geochelone **26** *1544*
Geococcyx californianus **20** 1178
Geoffrey's ground squirrel **4** *232*
Geoffroy's cat **3** 158
Geoffroy's long-nosed bat **12** *709*
Geoffroy's spider monkey **51** 3044
Geomalacus maculosus **48** 2822, 2824
Geomantis larvoides **40** *2400*
geometric tortoise **26** 1544, 1546
geometrid moths **44** *2613-15*
Geometridae **44** 2593
Geometroidea **44** 2609, 2613
Geomyidae **4** 233, 235
Geonemertes **49** 2920
Geophilomorpha **39** 2307
Geophilus **39** 2307
Georgia blind salamander **30** 1752
Georgian diving petrel **17** 976
Georychus capensis **5** 284
Geositta rufipennis **22** 1310
Geospiza scandens **24** 1429
Geospizinae **24** 1429
Geotria australis **31** 1818
Geotripetes seraphini **29** 1710
Geotrupes **42** 2492
stercorarius **42** *2497*
vernalis **42** *2497*, 2503

Geotrupidae **41** 2456; **42** 2492, 2503
Geranospiza caerulescens **18** 1070
gerbils **4** 218; **5** 243, 248, *253-4*, 255
gerenuk **9** *517-18*, *529*, 530
German cockroach **40** *2390*, 2391, 2394-5
German grasshopper **40** *2365*
Geronticus eremita **17** 1018
Gerridae **41** 2438, 2440, *2441*
Gerris lacustria **41** *2440*
Gerygone sulphurea **24** 1398
Gesner, Konrad **14** 784
gharial **29** *1682*, *1684*, 1687, 1692, *1695*; **51** 3027
gharial, classification **29** 1685
ghost bat **12** 699, 704
ghost crabs **38** *2230-1*
ghost frogs **30** 1799
ghost moths **44** 2595, 2599-2600
ghost pipefishes **34** 2000-1
ghost shrimp **37** *2219*
giant...
African land snail **47** *2804*
African snail **48** *2821-2*, *2829*
ant lion **43** *2567*, 2570, *2574*
anteater **1** 11; **4** *186*, *187-9*, *193*, 195; **10** 598
antpitta **22** 1310
armadillo **4** *186*, 197
Australian earthworm **50** 2952
bee fly **45** 2652, *2655*
Brazilian otter **1** 43-5, 55
chameleon **27** 1592
coot **19** 1114
coua **20** 1181
danio **32** 1894, 1901
devil ray **31** 1844, 1846
eland **8** 452, 457
forest hog **7** *364*, 365, 367, 370; **51** 3020, 3024
forest hog **7** *364*, 365, 367, 370; **51** 3020, 3024
golden mole **11** 655
gourami **35** 2068, 2070-1
ground sloth **4** 187
gumshoe chiton **45** 2684, 2688
hummingbird **21** 1227, 1228, *1234-5*, 1237
ibis **17** 1018
jungle runner **27** 1603
katydids **40** 2369, 2371
kelpfish **35** 2058-9
otter shrew **11** *646*, 651, 653, *654*
panda **1** 20, 28, *58*; **2** 62, *66*, 67-8; **51** *3051*, *3058-9*
pangolin **4** 189, *198-200*
petrels **17** *962*, 971, 974
classification **17** 973
pitta **22** *1311*
potoo **21** 1214
pouched rat **5** *245*, 248
sable antelope **9** 498
sailfin molly **33** *1972*, 1978, *1979*
salamanders **29** 1704, 1713, 1715, *1716-18*
sea-scorpion, fossil **38** 2237
Solomon Islands skink **27** 1593, 1598
squirrel **4** *220*, 234
toad **30** *1764*, 1789, *1790*, *1791*
top shell **45** 2700
top shell limpet **46** 2702
tropical damselfly **40** 2362
tun **46** 2737, 2743
tun shell **47** *2762*
turaco **20** 1173, 1178
water bugs **41** 2438, *2442-3*
weta **40** 2368, 2369
whip scorpion **38** *2242*
wood spider **38** *2233*
wood wasp **42** 2516, *2517-8*, *2519*
gibbons **14** *837-40*; **15** *841-7*, 848-9, 853, 855
classification **13** 728; **15** 842
distribution **15** 848
evolution **13** *727*, 780
hands **12** *719*, *720*
primate features **13** 722, *726*, 756; **15** *897*
Gibbula **46** 2700, 2703
gibel carp **32** 1894, 1897
Gigantocypris agassizi **36** *2156*
Gigantostraca **38** 2237-8
Giganturidae **33** 1946
GIGANTURIDS **33** 1944-5, 1946
gila monster **27** *1614-15*
gila woodpecker **22** *1296*
gilthead **34** *2012*
Ginglymostoma **31** 1839
Giraffa camelopardalis **8** 430
giraffe **5** 298; **6** 301, 304, *307*; **8** *425-30*; **10** *569*
national parks **51** 3018, 3022
giraffe stag beetle **42** 2502-3
Giraffidae **8** 430
GIRAFFIDS **8** 425-30
girdle of Venus **49** 2901, *2902*
girdle-tailed lizards **27** *1596-7*
classification **27** 1598
distribution **27** 1595
gizzard shad **33** *1922*
Glareolidae **19** 1121, 1137
Glareolus pratincola **19** 1137
glass catfish **32** *1906*, 1913, *1914*
glass eel **32** *1876*, 1877
glass frogs **30** 1799, 1800
glass lizard **27** 1602, *1603*
glass sponges **48** 2880
Glaucidae **47** 2800
Glaucidium passerinum **20** 1199
Glaucilla **47** 2792, 2800
Glaucomys volans **4** 233
Glauconycteris superba **12** 712
glaucous gull **20** 1142
Glaucus **47** 2792, 2800
gliders **11** 612, *616*, *621-3*, *626-7*, *630*, 631
Gliricola porcelli **41** 2428
Gliridae **5** 254
Glironia venusta **11** 615
Globigerina **50** 2986, *2987*, *2989*
Globorotalia **50** *2986*
Globotruncana **50** *2986*
glochidia **48** *2842*
Glomeridae **39** 2304
Glomeris **39** 2304
Glossina palpalis **45** *2658*, 2659
Glossiphonia **50** 2956, 2958
Glossiphoniidae **50** 2958
Glossodoris **47** *2774*, *2791*
Glossogobius giurus **35** 2060
Glossophaga soricina **12** 709
Glossoscolecidae **50** 2952
Glossosomatidae **43** 2580; **44** 2581
Glossus humanus **48** *2844*
glossy ibis **17** 1018, 1020; **51** 3014
glow-worms **41** 2458; **42** 2472, *2478-81*
glutton **1** *46*, 47
Glycimeridae **48** 2835, 2836-7
Glycimeris **48** 2836
glycoprotein **35** 2055
Glyphorhyncus spirurus **22** 1310
Gmelin's top shell **45** 2700
gnatcatchers **24** 1392
gnateaters **22** 1308, 1314
Gnathiidea **37** 2199
Gnathobdellae **50** 2958
Gnathodoridacea **47** 2785-6
Gnathonemus petersi **32** 1869, *1870*
Gnathostomulida **49** 2911
GNATHOSTOMULIDS **49** *2910*, 2917-18
gnats **45** 2643, *2644*
gnatwren **24** 1392
gnus **1** *13*; **9** *483-4*, 485, 486, *492-7*; **10** *569*
classification **8** 434; **9** 490
national parks **51** *3015*, 3018-19, 3022, *3023*
go-away birds **20** 1173, *1175*
goa **9** 525, 529
goat antelopes **8** 434; **9** 533-40; **10** 541-70; **51** *3012*
goat moths **44** 2605, *2609*
goatfishes **34** *2032 -3*
goats **5** 298; **6** 304-5
goatsucker **21** 1204
gobies **34** 2013; **35** *2060-5*
Gobiesocidae **33** 1962
Gobiesociformes **33** 1962
Gobiidae **34** 2013; **35** 2060
Gobio gobio **32** 1894
Gobiomorus dormitor **35** 2060
Gobiosoma oceanops **35** 2060
Gobius paganellus **35** 2060
goblin shark **31** 1832, 1839
goby **31** 1859
godwits **19** 1126, *1128*, 1129-30, 1135
Goeldi's monkey **13** 768; **14** 782, *787-9*, 790
goitred gazelle **9** 524-5, 529; **51** 3054
gold frogs **30** 1791, 1795
gold spot herring **32** *1887*
Gold terns **20** *1143-4*, 1145
gold-striped salamander **29** 1729, *1730*
goldcrest warbler **24** 1394, 1398
goldcrest wren **22** 1302
golden...
agouti **5** *285*
bowerbird **25** *1473*, 1475, 1476; **51** *3048-9*
cat **3** *142*, 154; **51** 3020, *3021*
conure **20** *1162*
dragonflies **40** 2351
eagle **18** *1053-4*, 1055, 1056-7, 1066-7, 1070
national parks **51** *3010*, 3011, 3013
frog **30** 1791, *1792*
hamster **5** *241*, 245
headed manakin **23** 1331
jackal **2** 111, *118*
leaf-folding frog **30** 1782
lion tamarin **14** *786*, 790
mantella **30** *1764*
moles **11** 649, 653-4, 655
monkey **14** 819
oriole **25** *1465-7*
pheasant **19** *1096*
pipit **23** 1352
plover **19** 1125, *1126*
potto **13** 748, 752
silk spider **38** *2261*, *2273*
snub-nosed monkey **14** *824*, 827, 831
sparrow **25** *1454*, 1455
tree snake **28** 1645
weaver **25** 1459
whistler **24** *1386*, 1400
golden-breasted starling **25** *1464*
golden-collared manakin **23** 1331, *1332*
golden-fronted leafbird **23** 1360, *1362*
golden-headed babbler **24** 1389, 1390
golden-headed lion tamarin **14** 790
golden-rumped elephant-shrew **11** 660
golden-rumped tamarin **14** 790
golden-shouldered parrot **20** 1170
golden-spangled spiculet **22** 1297
golden-striped grouper **34** 2023
golden-throated barbet **22** 1287-8
golden-winged parakeet **20** *1169*
golden-winged sunbird **24** 1417
goldenbacked woodpeckers **51** 3027
goldeneye **18** *1052*
goldfinch **25** 1442, *1443*
goldfish **32** *1894-5*, 1897
goldsinny wrasse **34** *2017*, 2023
goliath beetles **42** 2495, 2503
goliath frog **30** 1775-6, 1778, *1779*
goliath heron **17** 1000, *1004*, 1007
goliath spider **39** *2282*, 2283
Goliathus **42** 2493
Golofa porteri **42** 2500
golomyanka **51** 3053
goloveshka **35** 2060
Gomphocerippus rufus **40** *2373*
Gomphus vulgatissimus **40** *2355*
Gonaxis kiweziensis **48** 2822
Gongylus gongyloides **40** *2398*
Goniodorididae **47** 2786
Goniodoris **47** 2786-7
Gonoides colchicus **41** *2431*
gonolek **23** 1362, 1367
Gonorynchidae **32** 1892
Gonorynchiformes **32** 1892
Gonorynchus gonorynchus **32** 1892
Gonostoma **33** 1942, 1944
Gonostomatidae **33** 1944
Gonyaulax **50** 2985
Goodall, Jane **15** 867, 868, 872, 876, 881
goosander **18** 1050, 1051; **51** 3014
goose barnacles **36** 2147, *2156*; **37** *2171-6*
goosefish **33** *1957*, 1959-61; **35** *2083*
gorals **9** 535, 538-9; **10** 550
gordian worms **49** 2933, 2934
Gordioidea **49** 2934
Gordius **49** 2934
Gorgasia **32** 1874
Gorgonacea **49** 2889, 2899
gorgonia sea fan **35** *2098*
Gorilla gorilla **15** 852
gorillas **12** 719; **13** 721, *722-3*; **14** 838; **15** *847*, *849*, 852, *856-66*, 890
anthropoid features **13** 757, 758, 760
classification **14** 839; **15** 852
distribution **15** 848

evolution **15** *843*, *895*, *899*, *900*
feeding/social behaviour **15** *849*, *864-5*
hands **13** *728*; **15** 852
national parks **51** *3001*, *3024*
goshawks **18** 1059, *1063*, 1064-5, 1070; **51** 3014
gough fur seal **3** *168*
gouldian finch **25** *1448*, 1449, 1453
Gould's monitor lizard **27** *1608*, 1609
Goura victoria **20** 1156
gouramis **32** *1865*; **35** *2064*, *2067*, 2068-71
goureen **32** 1889
Gracula religiosa **25** 1462
grain thrips **41** 2428
grain-eating moths **44** 2600
Grallaria gigantea **22** 1310
Grallina **25** 1470
Grallinidae **25** 1470
Grammistes sexlineatus **34** 2023
granite night lizard **27** 1571
Grant's desert golden mole **11** 654, 655
Grant's gazelle **9** *519*, 520, *521* *526-7*, 529
Grant's zebra **5** *299*; **6** *336-8*, 340, *342-3*
granulated paper nautilus **48** 2870
grape-cutter beetle **42** 2493, *2498*
Graphium androcles **44** *2634*
Graphosoma italicum **41** *2439*
Grapsidae **38** 2231
Graptotemys **26** 1539
grass owl **20** 1194, 1195
grass pickerel **33** 1938
grass snake **26** *1521*; **27** *1619*; **28** 1644, 1645, *1654-5*
grass-green vine snake **28** *1650*
grassbird **24** 1393
grassfinch **25** 1449
grasshopper warbler **24** 1394-5, 1398
grasshoppers **39** 2320, 2323, 2326; **40** *2363-82*
body parts **39** 2313, *2319*, 2324
larvae **39** 2311, 2312
Grassi (eel researcher) **32** 1878
Grauer's broadbill **22** 1307
grayling **33** *1922*, 1924, 1934-6, *1938*; **51** 3041
grazing antelopes **9** 483-516
grazing starfish **36** 2130
great...
albatross **17** 962
apes **13** *727*; **14** 838; **15** *847-90*
classification **14** 839; **15** 852
argus pheasant **19** 1096
auk **20** 1145
barracuda **35** 2042-3
black-backed gull **20** 1142-3
blue heron **17** 1000
blue turaco **20** 1173, 1178
bustard **19** 1107, *1108*, 1112; **51** 3052, 3054
cormorant **17** 990
crane fly **45** 2643, 2645, 2647
crested flycatcher **22** *1317*; **23** 1321
crested grebe **16** *951*, 952, 956, *958-9*; **51** 3050
classification **16** 960
distribution **16** 957
head feathers **16** 957
crested newt **29** 1729, *1734-5*, 1738; **30** *1746*
curassow **19** *1086*, 1088, 1092
diving beetle **41** 2456; **42** *2464-7*
frigatebird **17** 994
green bush-cricket **40** *2368*, 2369, 2370-1
green grasshopper **40** *2368*, 2369, 2370-1
grey bowerbird **25** 1476
grey kangaroo **51** *3045*
grey shrike **23** *1364-5*
grey slug **47** 2802, *2812-13*, 2817; **48** *2825*, *2826*
hammerhead shark **31** 1839
hornbill **51** 3030
horned owl **20** 1196, *1198*, 1199
Indian hornbill **21** *1250*; **22** 1274, *1278*
jacamar **22** 1284
kiskadee **22** *1311*, *1320*
northern diver **16** *952*, *954-5*
peacock moth **44** 2606
peacock silk-moth **44** 2624-5
Plains skink **27** 1565, 1595, 1598
pond snail **47** *2804*, 2805, 2807, *2809*, *2814-15*
ramshorn snail **47** *2804*, 2805, *2811*, 2815
red sedge **44** 2583
red sedge caddisfly **43** 2580
rosefinch **25** 1448
scallop **48** 2837, *2840*
shearwater **17** *968*, 973
silver water beetle **42** *2465*
skua **19** *1139*, 1140; **20** 1142
slaty woodpecker **51** 3027
slug **47** *2804*
spotted cuckoo **20** 1175, *1178*, 1179-80; **51** 3008
spotted kiwi **16** 925, 931
spotted woodpecker **22** *1294-5*, 1297, *1298*, 1300
tinamou **16** 933
tit **22** *1301*, 1302; **24** 1402-3, *1404-5*, *1413*
whales **10** 572, 578
white egret **17** 1000-1, 1004, *1006*
bill colours **17** 999
classification **17** 1007
white pelican **17** 980, 982; **51** 3014
white shark **31** *1825-6*, *1832-3*, 1839
greater...
adjutant stork **17** 1012, 1015
bilby **11** 620
bird of paradise **25** *1477*, 1478, *1479*
bush baby **13** 748
eared nightjar **21** 1207
flamingo **18** *1022-3*, 1024, *1025*, 1026; **51** 3008-9
forkbeard **33** 1951, *1954*
glider **11** 627, 630-1
golden-backed woodpecker **22** *1297*
grison **1** 47
hedgehog tenrec **11** *651*, 652
honeyguide **22** 1288, *1289*
horseshoe bat **12** *678*, 690, 702, 704, *705*
kudu **8** *449-50*, *451*, 452
Malay chevrotain **7** 392
manakin **23** 1331
moonrat **11** 655
mouse-tailed bat **12** *678*, 696, 704
naked-backed bat **12** 693, 694
one-horned rhino **6** 355-6
pipefish **34** 2000, *2001*
prairie chicken **19** 1093, 1095
rabbit-eared bandicoot **11** 620
racket-tailed drongo **25** *1454*, 1465, 1468
roadrunner **20** 1178, *1180*, 1181
sandeel **34** 2033
sawfish **31** 1841-2
scaup **18** *1047*
short-tailed bat **12** 716
siren **29** *1712*, **30** 1753, *1754*
snow goose **18** 1043
spear-nosed bat **12** 703, 709
spotted dogfish **31** *1826*, *1831*, 1834, 1839
spotted eagle **18** 1067
wax moth **44** 2609, 2611-12
weasel lemur **13** *732*
weever **34** *2012*, 2033, *2035-6*
yellow-headed vulture **18** 1062, 1064
grebes **16** *951* 952, *955-60*; **51** 3014, 3050
classification **16** 960
distribution **16** 957
feather eaters **16** 957,´960
Greece, national park **51** 3002, *3014*
green...
anole **27** *1580-1*, 1582
catbird **25** 1474, 1476; **51** 3048
colobus monkey **51** 3020
discus **35** *2064*
drake **39** 2338
echiurans **50** 2950, 2958
frog **30** 1773, 1778
heron **17** 999, 1005
hydra **49** *2886*
ibis **17** 1018
iguana **27** *1563*, 1572, *1573*, *1576*, 1578
classification **27** 1579
distribution **27** 1565
imperial pigeon **20** 1156
kingfisher **21** 1253, *1259*
lacewings **43** *2567*, *2569*, 2570, *2571-2*
lizard **27** 1599, *1600*, 1603
magpie **25** 1489, *1490*, 1494
mamba **27** *1617-8*; **28** 1661, 1663, *1666*, 1667
monkey **14** 816
moray **32** 1874, 1880
oak tortrix moth **44** *2604*, 2609
palalo worm **49** *2936*
racer **28** *1660*
salamander **30** 1750, 1752
sandpiper **19** 1128-9, 1135
scarab beetle **39** *2325*; **41** 2456
snail **46** 2703
swordtails **33** 1980
tiger beetle **41** *2459*
toad **30** *1771*, *1787*, 1789, 1798
tree boa **28** *1624*, 1634, 1636, 1637, *1638*
tree python **28** 1633-4, 1637
turtle **26** *1527*, *1546*, 1552-3
wood-hoopoe **21** *1250*; **22** *1270*
woodpecker **22** *1293*, 1297, 1300
green-blood skink **27** 1593
green-tailed trainbearer **21** 1228
green-tongued nerite **45** 2700; **46** 2705
green-winged macaw **20** *1161*
green-winged teal **18** *1028*, 1045
green-winged trumpeter **19** 1117
greenback flounder **35** *2080*
greenbottles **45** *2658*, 2659, *2663-4*
greeneye **33** 1944, 1946
greenfinch **25** 1442, *1444-5*, 1446
greenflies **39** 2318; **41** 2438, *2451*
greenhouse thrips **41** 2428
Greenland right whale **10** 577
Greenland shark **31** 1841
greenlets **24** 1435
greenlings **34** 2007-8
greenshank **19** 1128, 1135; **51** 3010, 3046
gregarians **50** 2991-3
Gregarina annulata **50** *2992*
Gregarinia **50** 2991-3
gregarious turret shell **46** 2712
grenadiers **33** 1951, *1955*
Grevy's zebra **6** 334, *335*, 338-40
grey...
bat **12** 688
butcherbird **25** *1472*
caecilian **29** *1707*, 1710
catbird **23** 1379, *1380*
cuscus **11** 625
duck **51** 3050
duiker **8** 440
field slug **47** 2817
fox **2** *110*; **3** 126, 127
geese **18** 1040, 1044
gentle lemur **13** 742, 743
go-away bird **20** 1173, *1175*
ground jay **25** 1495
gurnard **34** 2007
heron **17** *999*, *1000-1*, *1006*, 1007
hornbill **22** 1278
hypocolius **23** 1372-3
jay **51** 3037
kangaroo **11** 635, *640-3*, *644*
kestrel **19** 1084
lesser mouse lemur **13** *735*, 742
mullet **34** *2037*; **35** 2042-3, *2044*
nurse shark **31** 1832
pampas fox **3** 127, 129
partridge **16** *913*; **19** 1096, 1097, 1099
pelican **17** 980, 981
phalarope **19** 1131
plantain-eater **20** 1178
plover **19** 1125, 1126
rhea **16** *923*, 925
rhebok **9** 508, 510, 516
seal **4** 183, 184
silky flycatcher **23** *1369*
slugs **48** *2825-6*
squirrel **4** *220*, 221-2, *232*
tree frog **30** 1782, 1785
triggerfish **35** 2087
wagtail **23** *1348-9*, 1352, 1353-4
warbler **51** 3050
whale **10** 577, *578-9*, *583*
wolf **2** 111, 117, 119; **51** 3012, *3056*
grey-backed fiscal shrike **23** *1367*
grey-bellied shrew opossum **11** 624

grey-breasted seedsnipe **19** *1137*
grey-breasted spurfowl **51** 3023
grey-breasted white-eye **24** 1417
grey-cheeked mangabey **14** *815*, 816
grey-headed albatross **17** 969
grey-headed fishing eagle **51** 3027
grey-headed flying fox **12** 693, 694, *700*
grey-headed kingfisher **21** *1252*, 1253
grey-headed lovebird **20** 1166
grey-headed shrike **23** 1367
grey-headed sparrow **25** 1455
grey-headed woodpecker **22** *1296*, 1297
grey-necked rockfowl **24** 1390, 1392
grey-rumped tree swift **21** 1224
greylag goose **18** 1034-5, 1040, 1044
gribble **37** 2196, *2200*
griffon vulture **18** 1070, 1077, *1078*
grison **1** 47, *48*
Grison **1** 47
grizzly bear **1** *19*, 20; **2** 71, 74, *79*; **51** *3037*, 3041
Gromphadorhina portentosa **40** 2391
Gronovius, Theodore **32** 1878
groove-billed ani **20** 1178
groove-toothed cowrie **46** 2730, *2731*
grosbeak weaver **25** 1455
grosbeaks **25** 1448
grotto salamander **30** 1750, 1752
ground beetles **41** 2456; **42** *2461-2*, *2465*
ground bugs **41** 2441
ground choughs **25** 1494
ground cockoo-shrike **23** 1357
ground cuckoo **20** *1172*, 1181
ground cuscus **11** 625
ground finches **24** *1424-5*, 1429
ground hornbill **22** 1274-5, 1278
ground jays **25** 1494-5
ground locust **40** 2369, 2382
ground rollers **21** 1253; **22** 1261, 1266-7
ground squirrel **4** 228, 229, 232
ground tyrant flycatcher **22** 1317
groupers **31** *1801*, 1803; **34** *2012*, 2020-1, 2023
  classification **34** 2013, 2023
  general features **34** 2022
grouse **19** *1086*, *1089*, 1092, *1093-6*, 1098; **51** 3010
grove snail **47** *2804*
Gruidae **19** 1107
Gruiformes **19** *1103-18*
grunion **34** 1982
grunt **34** 2032
Grus **19** 1107
Grylloblatta campodeiformis **40** 2385, 2387
grylloblattids **39** 2311; **40** *2384*, 2385, 2387
Grylloblattodea **39** 2311; **40** 2385, 2387
Grylloidea **40** 2369, 2374
Gryllotalpa **40** 2369
Gryllotalpidae **40** *2380-1*
Gryllus campestris **40** *2365*
grysbok **8** 444, 446
guanaco **7** *380*, *386*, 387-8
guanay cormorant **17** 990
guans **19** 1087, 1088, 1092, 1098
guasu pucu **7** 415
guavina sleeper **35** 2060, 2065
gudgeon **32** 1894-5, *1897*, 1898-9
guenons **13** 728; **14** 793-4, *795*, 796, *815-20*; **15** *897*
guereza **13** *755*; **14** *824*, *831-4*, 836
Guianan cock-of-the-rock **23** *1321*, 1322, *1330*
Guianan saki **13** *765*, 774
Guianas cattle heart **44** *2634*
guiara **5** 289
guillemots **19** *1119*; **20** *1141*, 1145, 1146, 1148
Guinea turaco **20** 1173
Guinea worm **49** 2925, 2929, 2933
guinea-pig family **4** 218; **5** *271-96*
guinea-pig louse **41** 2428
guineafowl **19** 1088, 1098, *1100*, 1101
guira **20** 1175, 1178, *1180*, 1182
Guira guira **20** 1178
guitarfish **31** *1838*, *1842*, 1843
Guivillea alabastrina **47** 2761
Gulf coast waterdog **30** 1743, 1745
gull-billed tern **20** 1143; **51** 3008
gulls **16** *913*; **19** 1139, *1140*; **20** *1141-3*, 1144; **51** 3008
  classification **19** 1121; **20** 1142; **51** 3008
  distribution **19** 1135
Gulo gulo **1** 47
gulper eel **32** 1874, *1882*, 1884; **34** 1988
gundi **5** 277, 286
gunnels **35** 2056, 2057
Gunther's dik-dik **8** 439-40, 444
guppies **33** *1970-2*, 1976, *1979-80*
  classification **33** 1978
gurnards **32** 1862-3; **34** 2007, 2010
  flying **34** *2004*, *2037*
Gustavia thrip **41** 2428
Guyonia flava **47** 2770
gwyniad **33** 1934
Gyliotrachela hungerfordiana **47** 2819
Gymnamoeba **50** 2991
Gymnarchidae **32** 1869
Gymnarchus niloticus **32** 1869, *1870*
Gymnobelideus leadbeateri **11** 627
Gymnocorymbus ternetzi **32** 1908
Gymnodinium **50** 2985
Gymnolaemata **50** 2966
Gymnophiona **29** 1701, *1707-10*
Gymnopis multiplicata **29** 1710
Gymnorhina tibicen **25** 1470
Gymnorhinus cyanocephala **25** 1489
Gymnosomata **47** 2767, 2783, 2784, 2786
gymnosome mollusc **47** *2774*
Gymnostomata **50** 2992, 2998
Gymnothorax funebris **32** 1874
Gymnotidae **32** 1920
Gymnotiformes **32** 1920
Gymnotus carapo **32** 1920
Gymnura micrura **31** 1844
gymnures **11** 654
Gynaikothrips ficorum **41** 2428
Gypaetus barbatus **18** 1070
Gyps **18** 1070
gypsy moth **41** 2457; **44** *2586*, *2589*, 2616-17, 2624
gyrfalcon **18** *1054*, *1079*, 1080; **19** 1081
gyrinid whirligig beetle **42** *2465*

ABOVE The hippoptamus's aggressive yawning gesture challenges another male to fight.

Gyrinidae **41** 2428, *2441*, 2456; **42** 2468
Gyrinocheilidae **32** 1894
Gyrinocheilus aymonieri **32** 1894
Gyrinophilus **30** 1750
Gyrinus natator **42** *2465*
Gyropidae **41** 2428
Gyrostoma **34** 2029

H

hadada ibis **17** 1018
haddock **31** 1859; **33** *1949-50*, 1951-2; **34** 1990
Hadogenes bicolor **38** *2246*
Hadrurus arionensis **38** *2246*
Haematomyzus **41** 2428
Haematopodidae **19** 1121, 1125
Haematopus **19** 1125
hagfishes **31** 1806-7, *1816-22*; **35** 2090
  classification **31** 1809
hailer shells **46** 2746
hair flies **45** 2646, 2647
hairless bat **12** 716
hairstreak butterfly **44** *2596*; **51** 3056
hairtail fishes **35** 2066-7
hairy armadillo **4** *197*
hairy blenny **35** 2059
hairy frog **30** 1782, 1785
hairy porcelain crab **38** *2224*
hairy-backed bulbul **16** 909
hairy-eared dwarf lemur **13** 745
hairy-flower wasps **43** 2529, 2534
hairy-fronted muntjac **7** 396
hairy-legged vampire bat **12** 679, 708, 709, *711*
hairy-nosed wombat **11** 633-4
hake **33** 1951, 1955
Halcyon **21** 1253
Halecium muricatum **47** 2797
Halesus digitatus **44** *2583*
halfbeaks **33** 1964, *1965-7*
Halgerdidae **47** 2796
Haliaeetus **18** 1070
halibut **32** 1884; **35** 2075, 2078, *2083*
Halicaridae **39** 2295
Halichoerus grypus **4** 184
Halichondria panicea **47** 2795
Halictidae **43** 2540
Halictus malachurus **43** *2538*, 2540
Halioma oculatum **50** 2991
Haliotidae **45** 2680, 2697-8
Haliotis **45** 2698
  lamellosa **45** 2699; **46** *2704*
  pourtalesii **45** 2697
  tubercolata **45** *2697*, 2699
Hall, K.R.L. **14** 820-2
Hall's giant petrel **17** 971
Halobaena caerulea **17** 973
Halobates **41** 2438, 2440
Halocynthia papillosa **35** 2094
Halocyprida **37** 2161
Halophiloscia **37** 2201
Halosauridae **32** 1872
Halosauropsis macrochir **32** 1872
halosaurs **32** 1872
Halpares libelluloides **43** *2567*
Haltica **42** 2504
hamadryas baboon **14** *792*, 808, *810-11*, 812-3; **51** 3017
hamerkop **17** 1008, 1011
Hamilton's frog **30** 1759

Hamlyn's monkey **14** 816
hammer oyster **48** *2832*, 2837
hammer shell **48** *2832*, 2837
hammer-headed bat **12** 693-5
hammer-headed stork **17** 1011
hammerhead sharks **31** *1836-9*
hammerheads **17** 997, *1008-10*, 1011
classification **17** 999,
distribution **17** 1005
hamster **4** 218; **5** 243, *245-7*, 248, *249*, 254
Handy Man **15** 899
hanging parrots **20** *1162*, 1166, 1168
hanging scorpion flies **43** 2575, 2576
hangul **7** 405; **8** 421
Hanno (explorer) **15** 858
Hanseniella **39** 2303
hanuman langur **14** *823-5*, 826, *828-9*, 834-6
Hapalemur **13** 742
Hapalemurinae **13** 742
Hapalochlaena
lupulata **48** 2868, 2869
maculosa **48** *2866*, 2868
Haplochromis **35** 2050
burtoni **35** 2049, *2054*
compressiceps **35** 2051
livingstonii **35** 2051, 2054
placodon **35** 2050
polyodon **35** *2051*
similis **35** 2050, *2051*
welcommei **35** 2051
Haplospora **50** 2992
Haplothrips tritici **41** 2428
harbour porpoise **10** 588, 593
harbour seal **3** *178*; **4** 184; **51** 3056
hard ticks **39** *2294*, 2295
hardun agama **27** 1584
hare wallaby **11** 636-7, 642
hares **4** *201-3*, 205-9, *210-11*, 214
harlequin beetle **42** *2510-11*
harlequin duck **18** 1051
harlequin frog **30** 1789, 1791
harlequin quail **19** 1096, 1099
harlequin rasbora **32** *1900*
harlequin shrimps **36** *2153*
Harlow, Harry **14** 803-5
harmless snakes **28** 1621, *1640-61*
harp seal **4** 183, *184*
harp shells **46** 2755, *2759*, 2760; **47** *2762*
Harpa **46** 2755
Harpa amouretta **47** *2762*
Harpactes **21** 1241
Harpacticoida **37** 2163, 2164
Harpadon nehereus **33** 1946
Harpagifer bispinis **35** 2055-6
Harpagiferidae **35** 2056
Harpia harpyia **18** 1070
Harpiosquilla **37** *2189*
harpy eagle **18** 1056, 1058, 1066, *1067*, 1070; **51** 3044
harrier-eagle **18** 1067
harrier-hawk **18** 1072
harriers **18** 1056, 1060, 1063-4, 1070, 1071-2
hartebeest **8** 434; **9** *484-8*, 490; **10** *569*; **51** 3018
Hartmann's zebra **6** *333*, 335, *338*, 340
harvest mites **39** 2295
harvest mouse **5** *242*, *259-60*
harvester ants **43** *2559*, *2560*, 2562
harvester termites **41** 2403, 2405, *2409*, *2420*
harvestmen **38** 2240, 2241, *2242*; **39** *2290-2*
hatchetfishes **32** *1906*, 1910-11; **33** *1940*, *1942-4*
classification **32** 1908
Hawaiian finches **24** 1435
Hawaiian goose **18** *1028*, 1044
Hawaiian honeycreepers **24** 1434-5
Hawaiian monk seal **3** 179, 180; **4** 184
Hawaiian petrel **17** 973
hawfinch **22** 1305; **25** 1442, *1446*, 1447
hawk eagles **18** 1066-7
hawk owl **20** 1191, *1195*, 1199
hawk-moths **44** 2595, *2596*, *2604*, 2617, *2621-3*
classification **44** 2624
feeding **44** *2587*, 2588, 2620
flight **44** 2597
migration **44** *2590-1*, 2622
hawker dragonflies **40** 2351, *2353*, 2354, 2359
hawks **1** 12; **18** *1054*, 1055, 1056, 1061, 1063-5
classification **18** 1057, 1070
courtship **18** 1059-60
hawksbill turtle **26** 1553, *1554-5*; **51** 3032
hazel grouse **19** 1092, 1093
heart cockle **48** 2846
heart shell **48** *2844*
heart urchins **36** 2124, 2127
heartworm **49** 2925
heath hen **19** 1095
hedge sparrow **24** 1381
hedgehog tenrec **11** *650*, 653
hedgehogs **1** *27*; **11** *645-50*, 655-7, *658-9*; **12** *664-5*
Heinroth, Oscar **16** 903
Heinroth's shearwater **17** 976
Helcion pectinatus **46** 2701
Heleomyia petrolei **45** 2642
Heleophryne rosei **30** 1799
Heleophrynidae **30** 1799
Helicacea **47** 2817, 2818; **48** 2826
Helicarionidae **48** 2823
Helicella **48** *2827*
Helicellidae **48** 2827
Helicidae **48** 2827, 2830
Helicigona **48** 2830
Helicinidae **45** 2700
helicinids **46** 2705
Heliconiinae **44** 2633, 2639
Heliconius **44** 2633, 2639
Heliocopris dominus **42** 2492
Heliophyra erhardi **50** 2979
Heliornis fulica **19** 1114
Heliornithidae **19** 1107, 1114
Heliothrips haemorrhoidalis **41** 2428
heliozoans **50** 2988, *2990-1*
Helix **47** *2813*
aspersa **48** 2828-9
pomatia **45** *2675*; **48** *2827-8*, **47** *2804*, 2812, 2817
hellbender salamander **29** *1712*, 1716, 1717-18
helmet shells **46** 2737, *2740-2*
helmet shrikes **23** 1367
helmeted guineafowl **19** 1100-1
helmeted iguana **27** 1572
helmeted lizard **27** 1579, *1582*
helmeted turtle **26** *1528-9*, 1530
Heloderma **27** 1614
Helodermatidae **27** 1614
Helops coerulens **42** 2472, 2490
Helostoma temmincki **35** 2070
Helostomatidae **35** 2070
Hemerobiidae **43** 2572
Hemerobioidea **43** 2570
Hemichromis bimaculatus **35** 2049
Hemicordata **50** 2971, *2972-3*
Hemicordulia tau **40** 2362
Hemidactylus turcicus **27** 1569
Hemiechinus auritus **11** 655
Hemifusus ternatana **46** 2751
Hemigalinae **2** 89, 92
Hemigalus derbyanus **2** 92
Hemignathus virens **24** 1435
Hemigrammus ocellifer **32** 1908
Hemimeridae **40** 2388
Hemimerina **40** 2388
Hemimycale **48** *2877*
Hemiphleboidea **40** 2351
hemipodes **19** 1115
Hemiprocne **21** 1224
Hemiprocnidae **21** 1218, 1224
Hemiptera **39** 2311; **41** *2433-52*
Hemiramphidae **33** 1965
Hemisus marmoratus **30** 1778
Hemitragus **10** 570
Hemmingway, Ernest **8** 449
Hemphillia glandulosa **48** 2824
hen **1** 39
hen harrier **18** 1070
Hepialidae **44** 2595
Hepialoidea **44** 2595, 2599
Hepialus humuli **44** 2595
Heptageniidae **40** 2343
Heptogenia sulphurea **40** *2343*
herbivore population **1** 26
Hercules beetle **42** 2491, 2500
Hereford cattle **8** 476
Hermann's tortoise **26** *1541-2*, 1544
hermit crabs **36** *2154-5*; **37** *2181*, 2220; **38** *2221-4*; **49** 2897
hermit hummingbirds **21** 1230, 1232
hermit ibis **17** *1015*, 1018
Hermodice carunculata **49** *2936*
Hermoine **49** 2937
hystrix **49** *2936*
herons **17** *996-9*, 1005, 1007
classification **17** 999, 1007
distribution **17** 1005
national parks **51** 3046, 3050
Herpestes **2** 98
Herpestidae **1** 28
Herpestinae **2** 89, 98
Herpetotheres cachinnans **18** 1080
herring gull **16** 915-16; **19** *1140*; **20** *1141*, 1142
herring smelts **33** 1937, 1941
herrings **31** 1806; **32** 1863, *1885-90*; **33** 1941
classification **31** 1858-9; **33** 1937
Herse convolvuli **44** 2624
Hesperarion niger **48** 2824
Hesperiidae **44** 2629, 2633
Hesperioidea **44** 2629, 2633
Hesperomynae **5** 243-9
Hesperornis **16** 905
hessian fly **45** 2646-7
Heterocephalus glaber **5** 284
heterocerid **42** *2465*
Heterocerus fossor **42** *2465*
Heteroconger **32** 1874
Heterodon nasicus **28** 1645
Heterodonta **48** 2833, 2837, 2843, 2845, 2847-8
Heterodontidae **31** 1828
Heterodontiformes **31** 1828
Heterodontus portjacksoni **31** 1828
Heterogastropoda **46** 2712, 2716
Heterohyrax **6** 313
Heteromys **4** 233
Heteroneris **49** 2939
Heteronetta atricapilla **18** 1052
Heteropeda venatoria **39** 2289
Heteropoda **46** *2726*, 2735-6, 2737
Heteropodidae **39** 2289
heteropods **45** 2677
Heteroptera **41** 2434, 2438
Heteropteryx dilatata **40** 2385
Heterostegina **50** *2986*
Heterostichus rostratus **35** 2059
Heteroteuthis dispar **48** 2855, 2860
Heterotricidae **50** 2999
Hexabranchidae **47** 2794
Hexabranchus **47** 2794
sanguineus **47** *2786*, 2794
Hexacorallia **49** 2889
hexacorals **49** 2889, 2893-9
Hexactinellida **48** 2880
Hexagrammidae **34** 2007
Hexagrammos decagrammus **34** 2007
Hexanchidae **31** 1828
Hexanchiformes **31** 1828
Hexanchus griseus **31** 1828
Hexapoda **36** 2140; **39** 2303, 2310, 2311, *2327-36*
Hiatellidae **48** 2849
hidden-necked turtles **26** 1528, 1532
hide beetles **42** 2503
Hierro giant lizard **27** 1603
higher annelids **50** 2956
highland anoa **8** 463, 468
hill kangaroo **11** 642
hill mynah **25** 1462, 1463; **51** 3030
hillstar hummingbird **21** 1232
hillstream loach **32** 1894, 1907
Himalayan snowcock **19** 1098
Himalayan tahr **9** *534*; **10** *551*, 554, 570
Himantopus himantopus **19** 1137
hinge-backed tortoise **26** 1526, 1546
hinged filter feeders **48** 2831-50
Hipparion **6** 333
Hippidion **6** 333
Hippocamelus **7** 418
Hippocampus **34** 2000, 2004
Hippodamia convergens **42** *2485*
Hippoglossus hippoglossus **35** 2075
Hippoidea **37** 2220
Hippolais polyglotta **24** 1394
Hippopotamidae **7** 378
HIPPOPOTAMIDS **7** *373-8*
Hippopotamus amphibius **7** 378
hippopotamuses **6** *302-3*, **7** *373-8*
classification **7** 378
distribution **7** 374
national parks **51** 3020, 3022, 3024
territory/breeding **7** 377-8
ungulate features **5** 298; **6** 301; **10** 569
Hippopus hippopus **48** 2847
Hipposideridae **12** 681, 704
Hipposideros fulvus **12** 704
Hippotraginae **8** 434; **9** 490, 502, 510; **10** 569

Hippotragini **8** 434; **9** 490, 495, 498-502
Hippotragus, equinus **9** 502
hirola **9** 490
Hirudinea **50** 2942, 2956, 2958
Hirudinidae **50** 2958
Hirudo medicinalis **50** *2956*
Hirundinidae **22** 1303; **23** 1345
Hirundininae **23** 1345
Hirundo **23** 1345
Hispaniola flower bat **12** 703
Hispaniola solenodon **11** *650*, 651
hispid hare **4** 209, 214
hissing adder **28** *1643*
hissing cockroach **40** 2391, 2395
hister beetle **42** *2473*
Hister quadrimaculatus **42** *2473*
Histioteuthidae **48** 2861, 2867
Histioteuthis
bonnellii **48** 2861, 2867
corona **48** 2867
heteropsis **48** 2867
meleagroteuthis **48** 2867
reversa **48** *2854*
Histrio histrio **33** 1961
Histriobdellidae **50** *2944*
hoary-headed grebe **16** 960
hoatzin **19** 1086, 1098, *1101*, 1102
hobby **19** 1081
Hochberg, Duke of **8** 478
Hochstetter's frog **30** 1759
Hodotermitidae **41** 2405
Hoffmann's two-toed sloth **4** *186*, 193, 195
hog deer **7** *397*, 398, 406
hog lice **37** 2200; **41** *2431*
hog-nosed badger **1** 55
hog-nosed skunk **1** 42, 55
hog-rat **5** 287-8
hogchoker **35** 2075
hognosed snake **28** 1641, *1643*, 1644-5
Hohnel's chameleon **27** 1589, 1592
Holarctic treecreepers **24** 1412
Holaus falos **44** *2634*
hollowsnout rat-tail **34** *1996*
Holocentridae **34** 1990
Holocentrus xantherythrus **34** 1990
hologymnura stickleback **34** 1992
Hololampra marginata **40** 2391, 2395
Holopedium gibberum **36** 2157
holothurian **36** *2123*
Holothuroidea **36** 2106, 2107, *2121-4*
Holvelia **41** 2438
Homalopteridae **32** 1894
Homaridae **37** 2214
Homarus gammarus **37** *2192*, 2214, *2218*
Homatus vulgaris **37** *2210*
homing pigeon **20** 1151, 1158
Hominidae **14** 839
HOMINIDS **13** 728; **15** *891-900*
Hominoidea **14** 839; **15** *897*
Homo **15** *895*, 899-900
Homoptera **41** 2434, 2438, 2446
Homotrena **50** 2987
Honduran disc-winged bat **12** 709
honey badger **1** *38*, 41, *49*, *52*; **51** 3026, 3054
honey buzzard **18** 1060, 1063, 1070, 1073
honey guide **1** 41
honey possum **11** 612, *621*, 631-2, 633
honey-bees **43** 2540, *2543-51*
drones **43** 2545
queen **43** 2544, *2547*, 2548
workers **43** *2542*, *2544-6*, *2548-51*
honeycomb coral **35** *2059*
honeycreepers **24** 1429
honeyeaters **16** *909*; **24** 1408, *1418-20*
honeyguides **20** 1175; **22** 1281, 1287-9
classification **22** 1284, 1288
distribution **22** 1282
honeypot ant **43** *2558*, 2564
Honshu sika deer **51** 3060
hooded crow **25** 1485, 1489, 1498, *1500*
hooded grebe **16** *960*
hooded merganser **18** *1028*
hooded racket-tailed tree pie **25** 1489, 1490
hooded scalyfoot **27** 1570
hooded seal **4** *182*, 183, 184
hooded skunk **1** *55*
hooded warbler **24** 1431, 1433
hoof snails **46** 2720, *2724*, *2726-7*
hoofed mammals **5** 297-300
hook-tentacled squid **48** *2854*
hooked-lipped rhino **6** 357
hookworms **49** 2928-9
hoolock gibbon **15** 842, 846
hoopoe lark **23** 1334, 1338-9
hoopoes **21** *1251*, 1253; **22** *1269-74*
classification **22** 1270
distribution **22** 1262
Hoplocampa **42** 2518
Hoplocarida **37** 2182
Hoplonemertea **49** 2920
Hoplopterus **19** 1125
hoppers **40** 2377-8
Hormogaster **50** 2952
horn shark **31** 1828-9
horn shells **46** 2712, 2718
horn-tails **42** 2516, *2517-18*
hornbills **21** 1251-2; **22** 1262, *1274-8*; **51** 3030
classification **22** 1253; 1278
distribution **22** 1262
horned frog **30** *1764*, 1795, *1800*
horned grebe **16** 957
horned hog **7** 370, *371*
horned lark **23** 1334, 1339
horned lizards **26** *1518*; **27** 1565, *1572*, 1573, 1576
classification **27** 1579
horned octopus **48** *2866*
horned puffin **20** 1148
horned screamer **18** *1028*, *1029*, 1030, 1031
horned toads **27** 1565; **30** 1768, 1769-70
horned tree-hopper **41** 2439
horned viper **28** 1673, *1674*
horneros **22** 1309
hornet moth **44** 2597, *2599*, 2608, 2609
hornets **42** *2516*; **43** 2530, 2532-3, *2536*
horns **6** 306-7, *308*
horny corals **49** 2889, 2899-2900
horny sponges **48** *2875*, 2880
horse antelope **9** 502
horse buffalo gnat **45** 2651-2
horse conchs **46** 2754
horse mackerel **32** 1863; **34** 2036, 2038, *2040*
horse mussel **48** *2832*, 2837, 2840
horse-like antelopes **8** 434; **10** *569*
horseflies **45** *2652-3*, *2458*
horsehair worms **49** *2933*, 2934
horses **5** *297*; **6** 331, 334, *346-7*, 348; **51** 3006-7, *3009*
classification **6** 340; **10** 568
distribution **6** 335
evolution **6** 300, 332-3
hooves **5** 298, 299; **6** 332
horseshoe bats **12** *678*, *690*, 699, 702, *705*; **51** 3046
body temperature **12** 688, 692
classification **12** 681, 704
navigation **12** 684-5
horseshoe crabs **36** 2140, 2141; **38** 2234, *2235-7*, 2241
horseshoe snake **28** *1642*
horseshoe worms **50** 2965-6, *2968-9*
Hospitalitermes **41** *2404*
Hottentot golden mole **11** 655
houbara **19** 1107, 1112
house cricket **40** 2369, 2374, *2375*
house crow **25** 1500
house finch **25** *1450-1*
house flies **45** 2659, *2660*, 2662
house gecko **27** 1568
house martin **16** *909*, 912; **23** 1343, *1344*
classification **23** 1345
nests **23** *1342*, 1343
house mouse **5** 243, 255, *258-9*
house shrew **12** 662
house sparrow **25** *1454*, 1455, *1456-7*, 1459
house spider **38** *2261*, 2279
house wren **23** 1377, 1379
houting **33** 1934
hover flies **45** *2655-7*, 2659
howler monkeys **13** 763-4, *766-7*, *775*; **14** 836; **51** 3038-9
classification **13** 728, 774
diet **13** *778*, 779
voice **13** *775*, 779-80
huemul **7** 417, 418
human body louse **41** 2428, 2430
human crab louse **41** 2428, 2429-30, *2431*
human flea **45** 2665-7
human head louse **41** 2428, *2429*, *2430-1*
human tapeworm **49** *2914*
human whipworm **49** 2925, 2929
humans **12** 718; **14** 839; **15** 849, *891-900*
evolution **13** *727*
hands **12** *719*, 720
origins **13** 728, 756
teeth **13** 726
Humboldt penguin **16** 938, 948, 949, 950
Humboldt's woolly monkey **13** *762*, 774, *779-80*; **14** 781-2
Hume's ground jay **25** 1484, 1489, 1495
humming frog **30** 1799
hummingbird hawk-moths **44** *2590-1*, 2597, 2622, 2624, 2633
hummingbird louse **41** 2428
hummingbirds **21** *1215*, *1216*, 1217, *1226-38*
classification **21** 1218, 1228
distribution **21** 1224
flight **16** 905, *908*, 909
heartbeat **16** 911
hump-headed Maori wrasse **34** 2023
humpback salmon **33** 1924
humpback whale **10** *575*, 577, *581-4*
migratory route **10** *572*
spout **10** *573*
Hunter's hartebeest **9** 490
hunting spider **38** *2274*
hunting wasps **43** 2529
huntsmen spiders **39** 2289
Huso huso **31** 1856
Hutchinsoniella macracantha **36** *2150*
hutia **5** 277, 287-8, 289
Huxley, Thomas **15** 893
hyacinth macaw **20** *1165*, 1168
hyacinth visor-bearer **21** 1228
Hyaenidae **1** 28
hyaenodons, evolution **1** 25
Hyaleus **43** 2539
Hydatina velum **47** *2775*
Hydatinidae **47** *2775*
hydra **49** *2886*, *2888-9*
Hydra viridis **49** *2886*
Hydrachnidae **39** 2295
Hydrobates pelagicus **17** 976
Hydrobatidae **17** 971, 976
Hydrobia **46** *2712*, 2713
Hydrobiidae **46** 2712, 2713
Hydrobiosidae **43** 2580; **44** 2581
Hydrocena **46** 2705
Hydrocenidae **46** 2705
Hydrochoeridae **5** 277, 289
Hydrochoerus **5** 279, 289
Hydrocorallina **49** 2889
Hydrocynus vittatus **32** 1908
Hydroida **49** 2889
Hydromantes italicus **30** 1750
Hydrometridae **41** 2438, 2440-1
Hydromyinae **5** 262
Hydromyles globulosa **47** 2783-4
Hydromylidae **47** 2783, 2786
Hydrophasianus chirurgus **19** 1123
Hydrophilidae **41** 2454
Hydrophinae **28** 1667
Hydropotes inermis **7** 396
Hydropotinae **7** 396, 411
Hydropsychoidea **43** 2580; **44** 2581, 2582-3
Hydroptilidae **43** 2580; **44** 2581
Hydrous piceus **42** *2465*
Hydrozoa **49** 2887, 2889
hydrozoans **49** *2886-92*
Hydrurga leptonyx **3** 179; **4** 184
Hyemoschus aquaticus **7** 392
hyena **1** 27, 28, 32; **2** *99-108*; **51** 3019, 3023, 3026
HYENIDS **2** *99-108*
Hyla **30** 1795
Hyles lineata **44** *2604*
Hylexetastes perrotii **22** 1310
Hylidae **30** 1756, 1795
Hylobates **15** 842, 846
Hylobatidae **14** 839; **15** 842
HYLOBATIDS **14** *837-40*; **15** *841-90*
Hylochoerus meinertzhageni **7** 370
Hylocylis striata **47** *2774*
Hylomanes momotula **22** 1270
Hylomys suillus **11** 655
Hylophilus olivaceus **24** 1435
Hymeniacidon sanguinea **46** 2719; **47** 2795
Hymenoptera **39** 2311; **41** 2402, 2404, 2426; **42** 2488, *2515-20*; **43** *2521-64*

Hymenopus coronatus **40** *2398*
Hymenostomata **50** 2992, 2997
Hynobiidae **29** 1713, 1716
Hynobius **29** 1716
Hyohippus **6** 333
Hyperiidea **37** *2206, 2207, 2208*
hypermastigina flagellate **50** *2980*
Hypermastiginae **41** 2408
Hyperoliidae **30** 1756, 1785
Hyperolius **30** 1785
Hyperoodon ampullatus **10** 593
Hypipamee National Park **51** 3048, 3049
Hypocolius ampelinus **23** 1372
Hypoderma bovis **45** *2658*, 2659
Hypogastrura viatica **39** 2333
Hypopachus cuneus **30** 1786
Hypositta corallirostris **23** 1368
Hypotrichidae **50** 2999
hypotrichs **50** *2993*
Hyppolite varians **37** *2212*
Hypsignathus monstrosus **12** 694
Hypsipetes amaurotis **23** 1359
Hypsiprymnodon moschatus **11** 642
Hypsypops rubicunda **34** 2024
Hyracoidea **6** 304, 313
Hyracotherium **6** 332, 333
hyraxes **5** 298-9; **6** *305, 309, 311-12*
classification **6** 304, 313
distribution **6** 316
evolution **1** 18; **6** 310, 319
hyspid hares **51** 3026
Hystricidae **5** 277

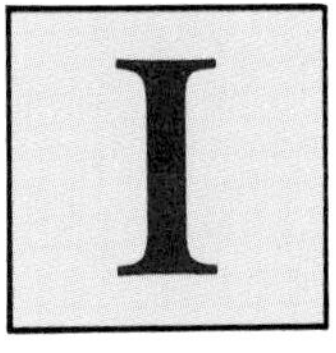

ibex **6** 308; **8** 434; **9** *534*, 535; **10** *552-4*, 555-6, 563, 570
ibex, national parks **51** 3016
Ibidorhyncha struthersii **19** 1137
Ibidorhynchidae **19** 1121, 1137
ibisbill **19** 1121, 1137
ibises **17** *996*, 997, *1018-20*; **51** 3014
classification **17** 999, 1018
distribution **17** 1019
Icaronycteris **12** 680
ice-birds **17** 972
ice-flea **39** 2331, 2333
Iceland gull **20** 1142
Icerya purchasi **42** 2486
ichneumon **2** 86, 98
ichneumon flies **42** 2516; **43** 2522
ichneumon wasp **42** *2519*; **43** *2521, 2523*
Ichneumonidae **42** 2516
Ichneumonoidea **43** 2522
Ichthyophis glutinosus **29** 1710
ichthyosaurs **26** *1507*
Ichthyotomidae **50** 2942
Ichthyotomus **50** 2944
Ictaluridae **32** 1913
Ictalurus nebulosus **32** 1913
Icteridae **24** 1440
ICTERIDS **24** 1430, *1438-40*
Icterus galbula **24** 1440
Icthyomyzon **31** 1818
Ictiobus bubalus **32** 1894
Ictonyx striatus **1** 47
Idiacanthidae **33** 1944
Idiacanthus **33** 1944
Idiurus **4** 233
idmi **9** 520, 529
Idolamantis **40** 2397
Idolothripinae **41** 2428
Idolum diabolicum **40** *2398*, 2399
Idotea **37** *2199*, 2200
Ifrita kowaldi **24** 1390
Iguana iguana **27** 1579
Iguanadon **26** 1508
iguanas **26** *1508*, 1517; **27** *1561, 1563, 1572-7*, 1578-9
classification **27** 1562, 1579
distribution **27** 1565
Galapagos Islands **27** 1578; **51** *3034*
Iguanidae **27** 1562, 1579
iiwi **24** *1426, 1434*, 1435
Ilyocriptus sordidus **36** 2157
impala **9** 520, *531*, 532
imperial angelfish **34** 2024, *2025*
imperial eagle **18** 1067
imperial mammoth **6** 319
imperial scorpion **38** *2241, 2246*, 2250-1
imperial woodpecker **22** 1297, 1300
Inachis io **44** 2633
Inachus dorsettensis **38** *2224*
Inarticulata **50** 2966, 2970
inch worms **44** 2609, 2613, *2614*
Incirrata **48** 2868, 2869
Incurvariidae **44** 2600
Incurvarioidea **44** 2595, 2600
India, national parks **51** 3002, *3028-9*
Indian...
bison **8** 468
black eagle **18** 1067
black vulture **18** 1078
blue jay **22** 1261
chameleon **27** 1565, 1592
chank **46** 2746
cobra **28** 1661, 1662, 1667
courser **19** *1122*
elephant **6** *320*, 324, 326, *329*
flapshell turtle **26** 1553, 1566
flying fox **12** *678, 695, 699*
fox **3** 127
grey hornbill **22** 1274, 1278
honeyguide **22** 1288
krait **26** *1520*
muntjac **7** *390*, 396
nightjar **21** 1206
pangolin **4** 189, 200
pitta **22** 1314, *1315*
python **28** *1624, 1629, 1633-4*
classification **28** 1637
incubation **28** 1632
rat snake **28** 1661
red dhole **3** *129*, 130
rhino **5** 300; **6** *354*, 355-6, *357*; **7** 361, 362; **51** *3026-7*
classification **6** 358
distribution **6** 356
roller **22** 1262
skimmer **20** 1145
spiny eel **35** 2072
spotted chevrotain **7** 392
spotted deer **7** 398-400, 406
star tortoise **26** *1523*, 1526, 1544
tiger **51** *3029*
tree shrew **13** *730*
wart snake **28** 1626, *1627*
Indiana bat **12** 716
Indicator **22** 1288
Indicatoridae **22** 1288
indigo bunting **24** *1427*, 1429
Indo-Pacific ark shell **48** 2834

ABOVE **A trio of female impalas survey the Masai Mara in Kenya.**

Indo-Pacific black marlin **35** 2041
Indostmatidae **34** 1997
Indostomus paradoxus **34** 1997
indri **13** 733, 735, 749; **15** *896*
classification **13** 728, 742
evolution **13** *727*
Indri indri **13** 742
Indriidae **13** 742
Indus dolphin **10** 586
infusorians **50** *2980*
ingolfiellids **37** 2208
Inia geoffrensis **10** 593
inland dotterel **19** 1125
innkeeper worm, host **35** 2061
Inostemma pyricola **42** 2516; **43** 2526-7
Insecta **36** 2140; **39** 2303, *2311-25*, 2326, 2335
Insectivora **11** 651, 655, 660; **12** 662, 670
INSECTIVORES **11** *645-60*; **12** *661-72*
primate ancestors **12** 718
INSECTS **36** 2103, 2140; **39 -45** *2309-2667*
body parts **39** *2312-17*
evolution **39** 2310-11; **45** *2670*
reproduction **39** 2318
INVERTEBRATES **36 -50** *2101-3000*
evolution **45** *2670*
introduction **36** *2101-3*
inviidae **46** 2720
io moth **44** *2594, 2596*
Iodopleura fusca **23** 1322
ioras **23** *1360*, 1361
Iowan **19** 1088
Iracundus signifer **33** *1960*
Ircinia **48** *2875-6*
Irena **23** 1360
Irenidae **23** 1360
Iriomote cat **3** 154
Iris oratoria **40** 2397, *2399*
isard **10** 549
Ischnocera **41** 2428
Ischnochiton rissoi **45** 2688
Ischnochitonida **45** 2684, 2686
Ischyropsalis heilwigi **38** *2242*
Isistius **31** 1841
island night lizard **27** *1563*, 1571
Isometrus maculatus **38** 2244, 2250
Isopoda **37** 2196
isopods **37** 2182, *2196-2203*
Isoptera **39** 2311; **41** *2401-26*
Isotoma saltans **39** 2331, 2333
Israel painted frog **30** 1762
Istiophoridae **35** 2043
Istiophorus platypterus **35** 2043
Isurus **31** 1839
Italian agile frog **30** 1775
Italian cave salamander **30** *1745, 1746*, 1747, 1750
Italian newt **29** 1738
Italian scorpion **38** *2244*
Italian sparrow **25** 1455
Italian tree cricket **40** *2366*
Italian wall lizard **27** *1594, 1599*
Italy, national park **51** 3002, *3012-13*
itch mite **39** 2295
Ivory Coast, national park **51** 3002, *3020-1*
ivory gull **20** 1142
ivory-billed woodpecker **22** *1298*
Ixobrychus **17** 1007
Ixodes ricinus **38** *2242*
Ixodidae **39** 2295

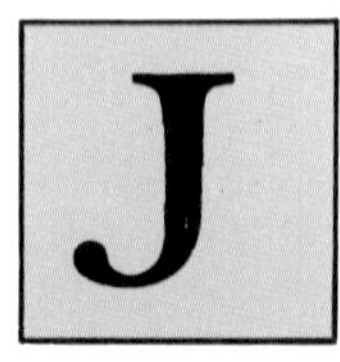

jabiru **17** *996*, 1011, 1012, *1014*, 1015
Jabiru mycteria **17** 1012
jacamars **22** *1281-3*, 1284
Jacamerops aurea **22** 1284
Jacana spinosa **19** 1123
jacanas **19** *1120-1*, 1123, 1129
Jacanidae **19** 1121, 1123
Jack Dempsey cichlid **35** 2049, *2055*
jack snipe **19** 1135
jackal **1** *24*; **2** 115, *116-18*; **3** *128*; **51** 3014
jackass penguin **16** *936*, 948, 949, *950*
jackdaw **25** *1488*, 1489, *1496-7*, 1498
jackrabbit **4** 202, *205-6*, 209
jacks **34** 2038
Jackson's chameleon **27** 1592
Jackson's francolin **19** 1096
Jackson's hartebeest **9** 486
Jackson's widow **25** 1459, 1460
Jacobson's organ **26** 1513; **27** 1562
Jaculus **5** 268, 270
jaeger **20** 1142
jaguar **1** 27, 60; **3** 140, *142*, 144, 149; **4** *193*
    national parks **51** 3038, *3039*, 3044
jaguarundi **2** 89; **3** *138*, *148-9*; **51** 3044
    classification **3** 158
    distribution 140
Jamaican flower bat **12** 703
Jamaican nutia **5** 287
Jamaican tody **22** 1268, 1270
James' flamingo **18** 1023, 1024
Janthina **46** 2736, 2758-9
    janthina **46** *2704*, *2719*
Janthinidae **46** 2712, 2719
Japan, national park **51** 3002, *3060*
Japanese...
    auk **51** 3060
    crane **19** 1105, 1106, 1107, *1109*
    crested ibis **17** 1018
    dormouse **5** 263; **51** 3060
    eel **32** 1874, 1877
    giant salamander **29** 1716, *1717*
    macaque **1** 14, *16*, *18*; **14** *796-9*, 800-1, 803, 805; **51** 3060
    medaka **33** 1965
    murrelet **20** 1148; **51** 3060
    night heron **17** 1007
    serow **9** 539, 540; **10** 541, 550
    sparrowhawk **51** 3060
    spider crab **37** 2178, 2189; **38** 2232
    waxwing **23** 1369
    wood pigeon **51** 3060
Japonacteon nipponensis **47** *2768*
Japygidae **39** 2333, 2334, 2335
Japyx solifugus **39** 2333, 2335
Jasper and Banff National Parks **51** 3002, *3036-7*
Jau National Park **51** 3002, 3004, *3038-9*
Java, national park **51** 3002, *3032*
Java fighting fish **35** 2069
Java sparrow **25** 1453

ABOVE The common jellyfish swims by pulsating its transparent umbrella or bell.

Javan frogmouth **21** 1213
Javan nawab **44** *2634*
Javan rhino **6** 356-7, 358; **7** 361, 362; **51** 3032
Javan slit-faced bat **12** 699
Javan wart snake **28** *1624*, 1626
Javan warty pig **7** 365, 366, *367*
    classification **7** 370
    extinction threat **7** 372
Javanese banteng **8** 473
Javanese pangolin **4** *189*, 200
javelinfish **33** 1945-6
jawless fishes **31** 1806-7, *1815-24*
jays **25** 1484, 1485, *1486-8*, 1490-1, *1492-3*
    breeding **25** *1490*, *1495*
    classification **25** 1489
    distribution **25** 1490-1
Jefferson salamander **29** 1720, 1722
jellyfishes **33** 1952; **36** 2103; **49** *2884-9*, *2891-3*
    classification **49** 2899
    hosts **34** 2038
Jemez mountain salamander **30** 1750
Jenkins' spire shell **46** 2712, 2713
Jentink's duiker **8** 438, 440; **51** 3020
jerboa **5** *242-3*, 254, 268, *269-70*; **51** 3052
jewel cichlids **35** 2049, *2052*, *2064*
jewelled squid **48** 2854, 2861, 2863
jimela **9** 488
Joenia annectens **50** *2980*
Johanssonia acetosea **44** 2600
John Dory **34** *1987*, 1990; *1996*
John's earth boa **28** *1635*
John's langur **14** 825-6
Johnston's hyrax **6** 313
Jordanella floridae **33** 1978
'jug o'rum' (bullfrog) **30** 1773
Julidae **39** 2304
Juliidae **47** 2776-7
jumping cockle **48** 2847
jumping mouse **5** 243, 254
jumping plant-lice **41** 2450, 2452
jumping spiders **38** 2258, 2263, 2277; **39** 2289
Junco hyemalis **24** 1429
jungle babblers **24** 1389
jungle nightjar **21** 1206
junglefowl **19** 1098
Jurus dufoureus **38** *2246*
Jynginae **22** 1297
Jynx **22** 1297

Kafue lechwe **9** 512
kagu **19** *1104*, 1107, 1117, *1118*
kaka **20** 1170
Kakadu National Park **51** 3002, *3046-7*
kakapo **16** 918; **20** *1162*, *1164*, 1168, 1169-70; **51** 3050
Kalahari Game Reserve **51** *3018-19*
Kallima inachus **44** *2596*
Kalotermitidae **41** 2403, 2405
Kaloula pulchra **30** 1786
kangaroo mouse **4** 233
kangaroo rat **4** *220*, 233, *238*
kangaroos **1** 16; **11** *607*, *609*, 610-12, *634-44*; **51** *3045-6*
    classification **11** 612, 642
    distribution **11** 634
    variations **11** *616*
Kaokoveld hyrax **6** 313
Karakul sheep **10** 570
Kashmir stag **7** 405; **8** 421
Kassina **30** 1785
katydids **40** 2364, *2369*, 2371-2
kauri moths **44** 2595, 2599
kea **20** *1162*, 1163, *1166*, 1168, 1170
keel-billed toucan **22** *1281*, 1290-1
keel-scaled boa **28** 1640
Kellia **48** 2845, 2847
kelp greenling **34** 2007-8
kelpfish **35** 2058-9
Kemp's ridley turtle **26** *1553*, 1554
Kenai Peninsular Dall's sheep **10** 566
Kentish plover **19** 1125, *1126*; **51** 3008
kestrel **18** 1055, 1056, 1057, 1060, 1080; **19** 1081, *1082*, 1083-4; **51** 3017
Ketupa zeylonensis **20** 1199
key deer **8** 424
keyhole limpets **45** 2674, 2680, *2694*, 2697, *2699-2700*; **46** *2704*
Khao Yai National Park **51** 3002, 3004, *3030-1*
Kheper aegyptiorum **39** *2325*; **41** 2456; **42** *2497*
kiang **6** 345, 346
killer whale **1** 10; **10** *571-2*, *574*, 592, *596*
    classification **10** 593
killifishes **33** 1968, *1973-5*, 1978
Kinetofragminophora **50** 2992, 2997, 2999
king bird of paradise **25** *1477*, 1480, *1481*
king cobra **28** *1661*, 1662, 1667
king cormorant **17** *990*
king eider **18** *1049*
"King of the Herrings" *see* oarfishes
King Kong film **15** 859
king penguin **16** *937*, *938-9*, 940-2
    classification **16** 949
    distribution **16** 944, 948
king salmon **33** 1924
"King of the Salmon" **34** 1987
King of Saxony bird of paradise **25** 1482
king snake **28** 1641, *1642*, 1645, *1658-9*
king thorny oyster **48** *2832*
king vulture **18** *1054*, *1061-3*, 1064
kingfishers **21** *1249-60*; **51** 3026
    classification **21** 1253
    distribution **21** 1252
kingklip **33** 1956
kinkajou **1** 18, *58*; **2** 62, *63*
KINORHYNCHS **49** 2923, *2924-6*
Kinosternidae **26** 1535
Kirk's dik-dik **8** 440, *441*, *444*
Kirtland's warbler **24** 1431, 1433
kissing gourami **35** 2068-70, *2071*
kit fox **3** 121-3, 127, *128*
kites **18** 1057, 1063-4, 1070, 1072-3
Kitti's hog-nosed bat **1** 9, 11; **12** 681, 704

ABOVE A koala rarely leaves its eucalyptus tree-top home.

kittiwake **20** *1141*, 1142
Kittlitz's murrelet **20** 1148
kiwis **16** 912, 918, 925, *931*, 933; **51** 3050
Klingel, Hans **6** 336
klipfishes **35** 2058-9
klipspringer **8** *435-6*, 438, 441, 444; **51** 3016
kloss gibbon **15** 842-3, 846
Kneria **32** 1892
Kneriidae **32** 1892
knifefishes **32** 1869
knob-billed goose **18** 1052
knot **19** 1127, *1130*, 1135
koala **11** *610*, *616*, *628-9*, 632
  classification **11** 612, 633
kob **9** 509-10, *511-13*; **34** 2032; **51** 3024
Kobus **9** 510
kodiak bear **2** 71, 75, *78*
kodkod **3** 158
koel **20** *1172*, 1174, 1180, 1181
Kogia
  breviceps **10** 593
  simus **10** 593
kokako **25** 1469, 1470
kokanee **33** 1925
kokoi poison-arrow frog **30** 1776, 1785
kolinsky **51** 3052
Komodo dragon **27** 1565, *1607*, 1608
  classification **27** 1609
  size **27** 1562, 1606, *1610-11*
'Kon-Tiki' expedition **32** 1880
kongoni **9** *487*, 490
kookaburra **21** 1252, 1253, *1260*
Korean grey whale **10** 579
kori bustard **19** *1108*, 1112
koringkriek **40** 2369, 2371
korrigum **9** *488*
Kortlandt, Adriaan **15** 876
Kotschy's gecko **27** 1566
kouprey **8** 468, 474-5
Kovalevskiids **35** 2098
kowari **11** *617*, 619
kraits **28** 1640, 1667, *1668*
krill **36** 2140, 2147; **37** 2182, *2188*, *2208-9*
  predators **37** *2209*, 2211
Krytopterus bicirrhus **32** 1913
kudu **8** *447*, *449*, 450-2, *458-9*
Kuhl's deer **7** 406
kulan **6** 345; **51** *3055*
kultarr **11** 619
Kynorhyncha **49** 2923, 2925

La Plata dolphin **10** 586, 593
Labidognatha **38** 2258
Labidostomis **42** 2504
Labiduridae **40** 2388
Labridae **34** 2013, 2023
Labrisomidae **35** 2059
Labrisomus nuchipinnus **35** 2059
Labroides **34** 2023
Labrus mixtus **34** 2023
labyrinth fishes **35** 2068, 2070
Laccifer lacca **41** 2452, 2454
lace bugs **41** 2438, *2439*, 2441-2
Lacerta **27** 1603
Lacertidae **27** 1562, 1603
lacewing-like flies **43** *2567*, 2570, 2573
lacewings **39** 2311, *2316*; **43** 2566, *2567*, *2569*, 2570
Lachesis muta **28** 1669
lackey moth **44** 2624, 2628
Lactophrys trigonus **35** 2082
Lactoria diaphana **35** 2082, 2086
Lacunidae **46** 2706
Lady Ross's turaco **20** *1173*, 1178
ladybirds **39** *2316*; **41** 2456, 2457, *2458*; **42** 2472, *2482-7*
Laevicardium **48** 2846, 2947
Lafresnaye's vanga **23** 1368
Laginiopsis triloba **47** *2784*
LAGOMORPHS **4** *201-14*
Lagopus **19** 1093
Lagostomus maximus **5** 289
Lagothrix lagotricha **13** 774
Lake Baikal gammarids **37** 2206
lake chars **33** 1934
Lake Maggiore shad **32** 1889-90
Lake Mikri Prespa National Park **51** 3002, *3014*
Lake Titicaca frog **30** 1795, 1798
lake trout **33** 1924, 1930, 1932, 1934
lake whitefish **33** 1934
Lalage suerii **23** 1357
Lama **7** 388
Lambis **46** 2720, 2723
  chiragra **46** *2726*
Lamellaria perspicua **46** *2727*, 2729
Lamellariidae **46** 2729
Lamellibranchs **48** 2833
Lamellidorididae **47** 2790
Lamellisabella **50** 2971
lamellose wentletrap **46** 2721
lammergeier vulture **18** *1070*, *1077*; **51** 3017
Lamna **31** 1839
Lamnidae **31** 1839
Lamniformes **31** 1838
lamp shells **50** 2966-7, *2970*
Lampanyctus **33** 1946
lampern **31** 1818, *1820*
Lampetra **31** 1818
Lampis noctiluca **42** 2472
lampreys **31** 1806-7, *1815-24*; **35** *2090*, 2100
  classification **31** 1809
Lampridae **34** 1987
Lampridiformes **34** 1987
Lampriformes **34** 1985-90, *1996*
Lamprina **42** 2502
Lampris guttatus **34** 1987
Lampropeltis getulus **28** 1645
Lamprosoma **42** *2507*
lampshells **36** 2103
Lampyridae **42** 2472, 2478, 2480
Lampyris noctiluca **42** *2479*; **48** 2825
lance-head snakes **28** 1675
lance-tailed manakin **23** *1330*
lancelets **31** 1803; **35** 2090-2, *2100*
lancetfish **33** 1946
land bugs **41** *2435-6*, *2438*
land iguana **27** *1577*, 1578, 1579
land leeches **50** *2956*, 2958
land operculate snail **46** *2704*, *2708*
land slugs **47** *2800-20*; **48** 2822
land snails **45** 2677, 2680, 2694; **46** *2704*, *2708*; **47** 2817, *2800-20*; **48** *2828*
  classification **45** 2674, 2697
langouste **37** *2214*
langurs **7** 399-400; **13** *721-2*, 728; **14** 794, *822-9*, 834-6
Laniarius barbarus **23** 1367
Laniidae **22** 1303; **23** 1367
Laniinae **23** 1367
Lanius **23** 1367
lanner falcon **19** *1081*; **51** 3017
lantern fishes **31** *1809*, 1858; **33** *1942*, 1946
lantern flies **41** *2438-9*, *2446*
lantern shark **31** *1838*
Lanternaria candelaria **41** *2446*
lanterneyes **34** 1988-90
Lanthanotidae **27** 1614
Lanthanotus borneensis **27** 1614
Lapidochromis vellicans **35** 2050, *2051*
lappet moth **44** 2624, *2628-9*
lappet-faced vulture **18** 1070, 1078
lapwing **19** *1123*, 1125, 1126
lar gibbon **14** *837*; **15** 842, *844-5*, *847*, 848
larder beetle **42** *2473*
large blue butterfly **44** 2595, 2632, 2633
large blue-tongued skink **27** 1593
large cuckoo-shrike **23** 1357
large frogmouth **21** *1213*, 1214
large green snail **45** 2700; **46** 2703
large ground finch **24** *1426*
large horse mussel **48** 2840
large mouse-eared bat **12** 679, *709*, 712-13
large raft spider **39** 2281
large red damselfly **40** *2355*
large white butterfly **44** 2633, 2636
large white plume moth **44** 2609, 2611
large-billed warblers **51** 3047
large-footed tapaculo **22** 1314
large-scaled sweepslang **27** 1598
large-tailed nightjar **21** 1206
largemouth bass **34** *2014-65*; **35** *2064*
larger mouse deer **7** 391, 392
Lari **19** 1121
Laridae **19** 1121; **20** 1142
lark quail **19** 1114
larks **22** 1303; **23** 1322, *1334-40*, *1356*
Larra anathema **43** 2537
Larridae **43** 2537
Larus **20** 1142
Larvacea **35** 2090, 2094-5, 2098
larvevorid **45** *2658*
Lasaea **48** 2845, 2847
Lasaeidae **48** 2845, 2847
Lasiocampa quercus **44** *2604*
Lasiocampidae **44** 2624, 2626
Lasiorhinus **11** 633
Lasius umbratus **43** 2555
Latiaxis **46** 2748
Laticauda **28** 1667
Latimeria chalumnae **31** 1850
Latimeriidae **31** 1850
Latrodectus **38** 2258, 2270; **39** *2282-3*
laughing dove **20** *1150*
laughing falcon **18** 1079-80

laughing jackass **21** 1260
laughing kookaburra **21** 1252, 1253, *1260*
laughing thrushes **24** *1386*, *1389*, 1390
laurel thrip **41** 2428
Lauterbach's bowerbird **25** 1475
Lawes' parotia **25** 1480, 1482
Laysan finch **24** 1434, 1435
Leach's storm petrel **17** 976
Leadbeatter's possum **11** 627
leaf beetles **42** *2503-7*
leaf bug **36** *2144*
leaf bush-hopper **40** 2369
leaf cricket **40** *2365*, 2369, *2374*
leaf fishes **34** 2025; **35** 2044, *2045*
leaf insects **39** 2311; **40** *2384*
leaf katydid **40** *2365*, 2385
leaf monkeys **13** 728; **14** 793, 796, 822, *824-6*; **15** *897*
leaf warbler **24** 1398
leaf-chinned bat **12** 681, 716
leaf-cutting bee **43** *2539*, 2540, 2541
leaf-hoppers **41** 2449, *2450*
leaf-nosed bats **12** 681, 684, *690*, 702-3, 704
leaf-rolling weevils **42** 2506, *2508-9*
leaf-suckers **41** *2450*
leaf-tailed gecko **27** 1566
leaf-toed gecko **27** *1566*
leafbirds **23** 1354, 1360-1, *1362*
leafcutter ants **39** 2323; **43** 2529, 2554, *2555*, 2558, 2563
leafscrapers **22** 1312
leafy plum-tree basilisk **27** 1579
leafy seadragon **34** 2000
Leakey, Louis and Mary **15** 899
least bittern **17** 1007-8
least cisco **33** 1934
least grebe **16** *956*, 960
least nighthawk **21** 1209
least seedsnipe **19** *1122*, 1137, 1138
least shrew **12** 662
least weasel **1** 40, 46
leather carp **32** 1896
leatherback sea turtle **26** *1524*, *1525*, 1552, 1553, 1555
leatherhead **24** 1420
leatherjacket **45** 2645
leatherjacket fishes **35** 2082
leathery crag lizard **27** 1598
Lebiasinidae **32** 1908
lechwe **9** *504*, 512-13, *514*, *515*
  classification **9** 510
  distribution **9** 508
Ledra aurita **41** *2450*
leeches **49** 2937; **50** 2942, 2950, *2956*, 2958
  crayfish parasite **37** 2219
  evolution **45** 2670
Leeuwenhoek, Antoni **50** 2976
left-eyed flounder **35** 2080
Legatus leucophaius **22** 1320
legionary ants **43** 2529
legless burrowing skink **27** *1594*
legless lizards **27** 1602, *1603*, *1607*
Leiopelma **30** 1760
Leiopelmatidae **30** 1760
Leiothrix lutea **24** 1390
Leipoa ocellata **19** 1088
Leishmania **50** 2985
  braziliensis **50** 2988
  donayani **50** 2988
  donovani **50** 2976
  mexicana **50** 2976, 2988
  tropica **50** 2988
Lelwel hartebeest **9** 486
lemming **5** *242*, 248, 249-51, 254
lemon sole **35** 2075, 2078
Lemur **13** 742
Lemuridae **13** 742
Lemurinae **13** 742

ABOVE **Apart from humans, the lion has no natural enemies.**

lemurs **12** 718, 719; **13** *732-3*, 734, *735-41*, 743, 748
  classification **13** 742; **15** *896*
  extinction threat **13** 745
Lentidium mediterraneum **48** 2848, 2849
Leontopithecus rosalia **14** 790
leopard **1** 27, 32, *33*; **3** 134-6, 158, 159
  classification **3** 144
  distribution **1** 24; **3** 136, 140, 149
  endangered species **51** 3016, 3018, 3020
  national parks **51** 3023, 3026, 3054, 3056, 3058-9
  predator **3** 154, 155
leopard cat **3** 154
leopard frog **30** 1773
leopard seal **3** 179; **4** 181, *182*, 184
leopard shark **31** 1835, 1839
leopard tortoise **26** *1524*, 1544
Lepadogaster lepadogaster **33** *1962*
Lepadomorpha **37** 2171, 2174
Lepas **47** 2799
  anatifera **36** *2156*
  pectinata **37** *2170*
Lepetidae **46** 2702
Lepidochelys **26** 1553
Lepidocyclina **50** *2986*
Lepidopleurida **45** 2684-6
Lepidopleurus **45** 2684, *2685*, 2686
Lepidoptera **36** 2103; **39** 2311; **44** *2636*, *2585-2640*
lepidosaurs **26** *1507*
Lepidosiren paradoxa **31** 1850
Lepidosirenidae **31** 1850
Lepidosireniformes **31** 1850
Lepidoteuthis grimaldi **48** 2861, 2862
Lepidotheuthidae **48** 2861, 2862
Lepilemur mustelinus **13** 742
Lepilemurinae **13** 742
Lepiodophyma flavimaculatum **27** 1570
Lepisma **39** 2335, 2336
Lepismina **39** 2336
Lepisosteidae **31** 1856
Lepisosteiformes **31** 1856
Lepisosteus osseus **31** 1856
Lepomis gibbosus **34** 2014
Leporidae **4** 209
Leptinotarsa decemlineata **41** 2456; **42** 2504, *2506*
Leptmotarsa **42** 2504
Leptocephalus morrisii **32** 1879
leptochephali **32** 1872, 1874, *1876-7*, *1879*
leptodactylid frogs **30** 1756, 1793, 1795, *1798*, *1799*
Leptodactylidae **30** 1756, 1795
Leptodactylus pentadactylus **30** 1795
Leptodora **36** 2157
  lungo **36** *2160*
Leptonychotes weddelli **3** 179; **4** 184
Leptonycteris nivalis **12** 709
Leptopilos **17** 1012
Leptopterus madagascarinus **23** 1368
Leptosomatidae **21** 1253; **22** 1261
Leptosomus discolor **22** 1261
Leptostraca **37** 2182, *2188*
Leptotyphlopidae **28** 1621, 1625
Leptotyphlops **28** 1625
Leptura **42** 2513
Lepus **4** 209
Lernaea branchialis **37** *2168*
Lesbia nuna **21** 1228
lesser...
  apes **14** 838, 839; **15** 848, 849, 895
  bilby **11** 620
  black-headed gull **20** 1142
  bulldog bat **12** 698, *704*
  bush baby **13** *744*, 748, *752*
  cuttlefish **48** 2855
  dog-faced fruit bat **12** *696*
  eared nightjar **21** 1207
  fairy armadillo **4** 196-7
  false vampire **12** *678*
  flamingo **16** *902-3*; **18** *1021*, 1023, 1024, *1026*
  florican **19** 1112
  frigatebird **17** *978*, 994; **35** *2041*
  goldfinch **25** 1448
  green broadbill **22** *1307*
  grey shrike **23** 1363, 1367
  grison **1** 47
  hedgehog tenrec **11** *651*, 652, *653*
  honeyguide **22** *1281*
  horseshoe bat **12** *692*, 702, 704
  kestrel **19** 1081
  kudu **8** 450-1, 452, *458-9*
  Malay chevrotain **7** 392
  moonrat **11** 655
  mouse deer **7** *390-1*, 392
  mouse lemurs **13** *732*, 733, *735*
  nighthawk **21** 1209
  one-horned rhino **6** 356-7
  panda **1** 28
  paper nautilus **48** 2870
  Papuan frogmouth **21** 1212-13
  pied kingfisher **21** *1251*, 1253, 1259
  prairie chicken **19** 1095
  rabbit-eared bandicoot **11** 620
  short-tailed bat **12** 679, 716
  siren **30** 1753, 1754
  spot-nosed monkey **14** *795*, 816, *818*
  spotted dogfish **31** *1831*, 1834, 1839
  spotted eagle **18** 1067
  spotted woodpecker **22** *1282*, 1297, *1299*, 1300
  stag beetle **42** *2503*

swallow-tailed swift **21** 1218
tree swift **21** 1224, 1227
yellow-headed vulture **18** 1062, 1064
waterboatmen **39** 2321-2; **41** 2438, 2444, 2446
Lestioidea **40** 2351
Lestoros inca **11** 624
Lethrinops brevis **35** *2051*
Lethrus apterus **42** 2493
Leucistus **32** 1894
Leucospis gigas **42** *2519*
Leuctridae **40** 2345
Leuresthes tenuis **34** 1982
Leurognathus marmoratus **30** 1750
Levaillant's barbet **22** *1286*
lewin honeyeater **51** 3048
L'Hoest's monkey **14** 819
Lialis
burtoni **27** 1570
childreni **28** 1637
Libellula
depressa **40** *2355*
pulchella **40** 2362
Libelluloidea **40** 2351
Libyan zorilla **1** 47
lice **41** *2427-32*
Lichanura trivirgata **28** 1637
Lichtenstein's hartebeest **9** *484*, 485, 488, 490
Lichtenstein's sandgrouse **20** *1150*, 1152
light-mantled sooty albatross **17** *963*, 971
lightfishes **33** 1944
Ligia **37** *2199*, 2201
Ligmes vettatus **48** 2822
Liguus dryas **47** *2804*
lilac-breasted roller **21** *1250*; **22** 1261, 1262
lilac-crowned wren **24** 1399
Lilioceris merdigera **42** 2504, 2506
Liloceris lilii **42** *2505*
lily-trotter **19** 1121, 1123
Lima **48** *2832*, *2841*, 2843
Limacidae **47** 2803; **48** 2823-5
Limacinidae **47** 2781-2, 2786
limaciud slug **48** *2825*
Limanda limanda **35** 2075
Limax maximus **47** *2804*, *2812*, 2817; **48** 2825, *2826*
limestone salamander **30** 1749
Limicina **47** 2784, 2786
Limidae **48** 2840, 2841-2, 2843
Limnadia lenticularis **36** *2156*
Limnephilidae **43** 2580; **44** 2583-4
Limnephiloidea **43** 2580; **44** 2581
Limnodynastes dorsalis **30** 1799
Limnogale mergulus **11** 651
Limnoperna fortunei **48** 2836
Limnophilus **43** *2578*; **44** *2583*
rhombicus **43** *2579*; **44** *2584*
Limnoria lignorum **37** 2196, *2200*
Limosa limosa **19** 1135
Limothrips
cerealium **41** 2428
oleae **41** *2431*
limpets **36** 2103; **45** 2676, 2680, 2694, 2696, *2698*, *2699-2700*, **46** 2701-2, *2704*, 2714-15; **47** 2805, *2815*
body parts **45** 2676, *2698*
classification **45** *2699-2700*
distribution **46** 2701
food **45** 2671, 2677
limpkin **19** *1104*, 1107, 1115, *1116*, 1117
Limulidae **38** 2236
Linckia
laevigata **36** *2111*, 2132
multiflora **36** *2111*
lined tiger heron **17** 1007
ling cod **34** 2007-8
lings **33** 1949, 1951, 1953-4
Lingulida **50** 2966
Linne's two-toed sloth **4** 195
linnet **25** 1442, 1446
Linophryne arborifer **33** 1960-1
linsang **2** *84*, 86, 89; **51** 3026
Linyphia triangularis **38** 2258; **39** 2283
Linyphiidae **38** 2258, 2263; **39** 2283
Liobagrus **32** 1913
Liomys **4** 233
lion **1** 29, 36; **3** *134*, *150-2*, 153
classification **3** 144
distribution **1** 27; **3** 135-6, 140
extinction threat **3** 159
prides **3** 146-7
teeth **1** 11-12, *22*
territory **1** 32; **3** 147, 152-3
lion fish **34** 2007, *2037*
lion tamarin **13** *758*; **14** *786*, 790
lion-tailed macaque **14** *792*, *802*, 803, 805
lions, national parks **51** 3018, *3022-3*, 3024
Liphistiidae **39** 2281
Liphistiomorphae **39** 2281
Liposcelidae **41** 2432
Liposcelis **41** *2431*
divinatorius **41** 2432
Lissemys punctata **26** 1553
Lister's river snail **46** 2706, 2712
Liszt monkey **14** 790
Lithobiomorpha **39** 2307
Lithobius **39** 2307, *2308*
Lithocelletidae **44** 2602-3
Lithophaga **48** 2836
aristata **48** *2837*
lithophaga **48** 2840
mytiloides **48** 2836
Lithuanian bison **9** 482
Litocranius walleri **9** 529
Litoria caerulea **30** 1795
auk **20** 1148
little...
auk **20** 1148
barreleye **33** 1937, *1941*
bee-eater **22** 1267
bittern **16** *916*; **17** 1007-8
blue penguin **16** *936-7*, 948-50
bustard **19** 1112
buttonquail **19** *1114*, 1115
crake **19** 1112
eagle **18** 1066
egret **17** *998*, 1000, *1005*, 1007
grebe **16** *915*, 955, *956*, 960
green-eyed monster **38** 2280
gull **20** 1143
owl **20** *1186-7*, 1191, 1198, 1199
red brocket **7** *412*, 418
ringed plover **19** 1125, *1126*
sargassum pipefish **34** 2000
skunk **1** 43, 48, 55, *56*
sole **35** 2075
sparrowhawk **18** 1064, *1065*
spotted kiwi **16** 925, 931
swift **21** 1218
tern **16** 914
water opossum **11** 615
wood swallow **25** 1470, 1471
Littorina **46** 2706-7; **47** 2801
littoralis **46** *2704*, *2710-11*
littorea **46** *2707*, 2712
neritoides **46** 2712
obtusata **46** 2714
saxatilis **46** *2708-9*, 2712
Littorinacea **46** 2706, 2708, 2712
Littorinidae **46** 2706, 2712
Lius iridis **42** *2505*
liver fluke **47** 2809
Livingstone's turaco **20** *1172*
Lixus junci **42** 2506, 2514
lizard snake **28** 1645, 1652-3
lizardfish **33** 1943-4, 1946
lizards **26** 1519, 1558; **27** *1561-1616*
classification **26** 1510; **27** 1562
defence **26** 1522; **27** 1565
distribution **27** 1565, 1595, 1606
evolution **26** *1507*, 1509
eyesight **26** 1514
feeding/eating habits **26** 1517
reproduction **26** *1515*; **27** 1564-5
llamas **6** 304; **7** 381, *387*, 388
Lo vulpinus **35** 2067
Loa loa **49** 2925, 2933
loaches **32** 1894-5, *1904-5*, *1907*, 1910
lobe shells **47** 2767, 2768-9
lobe-finned fish **31** 1808
Lobiger sowerbii **47** 2777
Lobodon carcinophagus **3** 179; **4** 184
Lobodontinae **3** 179
lobsters **36** *2148*; **37** *2192*, *2210*, *2212-18*
classification **36** 2140, 2147; **37** 2178, 2182
crustacean features **36** 2146
evolution **36** 2140; **37** 2212-13
front limbs **36** *2142*
locust fly **40** 2379
locust mite **39** *2293*
Locusta migratoria **39** *2314*; **40** 2365
locusts **36** 2144; **39** *2314*, 2323; **40** *2363-6*, 2369, *2376-82*
Loddigesia mirabilis **21** 1228
loggerhead sponge, host **35** 2061
loggerhead turtle **26** 1526, *1528*, *1547*, 1552-4
Loliginidae **48** 2861, *2868*
Loligo
forbesi **48** 2861
opalescence **48** 2861-2
pealei **48** 2861
vulgaris **48** *2854*, 2855, 2861
Lomechusa strumosa **42** 2478
Lonchura fringilloides **25** 1453
long-beaked echidna **11** 606
long-billed curlew **19** 1129
long-billed gnatwren **24** 1392
long-billed marsh wren **23** 1377, 1378, 1379
long-billed rail **19** 1108, 1115
long-crested helmet shrike **23** 1367, *1368*
long-ear sunfish **34** *2016-7*
long-eared bats **12** *690*, 712, *714*, 715
long-eared fox **2** *110*; **3** 127
long-eared hare **4** 203
long-eared hedgehog **11** *655*, 656
long-eared jerboa **5** 268
long-eared owl **20** *1191*, 1199
long-eared rabbit **4** 203
long-fingered bat **12** *715*
long-haired spider monkey **13** 728, *729*, 774; **14** 781
long-horned grasshopper **40** 2364, 2369
long-jawed orb-weaver **38** *2270*
long-legged bush-cricket **40** 2369, *2370*
long-nosed armadillo **4** *186*, *190-1*, 193, *195-6*
classification **4** 197
long-nosed bandicoot **11** *608*, 620, *621*, 624
long-nosed echidna **11** *601-4*
long-nosed seahorse **34** *1996*, 2000
long-spined nerite **45** 2700
long-spined sea scorpion **34** 2007, *2008*
long-tailed...
broadbill **22** 1307
chinchilla **5** 284
cuckoo **51** 3050
duck **18** *1051*, 1052
finch **25** *1454*
fruit bat **12** 694, 695
ground roller **22** 1261
hawk **18** 1064-5, 1070
manakin **23** 1332
nightjar **21** 1208
pangolin **4** *190-1*, 193, 200; **51** 3020
salamander **29** *1702*, *1712*
silky flycatcher **23** 1372
skua **19** *1122*; **20** 1142
skunk **1** 55
squid **48** 2861
tenrec **11** 651
tit **24** 1403, *1406-7*
water snake **28** 1648
weasel **1** 39, 53
widow **25** 1460
long-toed water beetles **42** 2472, *2481-2*
long-tongued fruit bat **12** *688*
long-wattled umbrellabird **23** *1323*, *1330*
long-whiskered catfish **32** 1913, 1915
long-winged antwren **22** 1310
longclaws **23** 1347, 1352, 1355
longhorn beetles **41** 2456; **42** *2504-7*, *2512-13*
Longhorn cattle **8** 476
longnose butterfly fish **34** *2012*, 2024
longnose chimaera **31** 1846
longnose gar **31** *1852*, *1855*, 1856
longnose lancetfish **33** 1946
longnose sucker **32** 1894, 1904
longsnout prickleback **35** 2056-7
longspine snipefish **34** *1996*, *2000*
loons **16** 954
Lophiidae **33** 1961
Lophiiformes **33** *1957-61*
Lophiomyinae **5** 249
Lophius piscatorius **33** 1961
lophophorates **50** *2967-70*
Lophopus **50** 2968
Lophorina superba **25** 1480
Lophorphorata **45** *2670*
Lopus lineolatus **41** 2437, 2438
Lord Derby's eland **8** 457
Lorenz, Konrad **16** 903, 915; **18** 1034-5; **20** 1141; **25** 1496-7

Loria's bird of paradise **25** 1480
Loricariidae **32** 1913
Loriculus galgulus **20** 1168
lories **20** 1163, 1164, 1168
lorikeets **20** *1162*, 1164, *1168*
Loris tardigradus **13** 748
lorises **12** 718, 719; **13** 733, 734, *744*, *746-50*, 751-2
classification **13** 728, 742, 748; **15** *896*
evolution **13** *727*
senses **13** 722, *731*
Lorisidae **13** 742, 748; **15** *896*
Lorisinae **13** 748
Lota lota **33** 1951
Lottia gigantea **45** 2697
Louisiade butcherbird **25** 1470
lovebirds **20** *1162*, 1165, 1166, 1168, *1170*
lovely wren **24** 1399
lowland anoa **8** *462*, 463, 468
lowland gorilla **15** 848, 852, 856, 864, 890
Loxia curvirostra **25** 1442
Loxocemus bicolor **28** 1637
Loxodonta africana **6** 324
Loxosceles reclusa **39** *2282*
Loxosomatidae **49** 2920
Loxosomella claviformis **49** 2920
Lubricus terrestris **50** 2948
Lucanidae **41** 2456; **42** 2503
Lucanus cervus **42** 2502
lucerne flea **39** 2330, 2333
Lucilia **45** 2659
caesar **45** *2658*
Luciocephalidae **35** 2072
Luciocephalus pulcher **35** 2072
"Lucy" *see* humans
lugworms **49** 2935, *2936*, 2939; **50** 2942, *2943-4*
Luidia ciliaris **36** 2121, *2136*
Lullula arborea **23** 1334
Lumbricidae **50** 2952
Lumbriculid worms **50** 2948
Lumbriculidae **50** 2952
Lumbricus terrestris **50** 2952, *2953*
Lumpenella longirostris **35** 2056
lumpsucker **31** *1804-5*, 1814; **34** 2007, 2010, *2037*
lungfishes **31** *1806*, 1808-9, *1848-52*
lungless salamanders **30** *1744-52*
classification **29** 1713; **30** 1750
Luscinia **24** 1388
Lutra **1** 41, 55
Lutraria elliptica **48** *2844*
Lutreolina crassicaudata **11** 615
lutrine opossum **11** 615
lutrines **1** 46, 55
Lybius **22** 1288
Lycaenidae **44** 2632, 2633
Lycaon pictus **3** 132
Lychnocanium tripus **50** *2974-5*, 2977
Lycosa **39** 2266, *2282*
Lycosidae **38** 2258, 2263, 2266; **39** 2283
Lycoteuthidae **48** 2861, 2863
Lycoteuthis diadema **48** *2854*, 2861, 2863
Lygaeidae **41** 2441
Lymantria dispar **44** 2624
Lymantriidae **44** 2616, 2624
lymmaean pond snails **47** *2807-8*
Lymnaea **47** *2807-8*
hookeri **47** 2815
stagnalis **47** *2804*, 2805, 2807
truncatula **47** 2805, 2809
Lymnaeidae **47** 2805, 2806-7, *2809*
Lymnocryptes minimus **19** 1135
Lymnodromus griseus **19** 1135
Lymnodytes dominicus **16** 960
Lyncodon patagonicus **1** 47
lynx **1** *26*, 27; **3** *139*, *142*, 143
national parks **51** 3036, 3056
Lyonogale tana **13** 730
lyre-tailed honeyguide **22** 1288
lyrebirds **22** 1303, 1304, *1306*; **23** 1322, *1325-9*, *1356*
lyretail **33** *1972*, *1974*, 1978
Lytta vesicatoria **42** 2472, 2488

Mabuya heathi **27** 1598
Macaca **14** 803
macaques **12** *718*, 719; **14** *792-805*, 808, *825*; **51** 3060
body shape **12** 720; **15** *895*, *900*
classification **13** 728; **14** 796, 803; **15** *897*
diet **14** 825, 834-5; **15** 841
distribution **14** 794, 814
infant care **13** *722*; **14** 803-5
macaroni penguin **16** 948, 949
macaws **20** *1161*, *1165*, 1168, 1170
McCormick's skua **20** 1142
MacGregor's gardener **25** *1473*, 1475, 1476, *1477*
Machaerhamphinae **18** 1070
Machaerhamphus alcinus **18** 1070
Machaon brittanicus **44** 2636
Machetornis rixosus **22** 1320
machilids **39** *2334*
mackerel sharks **31** 1827, *1832-3*, 1839
mackerel **31** 1859; **32** 1862, *1863*; **34** 2039-40
classification **31** 1806; **34** 2036
MacKinnon, John **14** 840; **15** 876, 878, 880
Macleays spectre **40** 2385
Macoma baltica **48** 2847
Macrobiotus hufelandi **50** *2963*
Macrocephalon maleo **19** 1088
Macrocheira kaempferi **38** 2223
Macroclemys temminckii **26** 1535
Macrodasyida **49** 2923
Macroderma gigas **12** 704
Macrodipteryx longipennis **21** 1206
Macrodontia cervicornis **42** 2506, 2513
Macrogalidia **2** 89
Macroglossum **44** 2624
Macroglossus minimus **12** 694
Macrognathus aculeatus **35** 2072
macrolepidoptera **44** 2586, 2598
Macronectes giganteus **17** 973
Macronyx croceus **23** 1352
Macroperipatus insularis **50** *2962*
Macropleurodus bicolor **35** 2050
Macropodidae **11** 612, 642
Macropodus opercularis **35** 2070
Macropus **11** 642
Macroramphosidae **34** 2000
Macrorhamphosus scolopax **34** 2000
Macroscelidea **11** 660
Macroscelides proboscideus **11** 660
Macrosiphum rosae **41** *2439*, *2451*
macrospectum **49** 2939
Macrotermes **41** 2405
bellicosus **41** 2405, 2408, *2421*
natalensis **41** *2416*, *2424*
Macrotermitinae **41** 2408
Macrotis **11** 620
Macrotus californicus **12** 709
Magellanic plover **19** 1121, 1125
maggot **39** *2312*
Magicicada septemdecim **41** 2438, 2448
Magilus antiquus **47** *2762*
magilus coral shell **47** *2762*
magistrate black colobus monkey **13** *755*
magnificent frigatebird **17** *991*, *993*, 994
magnificent night heron **17** 1007
magnificent bird of paradise **25** 1480, 1482, *1483*
magnificent riflebird **25** *1477*, 1480, 1483

ABOVE A flamboyant tuft of silky hair adorns a marmoset's head.

Macrouridae **33** 1951
Macrozoacres americanus **35** 2056
Macrura **37** 2212
Maculinea arion **44** 2633
Madagascan civet **2** 92, *96*
Madagascan day-flying uranid moth **44** *2604*
Madagascan harrier-hawk **18** 1072
Madagascan hawk-moth **44** *2587*
Madagascan leaf-tailed gecko **27** *1569*
Madagascan moon moth **44** *2604*
Madagascan primates **15** *896*
Madagascan rat **5** 249, 254
Madagascar boas **28** 1636, 1639
Madagascar day gecko **27** 1566
Madagascar squacco heron **17** 1004
Madoqua **8** 444
Madreporaria **49** 2889
madrepores **49** 2889, 2894
Magellan diving petrel **17** 976
Magellan goose **18** *1032*, 1044
Magellan penguin **5** *280*
Magellanic penguin **16** 948, 949, *950*
magnificent wentletrap **46** 2721
magnolia warbler **24** *1426*
magpie **25** 1484, 1485, *1488*, 1491, *1494*
classification **25** 1489
cuckoo host **20** *1178*, 1179
plumage **25** *1490*, 1491
magpie goose **18** *1028*, 1030, 1033, *1035*, 1036
magpie larks **25** *1469-70*
classification **25** 1470
distribution **25** 1468
magpie mannikin **25** 1453
magpie moth **44** *2604*, 2609, 2613, *2614*
maguari stork **17** 1015
mahseer **32** 1894
mail-cheeked fishes **34** 2006
mainland serow **9** *534*, 539-40; **10** 550
Maja squinado **38** *2230*
Majidae **38** 2232
Makaira nigricans **35** 2043
mako shark **31** 1832-4, 1844
Malabar squirrel **4** 234

malachite kingfisher **21** 1253, *1258*
Malaconotinae **23** 1367
Malaconotus cruentus **23** 1367
Malacoptila panamensis **22** 1284
Malacosoma neustria **44** 2624
Malacostraca **36** 2140, 2147; **37** 2178, 2182, 2212; **38** 2223
malacostracans **37** *2179-2220*
Malagasy hissing cockroach **40** 2391, 2395
Malapteruridae **32** 1913
Malapterurus **32** 1913
Malayan badger **1** 39
Malayan colugo **12** *673-5*, 676
Malayan pangolin **4** 200
Malayan sun bear **2** 81
Malayan tapir **6** *301*, *349-50*, 351, 352
Malaysian elephant **6** 324, 326
Malaysian hill froglet **30** 1782
Malaysian horned toad **30** 1769
Malaysian wood nymph **40** 2385
maleo **19** 1088, *1091*
malkoha **20** 1175
mallard **18** *1034*, 1044-5, 1047
mallee fowl **16** 913; **19** *1086*, 1088, *1091*
Malleus
albus **48** 2837
malleus **48** *2832*, 2837
vulgaris **48** 2837
Mallophaga **39** 2311; **41** 2428-9
Mallotus villosus **33** 1924
malmignatte **38** 2277; **39** *2282*, 2283, *2284*, 2285
Malpolon monspessulanus **28** 1645
Maluridae **24** 1398
Malurus cyaneus **24** 1398
mambas **28** 1640, 1661, 1663, *1666*, 1667
MAMMALS **1-15** *7-900*
carnivore families **1** 28
egg-laying **11** 601-6
evolution **1** 8-11, 17-18; **26** *1506-8*
intelligence **1** 12-14
reproduction **1** 14-16
mammoth **6** 319
man-of-war bird **17** 993
Manacus **23** 1331
manakins **22** 1308; **23** *1330*, *1331-3*, 1334
manatee **5** *298*; **6** *313*, 314, *315*, *316*; **51** 3038
Manchurian crane **19** 1107
Manchurian red-footed falcon **19** 1083
mandarin duck **18** *1048-9*, 1052
mandrills **14** 793-4, 808, 811, *813-14*
Mandrillus **14** 811
maned sloth **4** 195
maned wolf **2** *110*; **3** 130, *131-2*
mangabeys **13** 728; **14** 796, 814, *815*, 816
Mangelia powisiana **47** 2765
mangrove kingfisher **51** 3047
mangrove monitor **27** *1614*
mangrove robin **51** 3047
mangrove snake **28** *1642*, 1645, *1648*, 1649
Manidae **4** 200
Manis **4** 200
Manoria melanocephala **24** 1420
Manta birostris **31** 1844
manta rays **31** *1838*, *1844*, 1845-6
Mantekina **50** *2986*
mantellin **30** *1778*
mantids **39** 2311; **40** 2391, 2395-2400
mantis flies **43** *2567*, 2570, 2572-3; **45** *2658*
Mantis religiosa **40** 2391, *2396*, 2397, *2398*
mantis shrimps **37** *2182-3*, *2186-9*, 2190
Mantispa syriaca **43** *2567*, 2570
Mantispidae **43** 2570
mantled howler monkey **13** 774, 780
Mantodea **39** 2311; **40** 2391, 2395-2400
Manucodia keraudrenii **25** 1480
Manx shearwater **17** *972*, 973, 974
many-toothed snake **28** 1644
Maori humpback wrasse **34** 2023
map turtles **26** 1537, 1539
mara **5** *271-2*, 275, 278-9, *280-1*
marabou stork **17** 1011, 1012, 1013, *1015*
marble blenny **35** 2059
marble cichlid **35** 2049, *2050*
marble cone shell **46** 2746; **47** *2762*, 2764-5
marbled cat **3** 154
marbled electric ray **31** 1842
marbled godwit **19** 1129-30
marbled hatchetfish **32** *1906*, 1908
marbled murrelet **20** 1148
marbled newt **29** *1705*, *1711*, 1729, *1736*, 1738; **30** *1746*
marbled polecat **1** 39, 41, 46
intelligence **1** 12-14
marbled rush frog **30** *1785*
marbled salamander **29** 1720
marbled swamp eel **34** *1996*
marbled whiptail **27** 1600-1
marbled white butterfly **44** 2633, 2640
march-flies **45** *2644*, 2646-7
Marco Polo sheep **10** 566
Marcusenius longianalis **32** 1869, *1870*
Margaritifer margaritifer **48** *2832*, 2843
margay **3** 138, 158
margin shells **47** *2761-3*
marginated cockroach **40** 2391
marginated tortoise **26** 1542
margined flying fish **33** 1965
Marginellidae **47** 2761
Marginelloninae **47** 2761-3
Marifugia cavatica **50** 2941
marine amphipod **37** 2203
marine bristletails **39** 2311, 2335, 2336
marine hatchetfish **33** 1944
marine iguanas **27** *1561*, 1572, *1574-5*, 1578-9; **51** *3034*
marine mites **39** 2295, 2297
marine skink **27** 1593
marine slugs *see* sea slugs
marine snails **45** 2680, *2693*, 2694, 2697; **46** 2758
marine sunfish **35** 2087
marine toad **29** 1701, 1703; **30** 1789, 1790, *1791*
marine water-strider **39** 2323
marine worms **50** 2958
mariqua flycatcher **24** 1399
markhor **9** *534*, 538; **10** *555*, 557-8, 570
marlins **35** 2041, 2043
marmosets **12** 719; **13** *756*, 763-4; **14** 782, *783-5*, 786-7
classification **13** 728; **14** 790; **15** 897
distribution **13** 768
Marmota monax **4** 233
marmots **4** *220-1*, *224-6*, 233; **51** 3036
marsh babbler **24** 1389
marsh deer **7** 415, 417, 418; **8** 424
marsh frog **30** 1771, *1772-3*, 1778
marsh harrier **18** 1070, 1072; **51** 3008, 3014
marsh hawk **18** 1070
marsh mugger crocodile **51** 3027
marsh snails **47** 2803, 2815
marsh terns **20** 1144, 1145
marsh tit **24** *1401*, 1403, 1406
marsh warbler **24** 1394, 1395
marsupial frog **30** 1793, 1795
marsupial mole **1** 18; **11** *608*, 609, 619, 620
marsupial mouse **11** *608*, 619
MARSUPIALS **1** 15-16, 18; **11** 607-44
martens **1** 26, *38*, 44, *45*
classification **1** 46-7
reproduction **1** 48, 49-52
Martes **1** 46
Marthasterias glacialis **36** 2121
martial eagle **18** 1066-7
martins **22** 1304; **23** *1340*, *1344-5*, 1346-7
classification **23** 1345
distribution **23** 1322
nests **23** 1343
marvellous spatuletail **21** *1216*, 1228, 1232, 1236
Masai giraffe **8** 428, 430
Masai ostrich **16** 918-19, 925
masked booby **17** 989, 992, 994
masked lovebird **20** *1162*, 1168, *1170*
masked owl **20** 1194
masked shrew **51** 3006
masked weaver **25** 1455, 1458
masked wood swallow **25** 1471
mason bees **43** *2539*, 2540, 2541-2
mason wasps **43** *2532*, 2527-8, 2529
massasagua **28** 1669
Massoutiera mzabi **5** 286
Mastacembelidae **35** 2072
Mastacembelus **35** *2072*
mastiff bat **12** *690*
Mastigophora **50** 2974, 2976
Mastigoproctus giganteus **38** *2242*
Mastigoteuthis glaukopsis **48** *2854*
Mastotermes darwiniensis **41** 2403, 2405
Mastotermitidae **41** 2403, *2404*, 2405
Matadi hyrax **6** 313
matamata **26** 1520, 1526, 1530, *1531*
Mauremys **26** 1539
Mauritian kestrel **19** 1084
Maurolicus muelleri **33** 1944
Maxwell's duiker **8** 437, 440
Mayetiola destructor **45** 2646, 2647
mayflies **39** 2311, 2318, 2321, 2322-3, *2337-40*; **40** *2341-4*
Mayotte lemur **13** 737
Mazama **7** 418
meadow jumping mouse **5** 248
meadow pipit **20** *1177*; **23** 1352, *1353*, 1354, *1355*
meadow spittlebug **41** 2449
meadowlark **24** 1440
meagre **34** 2032, 2033
meal moths **44** 2606
mealworm beetle **42** 2472, *2492*
measuring worm moth **44** 2609
Mecoptera **39** 2311; **42** 2516; **43** 2574, 2576
medakas **33** 1965
medicinal leech **50** *2956*
Mediterranean...
beaded nasset **46** 2715
chameleon **27** 1592
cigar-shell **48** 2840
cone **46** 2703, 2746
cone shell **47** 2764
deep-water sepiolid **48** 2855, 2860
feather star **36** *2117*
flour moth **44** *2604*
flying fish **33** 1965
fruit flies **45** *2657-9*
land winkle **46** 2708, 2712
limpet **46** 2701
malgmignatte **39** *2282*
marginated cockroach **40** 2391
mole **12** 670
monk seal **3** 179, 180; **4** *181*, 183, 184
moray **32** 1874, 1880, *1882*
mussel **48** 2837
odd-eyed squid **48** 2861
sea anemone **49** 2889, *2896*
sea slug **47** *2798*
spur-thighed tortoise **26** *1540*, 1541, 1544
umbrella shell **47** 2767
worm shell **46** 2712, 2718
meercat **2** 86, *90-1*, *98*; **13** 740
Megachasma pelagias **31** 1839
Megachasmidae **31** 1839
Megachile centuncularis **43** 2540, 2541
Megachilidae **43** *2540*, 2541
Megachiroptera **12** 681
Megadenus arrhynchus **46** *2720*
Megadermatidae **12** 681, 704
Megadyptes antipodes **16** 949
Megadytes **42** 2468
Megalaima **22** 1288
Megalobatrachus **29** 1716
Megalonychidae **4** 195
Megalopidae **32** 1872
Megaloprepus coerulatus **40** 2362
Megalops cyprinoides **32** 1872
Megaloptera **39** 2311; **43** *2565-70*
megamouth shark **31** 1827, 1832, 1839
Meganyctiphane norvegica **37** *2188*, *2209*
megapodes **19** 1087-8, *1090-1*, 1098
Megapodiidae **19** 1088
Megapodius freycinet **19** 1088
Megaptera novaeangliae **10** 577
Megascolecidae **50** 2952
Megascolides australis **50** 2952-3
Megasoma elephas **42** 2500
Megatura crenulata **46** *2704*
Megophrys monticola **30** 1769
Megopsis scabricoinis **42** 2506, 2512
Melanargia galathea **44** 2633, 2640
Melanerpes erythrocephalus **22** 1297

Melanidae **46** 2713
Melanitta nigra **18** 1052
Melanocetus johnsonnii **33** *1959*, 1961
Melanocorypha calandra **23** 1334
Melanogrammus aeglefinus **33** 1951
Melanosuchus niger **29** 1685
Melanotaenia maccullochi **34** 1982
Melanotaeniidae **34** 1982
Melanotis caerulescens **23** 1380
Melasoma populi **42** 2504
Meleagrididae **19** 1088, 1101
Meleagris gallopavo **19** 1101
Meles meles **1** 55
Melichneutes robustus **22** 1288
melines **1** 46, 55
Meliphaga **24** 1420
Meliphagidae **24** 1420
Meliponinae **43** 2540, 2543
Melitaea phoebe **39** *2320*
Melittidae **43** 2538, 2539
Meller's chameleon **27** *1563*, 1592
Mellivora capensis **1** 49
mellivorines **1** 46, 49
Melo amphora **47** *2762*
melodious warbler **24** 1394, *1395*
Meloe **42** 2487
Melogale **1** 55
Meloidae **42** 2472, 2486-7
Melolontha melolontha **42** 2498
Melolonthinae **42** 2503
melon-headed whale **10** 588, 592
Melongenidae **46** 2746, 2751
Melopsittacus undulatus **20** 1168
Melospiza melodia **24** 1429
Membracidae **41** 2449-50
Membranipora **50** *2968*
menhaden **34** 2036
Mentawai Islands langur **14** 826
Menura **23** 1328
Menurae **22** 1303
Menuridae **22** 1303; **23** 1328
mephitines **1** 46
Mephitis **1** 55
Mercenaria mercenaria **48** 2849
Merganetta armata **18** 1047
mergansers **18** 1050-1, 1052
Mergini **18** 1030, 1052
Mergus **18** 1052
Merino sheep **10** 570
Merlangius merlangus **33** 1951
merlin **18** 1080; **19** *1081*, 1083
merluccid hake **33** 1951
Merlucciidae **33** 1951
Merluccius **33** 1951
Meropidae **21** 1253; **22** 1270
Merops **22** 1270
Merostomata **38** 2234, 2241
Merulaxis ater **22** 1314
Merychippus **6** 332, 333
mesites **19** 1107, 1114, 1116
Mesitornithidae **19** 1107, 1114
Mesogastropoda **45** 2697; **46** 2706, *2712*, 2720, 2737
mesogastropods **46** *2712-13*, 2740, 2742
Mesogastropods **47** 2801
Mesolimbus walchii **38** *2234*
mesopelagic fishes **33** *1940-6*
Mesoplodon bidens **10** 593
Mesosemia **44** *2634*
Mesostigmata **39** 2295, *2296*
Mesothelae **38** 2258
mesozoa **48** 2874
MESOZOANS **36** 2103
Messor barbarus **43** *2525*, *2560*, *2562*
metacecarian **49** *2911*
metaltails **21** 1232
metamonad flagellate **50** *2980*
Metastigmata **39** 2295
METAZOANS **48** *2872-80*; **49** 2919, 2923, 2925
Metridium senile **47** 2800
Mexican...
  axolotl **29** 1714, 1718, 1719, *1721*, 1722
  beaded lizard **27** *1607*, 1614-15
  blind lizard **27** 1570, 1572
  bulldog bat **12** *678*, 697-8, 704
  burrowing python **28** 1634-5, 1637
  cross-breasted turtle **26** 1535
  free-tailed bat **12** 716
  howler monkey **13** 774, *778*, 780
  long-nosed bat **12** 705, 708, 709
  musk turtles **26** 1533, 1535
  narrow-mouthed frog **30** 1784, 1786
  tiger heron **17** 1007
  tree porcupine **5** 283
  worm-lizard **27** 1616
miacids **1** 25, 41
Michoacan pocket gopher **4** 233
Micrathena **38** *2261*
Micrathene whitneyi **20** 1199
micro whip scorpions **38** 2240, 2241, *2254*
Microbiotheriidae **11** 612, 642
Microbuthus pusillus **38** 2245, 2250
Microcebus **13** 742
Microchiroptera **12** 681
Microciona atrasanguinea **47** 2794
Microcosmus **35** 2094
Microdipodops **4** 233
microeca **24** 1400
Microhierax erythrogonys **18** 1080
Microhyla carolinensis **30** 1786
Microhylidae **30** 1756, 1786
microlepidoptera **44** 2586, 2598
Microperoryctes murina **11** 620
Micropogon undulatus **34** 2033
Micropotamogale ruwenzorii **11** 651
Micropsitta bruijnii **20** 1168
Micropterigidae **44** 2595, 2597-8, 2599
Micropterus **34** 2014
Microsaura **27** 1592
Microspora **50** 2976, 2992
Microstigmus comes **43** 2525
Microstomus kitt **35** 2075
Microtinae **5** 249-53
Micrurus fulvius **28** 1667
Middle American night lizard **27** 1570, *1571*
middle spotted woodpecker **22** 1297, 1300
midges **45** 2643, *2644*, 2650-1, 2652
midshipmen **33** 1958-9
midwater shark **31** 1839
midwife toad **29** 1704, 1706; **30** 1760, *1761*, *1771*
migratory locust **40** *2365*, *2377-9*
mildew-eating ladybird **42** 2472
milkfish **32** *1892-3*
Millepora **49** 2889
millepore coral **49** 2889
miller's thumb **34** 2007-8
millipedes **36** 2103, 2140; **39** *2303-6*
Milneria minima **48** 2845
Milvinae **18** 1070
Milvus **18** 1070
Mimela aurata **42** 2499
Mimidae **23** 1380
Mimonectes **37** 2207
Mimus polyglottos **23** 1380
miners **22** 1309, 1310
Miniopterus schreibersi **12** 712
minivets **23** *1357*, 1358; **51** 3030
mink **1** 40, 44, 46, *47*
minke whale **10** 577, *579*, 581
minnows **32** 1892, 1896, *1898-900*
  classification **32** 1894
minotaur beetle **42** 2492, 2497
minowa **26** 1553, *1555-6*
minute ptiliid **42** *2465*
Miohippus **6** 333
Miopithecus talapoin **14** 816
miracadium **49** *2911*, *2912*
Mirafra javanica **23** 1334
Miratesta celebensis **47** 2807
Miridae **41** 2437-8, 2447
Mirounga **4** 184
mirror carp **32** 1896
Misophrioida **37** 2163
Mississippi kite **18** 1072
Missosporidium **37** 2219
mistle thrush **24** *1382*, *1388*
mistletoe bird **24** *1415*, 1416, 1417
Misumena vatia **38** *2261*
mites **36** 2140; **38** 2240, 2241, *2242*; **39** *2293-8*
mithan **8** 473
Mitra
  mitra **47** 2761
  zonata **46** 2760; **47** *2762*
mitre shells **46** 2746, 2760; **47** *2761*, *2762*
mitred langur **14** 826
Mitridae **46** 2746, 2760; **47** 2761
Mitsukurina owstoni **31** 1839
Mobula mobular **31** 1844
Mobulidae **31** 1844
Mochokidae **32** 1913
mockingbird **23** 1378-9, *1380*
Modiolus
  barbatus **48** 2837
  capax **48** 2840
  difficilis **48** *2832*
  modiolus **48** 2837
  phaseolinus **48** 2840
Mola mola **35** 2082
molas **35** 2082, 2087
mole crabs **37** 2220
mole crickets **39** 2320; **40** 2369, 2374, *2380-1*; **41** 2402; **43** 2537
mole salamanders **29** 1713, *1718-21*, 1722
mole-rat **5** *242*, 243, 254-5, 284, 295-6
  distribution **5** 248, 275
mole-shrew **12** 662
molecowrie **46** 2734
moles **1** *8*, 9, 18, 34; **11** *646-7*, 648-9, 653-4; **12** 663, *668-71*
  classification **11** 651; **12** 670
  distribution **11** 647
Molidae **35** 2082
mollies **33** *1963*, *1972*, 1976
  classification **33** 1978
  varieties **33** 1979-80
Mollusca **36** 2103; **45** 2674
MOLLUSCS **36** 2103; **45** *2668-2700*; **46** *2701-80*; **48** *2821-71*; **50** 2966
  bitterling host **30** 1903, *1904*
  communication **46** *2714-5*
  distribution **45** 2695
  evolution **45** 2670-1
  shell **45** *2672-4*
mollymauk **17** 962
moloch **27** 1585, *1587*
moloch gibbon **15** 842, 846, 848
Moloch horridus **27** 1585
Molossidae **12** 681, 716
Molothrus **24** 1440
Molva molva **33** 1951
Momotus momota **22** 1270
mona monkey **14** *795*, 816, *820*
Monachinae **3** 179
Monachus **3** 179; **4** 184
monarch butterflies **44** *2588*, 2590, *2601*, 2607
monarch flycatchers **24** *1399*, 1400
Monarcha alecto **24** 1400
Monasa atra **22** 1284
Mondini, Professor **32** 1878
money cowrie **46** 2720, 2734
money spiders **38** 2257, 2276; **39** 2283
Monezia expansa **49** *2917*
Mongolian gazelle **9** *518*, 520, 525, 529
Mongolian saiga **9** 535, 536, 538
mongoose **1** 28, 59; **2** 85-7, *88*, 89; **28** 1665; **51** 3023
mongoose lemur **13** 737, *738*, 742
Monias **19** 1114
monito del monte **11** 612, 642
monitor lizard **27** 1562, 1565, *1606-14*
monk parakeet **20** 1163, 1168
monk seal **3** 179, 180; **4** 181, *182*, 183, 184
monkey-eating eagle **18** 1058, 1066, 1070
monkeys **15** 841, 852, 895, *899*; **51** 3038
  evolution **13** *727*
  New World **13** *727*, 728, *761-80*; **14** 781-90; **15** 897
  Old World **13** *727* 728, 763; **14** 791-836; **15** 897
  primates **12** 718; **13** 722-3, 726, 728, *755-60*
monkfish **31** *1840-1*
Monocentrididae **34** 1990
Monocentris japonicum **34** 1990
Monocirrhus polyacanthus **35** 2044
Monocystis **50** 2993, 2992
Monodon monoceros **10** 593
Monodonta **46** 2702
  concamerata **46** 2702
  lineata **46** *2703*
  turbixata **45** 2700
Monodontidae **10** 593
Monogenea **49** 2905, 2911, 2912
Monolistra **37** 2197
Monoplacophora **45** 2674, 2678-80, 2684, *2690*, 2692
Monopterus **34** 2006
Monotremata **11** 606
MONOTREMES **1** 15, 16, 18; **10** *597-600*; **11** *601-6*
Monotrysia **44** 2595, 2599, 2600
monstrilloid copepods **37** 2167-8
Monstrilloida **37** 2163
Montacuta **48** 2847
Montezuma oropendula **24** *1438*, 1440

Monticola saxatilis **24** 1388
Montifringilla nivalis **25** 1459
Montpellier snake **28** 1645, *1652-3*
moon shells **45** 2676, 2678, *2679*; **46** *2726*, *2736-7*, *2740*
mooneye **33** *1922*
moonfish **34** 1986, *1987*
moonrats **11** 654-5
moor frog **29** *1700*; **30** *1777*
Moor macaque **14** 808
moorhen **19** 1108, *1112*, 1114-15
Moorish gecko **27** *1562*, *1564*, 1565, 1569
Moorish idol **35** *2066*, 2067
moose **6** 301, 307; **7** 417, 418; **51** *3036*, 3041
Mopaliidae **45** 2684, 2686
moray eels **32** 1874, *1880-2*
Mordacia **31** 1818
Morelet's crocodile **29** 1692
Mormoopidae **12** 681, 716
Mormoops blainvillei **12** 716
Mormyrus kannume **32** *1870*
Moroccan edge-snouted worm-lizard **27** *1607*, *1616*
Morone saxatilis **34** 2023
Morphidae **44** 2633
Morpho **44** 2586, 2633, 2640
  didius **44** *2634*
Moschidae **7** 395
MOSCHIDS **7** *389-93*, 395, 414
Moschus **7** 395
mosquito fish **33** 1978; **34** 1981
mosquitoes **39** 2310, 2313, 2321, 2324; **45** 2643, *2644*, *2647-50*
  classification **45** 2652
  disease carriers **45** 2650
  larvae *2646-7*
  nematode carrier **49** 2933
moss animals **36** 2103; **50** *2965*, 2966, *2967-8*
mossbunker **32** 1890
Motacilla **23** 1352
Motacillidae **23** 1352
moth-butterfly **44** 2633, 2635
moths **39** *2310*, 2311, 2313, 2318, 2324; **44** *2586-2629*
  anatomy **44** 2586-9
  bat evasion **12** 685
  migration **44** *2588*, 2590
  scent **44** *2606-7*
Motmotidae **21** 1253; **22** 1270
motmots **21** 1252, 1253; **22** *1269*, 1270
mottled burrowing frog **30** 1776, *1778*
mottled cone **46** 2714
mottled grasshopper **40** *2373*
mottled shrike-tit **24** 1400
mottled sunfish **34** 2016
mottled umber moth **44** 2614-15
mouflon **10** *560-1*, 562-3, 567
  classification **8** 434; **9** 535; **10** 570
Mount Lyell salamander **30** 1747
Mount Nimba least otter shrew **11** 653
Mount Shasta salamander **30** 1747
mountain...
  anoa **8** 463, 468
  beaver **4** *220*, *221*, 222
    classification **4** 233
  brushtail possum **11** 625
  cat **3** 158
  cuscus **11** 625
  gazelle **9** *518*, 520, *524*, 529
  goat **8** 434; **9** 535, *537*, 538, *539*; **10** 541, 544-5
  gorilla **1** 18; **15** 848, 852, 856, *862*, 890; **51** 3024
  hare **1** *26*
  lion **3** 135; **51** 3036, *3040-1*
  nyala **8** 451, 452
  pygmy possum **11** 627
  quail **19** *1086*
  reedbuck **9** 503, 510, 515-16
  sheep **10** 570
  shrew **12** 662
  tapir **6** *351*
  thornbill **24** 1398
  viscacha **5** 285, *287*
  weasel **51** 3052
  zebra **6** 334-5, 338, 340
mourning dove **20** 1156, *1159*, 1160
mouse bandicoot **11** 620
mouse deer **7** *390-91*, 392
mouse family **4** 218; **5** 241-70
mouse lemurs **13** *732*, 733, *735*; **15** *896*
  classification **13** 728, 742
  extinction threat **13** 745
mouse opossum **11** 611, *613-15*
mouse shrews **12** 662
mouse-tailed bats **12** *678*, 681, *690*, 696, 704
mousebirds **16** 912; **21** *1240*, 1241, *1245-8*
moustached monkey **14** *795*, 816, *820*
moustached tamarin **14** 782
moustached tree swift **21** 1224
mouth-brooding frogs **30** 1798-9
mouthbrooders *see under* FISHES
Mozambique mouthbrooder **35** 2048
Mozena lunata **41** *2439*
Mrs Gray's lechwe **9** 510, 514
mucous-coated pelagic squid **48** *2866*
Mucronalia **46** 2720, 2721
mud lobster **35** 2061
mud salamander **30** 1750, 1751
mud shrimps **37** 2212, 2213, 2220
mud snails **46** 2746, 2751, 2758-9; **47** 2805, 2809
mud turtles **26** *1532-3*, 1535
mud-loving caddisflies **44** 2584
mud-nester **25** 1470-1
mudhoppers **35** 2062
mudlark **25** 1469
mudminnows **33** 1937, 1938
mudpuppy **29** *1712*, 1713; **30** 1742, 1743, *1744*, 1745
mudskippers **35** 2060, *2061-5*
Mueller's sand boa **28** 1637
mugger crocodile **29** 1685, 1690, 1693; **51** 3027
Mugil cephalus **35** 2043
Mugilidae **35** 2043
mule deer **7** 398, *407*, 414-15, 418; **51** 3036
Muller's gibbon **15** 842, 848
Müller's topknot **35** *2073*
mullets **34** *2012*, *2032-3*, *2037*; **35** 2042-4
Mullidae **34** 2033
Mulliodichthys martinicus **34** 2033
Mullus barbatus **34** 2033
mummichog **33** *1974-5*, 1978
mungo **2** 86
Mungotictis decemlineata **2** 92
Mungus mungo **2** 98
Muntiacinae **7** 396
Muntiacus **7** 396
muntjac **7** *390*, *393*, 394-6, 414
Muraena helena **32** 1874
Muraenidae **32** 1874
Murchisonia subsulcata **45** *2694*
murexes **46** *2745-9*, *2762*
Muricacea **46** 2745, 2746, 2755
Muricanthus fulvescens **46** 2746
Muricidae **46** 2745-7
Muridae **5** 243, 254
Murina aenea **12** 712
murine opossum **11** 614
muriqui monkey **13** 774
murre **20** 1148
murrelets **20** 1148
Musca domestica **45** 2659
Muscicapa striata **24** 1400
Muscicapidae **22** 1303; **24** 1400
Muscidae **45** 2659, 2662
Muscivora forficata **22** 1320
muscovy duck **18** 1049, 1052
music volute **46** 2746
musk beetle **42** 2506-7
musk deer **7** *390-3*; **10** *569*; **51** 3052, 3056, 3068
  classification **7** 395
  distribution **7** 414
musk octopus **48** 2869, 2870
musk ox **6** 306; **8** 434; **9** 535, 538; **10** *548-9*, 550, 551-2
musk turtles **26** *1532-3*, 1535
muskellunge **33** 1937-8
muskrat **5** 249, *252*, 253
musky rat kangaroo **11** 635, 642
Musophaga rossae **20** 1178
Musophagidae **20** 1178
mussel shrimps **36** 2147, 2149, *2156*, 2158-60; **37** 2161
musselcracker **34** 2033
mussels **45** 2674; **48** *2832-4*, *2835-43*
  bitterling host **32** 1903, *1904*
  classification **48** 2835, 2837, 2843
  distribution **48** 2834, 2840
mussurana **28** 1644, 1645, *1652*, 1653
mustang **6** 348
Mustela **1** 46
Mustelidae **1** 28, 39
MUSTELIDS **1** *37-56*
mustelines **1** 46-7
Mustelus canis **31** 1839
mute swan **18** *1036*, *1037-9*, 1044
Mutilla
  barbara **43** 2529
  europaea **43** 2529, 2533, *2536*
Mutillidae **43** 2529, 2533
mutton bird **17** 969
Mya arenaria **48** 2848
Myacea **48** 2848
Mycetophilia fungorum **45** *2644*
Mycidacea **37** 2193-4
Mycteria **17** 1012
Myctophidae **33** 1946
Myctophiformes **31** 1858; **33** 1946
Myctophum **33** 1946
  punctatum **33** *1942*
Mydaus javanensis **1** 55
Mygalomorphae **38** 2258; **39** 2281
Myidae **48** 2848
Myioborus torquatus **24** 1431
Myiopsitta monachus **20** 1168
Myiornis ecaudatus **22** 1320
Mylabris variabilus **42** 2488
Myliobatididae **31** 1844
Myliobatis aquila **31** 1844
mynah birds **25** 1462
myobatrachid frogs **30** 1799-1800
Myobatrachidae **30** 1799
Myocastor coypu **5** 289
Myocastoridae **5** 277, 289
Myodocopa **36** *2160*; **37** 2161
Myoida **48** 2845, 2847, 2848
Myomorpha **4** 233; **5** 254, 268, 277
MYOMORPHS **5** *241-70*
Myopsida **48** 2861
Myotis **1** *8*, 9
  myotis **12** 712
myotis bat **12** *690*
Myrianida **49** *2936*, 2939
Myriapoda **36** 2140; **39** *2301-7*
Myrichthys oculatus **32** 1874
Myriozoum truncatum **50** *2965*, 2967
Myripristis murdjan **34** 1990
Myrmarachne **38** *2261*, *2280*
Myrmecium **38** *2280*
Myrmecobiidae **11** 612, 619
Myrmecobius fasciatus **11** 619
Myrmecophaga tridactyla **4** 195
Myrmecophagidae **4** *195*
Myrmecophila acervorum **43** 2560
Myrmeleon formicarius **43** *2567*, 2570
Myrmeleontidae **43** 2570, 2573
Myrmeleontoidea **43** 2570
Myrmeleotettix maculatus **40** *2373*
Myrmica **42** 2478
Myrmicinae **43** 2562
Myrmotherula longipennis **22** 1310
Mysis relicta **37** *2188*, 2194, *2195*
Mysosorex **12** 662
Mystacina **12** 716
Mystacinidae **12** 681, 716
Mystacocarida **36** 2147; **37** 2168, 2169
Mysticeti **10** 577
Mytilacea **48** 2837
Mytilidae **48** 2836, 2840
Mytiloida **48** 2835-7, 2842, 2843
Mytilus **48** 2836
  edulis **48** 2834, 2836-7
  galloprovincialis **48** 2836-7
Myxine glutinosa **31** 1818
Myxini **31** 1809, 1818
Myxinidae **31** 1818
Myxiniformes **31** 1818
Myxobolus **50** *2992*
Myxocephalus scorpius **34** 2007
Myxophaga **41** 2456
Myzopoda aurita **12** 709
Myzopodidae **12** 681, 709
Myzostoma **50** 2942
Myzostomida **50** 2942, 2944-5
Myzostomidae **50** 2942, 2944, *2946*
Mzab gundi **5** 286

nacunda nighthawk **21** 1209
Nahan's francolin **51** 3024
naidid worms **50** 2947

Naididae **50** 2947, 2952
nail-tail wallaby **11** 637, 642
Naja **28** 1667
naked amoebas **50** 2989, 2991
naked bat **12** *693*, 716
naked mole-rat **5** 284, 295-6
naked sea butterflies **47** *2783-4, 2785*, 2786
naked-backed knifefish **32** 1910, 1920
naked-tailed armadillo **4** 197
Nandidae **35** 2044
Nandinia binotata **2** 89
Nankeen night heron **17** 1006
Nannopterum harrisi **17** 990
Nannostomus eques **32** 1908
narcissus fly **45** 2656
Narina's trogon **21** *1240, 1241*, 1243
narrow-bridged musk turtle **26** 1533, 1535
narrow-headed softshell turtle **26** 1553, 1556
narrow-mouthed frogs **30** 1756, 1776, 1783, 1786
narwhal **10** *586*, 587-8, 593
Nasalis **14** 831
Nascella mytilina **46** 2701
nase **32** 1894, *1899*, 1900
Naso **35** 2065, 2067
Nassariidae **46** 2746, 2751
Nassarius **45** 2677; **46** *2715*
incrassatus **45** *2693*; **46** 2746
reticulatus **45** 2677, *2679*; **46** 2715, 2746
Nassula **50** 2992, 2998
nasuti **41** 2406-7
Nasutitermes arborum **41** *2424*
Nasutitermitinae **41** 2406-7
Natalidae **12** 681, 709
Natantia **37** 2212
Natica **45** 2679; **46** *2737*
Naticacea **46** 2737
Naticarius millepunctatus **46** *2726*
Naticidae **46** *2737, 2740*
NATIONAL PARKS **51** *3001-60*
native cat **11** 619
Natrix natrix **28** 1645
natterjack toad **30** *1787*, 1789
natural selection theory **15** 892
Naucoridae **41** 2438, 2442
Naucrates ductor **34** 2036
Nautiloidea **48** 2853, 2855
Nautilus **48** 2855
disculus **48** *2853*
macrophalus **48** *2853*, 2855, 2857
pompilius **48** *2854-5, 2856-7*
scrobiculatus **48** 2855, 2857
nautiluses **36** 2103; **45** 2681; **48** *2852-7, 2866*, 2869-70
Neactaeonina cingulata **47** 2771
Neanderthal man **15** 900
'near insects' **39** 2311, 2320
Nebalia bipes **37** *2188*
Necator americanus **49** 2925
Necrophorus
germanicus **42** *2473-4*
humator **42** 2472, 2474
vespillo **42** *2472-4*
vestigator **42** 2474
Nectarinia **24** 1417
Nectariniidae **22** 1303; **24** 1417
Nectogale elegans **12** 662
Nectonema **49** 2934
Nectonematoidea **49** 2934
Nectophrynoides occidentalis **30** 1789
Necturidae **30** 1745
Necturus **30** 1745
needle-clawed bush baby **13** 748
needlefishes **33** *1964-6*; **34** *1996*
Neophocoena phocoenoides **10** 593
Neophron percnopterus **18** 1070
Neopilina **45** 2678-9, 2691
galatheae **45** *2690*, 2691-2

ABOVE A smooth newt reveals its bright orange, black-spotted underside.

Nemamyxine elongata **31** 1818
Nematocera **45** 2643, 2647, 2652
Nematoda **49** 2925, 2926
NEMATODES **49** *2925, 2926-33*
Nematomenia banyulensis **45** 2684, 2690
Nematomorpha **49** *2933*, 2934
Nematus ventricosus **42** *2519*
Nemertea **49** 2918, 2920
nemerteans **49** *2918-20*
Nemertesia antennina **47** 2797
Nemichthyidae **32** 1874
Nemichthys scolopaceus **32** 1874
Nemocardium centifilosum **48** 2846
Nemoptera sinuata **43** 2570
Nemopteridae **43** 2570, 2574
Nemorhaedus **10** 550
Nemotaulius punctatolineatus **44** *2583*
Nemouridae **40** 2345
Neobatrachus pelobatoides **30** 1799
Neoceratodus forsteri **31** 1850
Neoclinus blanchardi **35** 2059
Neodrapanis curuscans **22** 1316
Neogastropoda **45** 2697; **46** 2744-5, 2746, 2758; **47** 2766
Neomeniamorpha **45** 2684
Neomys fodiens **12** 662
Neomyxine biplinicata **31** 1818
neon goby **35** 2060, 2061
neon tetra **32** 1908, 1910
Neophoca cinerea **3** 172
Neositta papuensis **24** 1409
Neotetracus sinensis **11** 655
neotony **35** 2094
Neotragini **8** 434, 435-6, 438-46
Neotragus **8** 444
Neotrigonia margaritacea **48** 2843
Nepa **41** 2443
Nepal, national park **51** *3026-7*
Nephila **38** *2234, 2261*
Nephrotoma crocata **45** 2643, 2647
Nepidae **41** 2438, 2443
Nepticulidae **44** 2600
Nepticuloidea **44** 2595, 2600
neptune shell **46** 2746, 2751
Neptunea contraria **46** 2746
Nereidae **50** 2942
Nereis **49** 2937; **50** 2941
diversicolor **49** *2940*; **50** 2942
Nerilla mediterranea **50** *2946*
Nerita textilis **45** 2700
Neritacea **45** 2700; **46** 2705
Neritidae **45** 2700; **46** *2705*
Nerophis lumbriciformes **34** 2000
Nesiarchus nasutus **35** 2067
Nesolagus netscheri **4** 209
Nesomyinae **5** 249
Nestor notabilis **20** 1168
net-spinning caddisflies **43** 2580; **44** 2582-3
Nethrops norvegicus **37** *2214*, 2218
Netta rufina **18** 1047
Nettapus auritus **18** 1052
netted dog whelk **46** 2746, *2751*
Neuroptera **39** 2311; **43** 2565, 2570-4
Neuroterus **42** 2516, 2520
Neuse river waterdog **30** 1743
New Caledonian pearly nautilus **48** *2853*
New Guinea blind burrowing lizard **27** *1594*
New Guinea long-nosed bandicoot **11** 620
New Guinea tiger heron **17** 1007
New World false vampire **12** 705
New World orioles **24** 1438, 1440
New World porcupine **5** 276-7, 283
New World vultures **18** 1056, 1057, 1061-3, 1064
New Zealand, national park **51** 3002, 3004, *3050*
New Zealand dabchick **16** 960
New Zealand frogs **30** 1759-60, 1768
New Zealand fur seal **3** *166*
New Zealand sea lion **3** *170-1*, 172
distribution **3** 164
New Zealand shelduck **18** 1041, 1044
New Zealand wattlebirds **25** 1468, 1469, 1470
New Zealand wrens **22** 1302, 1316-17
classification **22** 1316
distribution **22** 1308
newts **29** 1702, 1703, *1704-5, 1711-14*, 1722-3; **30** *1746*
body features **29** *1731-40*
classification **29** 1701, 1713, 1729
distribution **29** 1715
Nierstraszia **45** 2690
night adder **28** 1673
night herons **17** 997, *1002-3*, 1005-7
night lizards **27** 1570, *1571*, 1572
night monkey **13** *761-3*, 764-5, 768, 774; **51** 3038
nighthawk **21** 1206, *1207*, 1208-9
nightingale **16** 909; **24** 1382, *1383*, 1387-8
nightingale monkey **14** 790
nightingale wren **23** 1377
nightjars **16** 912; **21** *1202, 1203-9*
classification **21** 1206
distribution **21** 1204
Nile bichir **31** 1850, 1853
Nile crocodile **29** *1684*, 1685, *1688-9*, 1690, 1693
Nile electric eel **32** 1869, *1870-1*
Nile lechwe **9** *504*, 508, 510, 514
Nile monitor **27** 1606, 1609, *1612-13*
Nile rat **5** 260
nilgai **8** *448, 451, 453, 456*, 460
distribution **8** 450
nilgau **6** 308
Nilgiri langur **14** 826
Nilgiri tahr **9** *534*; **10** 554-5, 570
nine-banded armadillo **4** 195-7
nine-spined stickleback **34** *1992*, 1993
ninguai **11** 619
Niphargellus **37** 2206
Niphargidae **37** *2206*
Niphargus **37** *2206*
Nipponia nippon **17** 1018
nits **41** 2430
noble crayfish **37** 2218

Noctilio leporinus **12** 704
Noctilionidae **12** 681, 704
noctuid moths **44** 2615, 2617, 2624
Noctuidae **44** 2624
noctule bat **12** *683*, *713-14*
classification **12** 712
echolocation **12** 685, *689*
migration **12** 690
Noctuoidea **44** 2598, 2624
nocturnal curassow **19** 1088
nocturnal flying squirrel **4** *234*
nocturnal guan **19** 1092
nocturnal kangaroo rat **4** *238*
noddy **20** 1144, 1145
Nodosaria raphanus **50** *2980*
Noemacheilus barbatulus **32** 1894
noisy friarbird **24** *1413*, 1420
noisy miner **24** *1419*, 1420
noisy scrub-bird **23** 1328, 1329
Nomada **43** 2540
Noniona depressula **50** *2987*
North African ass **6** 341, 344
North African elephant-shrew **11** *646*, *657*, 660
North African gundi **5** 286
North African ostrich **16** 918-19, 925
North American...
anchovy **32** *1889*
beaver **4** 233, 239, *240*
black bear **2** *70*, 71, *80-1*
cacomistle **1** *59*
catfish **32** 1911, 1913
flying squirrel **4** 235
hairy scorpion **38** *2246*
lungless salamander **30** *1751*
mudpuppy **30** *1744*
mummichog **33** *1975*
passenger pigeon **20** 1160
pika **4** *203-5*, 207, 209
porcupine **5** 275, *276*, 277-8, 283
red salamander **30** *1749*
spadefoot **30** 1768
North Atlantic barreleye **33** 1941
North Atlantic grey whale **10** 579
North Atlantic hake **33** 1951, 1955
North Canadian ground squirrel **4** *229*
North European scorpion **38** *2246*
North Pacific cod **33** 1950
north-west European periwinkle **46** 2707
northern...
alligator lizard **27** 1601, 1606
bottlenose whale **10** 586, 593
brushtail possum **11** 625
cardinal **24** *1423*
elephant seal **4** 184
flicker **22** *1298*
fluke **35** 2075
fulmar **17** *962*, *968*, 971, 973, *975*
fur seal **3** *162*, *167*, 172, 174
distribution **3** 164
hairy-nosed wombat **11** 633-4
hartebeest **9** 485
jacana **19** 1123
lapwing **19** 1125, 1126
leaf-tailed gecko **26** *1519*
midshipman **33** 1958-9
mockingbird **23** 1378-9, *1380*
oriole **24** *1438-9*, 1440
phalarope **19** 1135
pika **4** 204
pike **33** *1922*, 1937
pudu **7** 418; **8** 424
rough periwinkle **46** 2707, 2712
royal flycatcher **22** 1320
sea lion **3** 172
sea-robin **34** 2007
shrike **23** 1364
tamandua **4** 195
two-lined salamander **30** 1752
waterthrush **24** 1431, *1433*
whelk **46** 2715
white rhino **7** 361
wryneck **22** 1297, 1299
Northocercus bonapartei **16** 933
Northoprocta ornata **16** 933
northwestern salamander **29** 1721, 1722
Norway lemming **5** *249*
Norway rat **5** *255-8*
Norwegian cockle **45** 2676
Norwegian herring **32** 1890
Norwegian lobster **37** *2214*, 2218
Nosopsyllus fasciatus **45** 2665
Notacanthidae **32** 1872
Notacanthiformes **32** 1872
NOTACANTHS **32** 1868, 1872
Notacanthus chemnitzii **32** 1872
Notaden nichollsi **30** 1799
Notarchus **47** 2779
Notaspidea **47** 2767, 2779
Notechis scutatus **28** 1667
Notharchus macrorhyncus **22** 1284
Nothocrax urumutum **19** 1088
notochord **35** *2090*
Notodontidae **44** 2615, 2624
Notomyxine tridentiger **31** 1818
Notonecta glanca **41** *2445*
Notonectidae **39** 2322; **41** 2438, 2441, 2444
Notophthalmus viridescens **29** 1729
Notopteridae **32** 1869
Notopterus chitala **32** 1869
Notoryctes typhlops **11** 619
Notoryctidae **11** 612, 619
Notostraca **36** 2150
Nototheneiidae **35** 2056
Nubian ass **6** 335, *341*, 344
Nubian ibex **10** 555
Nucella lapillus **46** 2746, 2751, *2752-3*
Nucifraga **25** 1489
Nucula **45** 2677; **48** 2834, 2837
nucleus **48** *2835*
Nuculana, acinace **48** *2832*, 2834
Nuculoida **48** 2834, 2837
Nuda **49** 2901, 2902
Nudibranchia **47** 2767, *2784-2800*
nudibranchs **45** *2674*
numbat **11** *608*, 612, *619-20*, 621
Numenius arquata **19** 1135
Numida meleagris **19** 1101
Numididae **19** 1088, 1101
Nummulites **50** 2977, *2986-7*
nurse shark **31** *1830*, 1831, 1839; **35** *2047*
nutcracker **25** 1489, *1491*, 1495, 1498; **51** 3007, 3056
Nutcracker Man **15** 899
nuthatches **24** 1408, 1409, *1410-11*
distribution **24** 1408
nutmeg shell **46** 2746, *2760*
nutria **5** 288
nutshells **48** *2832*, 2834, *2835*, 2837
nyala **8** *448*, *450-1*, 452, *454-5*
Nyctalus noctula **12** 712
Nyctea scandiaca **20** 1199
Nycteridae **12** 681, 704
Nycteris thebaica **12** 704
Nyctibiidae **21** 1206, 1214
Nyctibius griseus **21** 1214
Nycticebus coucang **13** 748
Nycticorax nycticorax **17** 1007
Nycticryphes semicollaris **19** 1123
Nyctidromus albicollis **21** 1206
Nyctimene cephalotes **12** 694
Nyctiphanes **37** 2209
Nyctunguis **39** 2307
Nyctyornis athertoni **22** 1270
Nymphalidae **44** 2598, 2633, 2638
Nymphalinae **44** 2633, 2639
Nymphalis antiopa **44** 2633
Nyssonidae **43** 2535, 2540

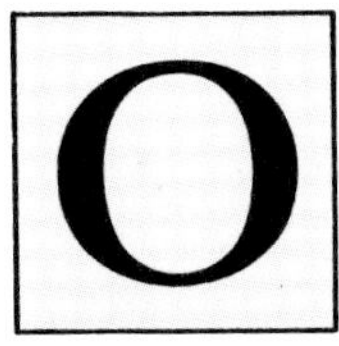

Oceanites oceanicus **17** 976
Oceanodroma leacorhoa **17** 976
ocellated electric ray **31** *1838*
ocellated green lizard **27** 1599, 1603
ocellated shieldtail snake **28** 1628
ocellated skink **27** 1595-6, 1598
ocellated turkey **19** 1086, 1101, 1102
ocelot **3** *141-2*, 158; **51** *3044*
Ocenebra inermicostata **46** 2745
Ochotona **4** 209
Ochotonidae **4** 209
Ochtera mantis **45** *2658*
Octanemids **35** 2094
Octocorallia **49** 2889, 2899
Octodon degus **5** 28
octodont **5** 288, 289, 294
Octodontidae **5** 277, 289
Octodontomys gliroides **5** 289
Octopoda **48** 2855, 2868-70, *2871*
Octopodidae **48** 2868
Octopodoteuthidae **48** 2861
Octopoteuthis sicula **48** 2861, 2867
Octopus
cyanea **48** *2866*

ABOVE The great horned owl nests in forests and suburban gardens.

oak bell-moth **44** 2603-5
oak eggar **44** *2604*
oak gall wasp **42** 2516, 2520
oak moth **44** 2626-8
oak processionary moth **44** 2623
oarfishes **34** 1985-7
Oaxacan boa **28** 1639
Obelia **49** 2889
Oberea oculata **42** *2505*
ocean perch **34** 2007
ocean pout **35** 2056-7
ocean squid **48** *2863-5*
ocean sunfish **35** *2082-3*, 2087
dofleini **48** 2852, *2869*
hubbsorum **48** 2852
macropus **48** 2852, 2869
salutii **48** 2869
vulgaris **48** 2852, *2866*, 2869
octopuses **36** 2103; **45** 2670, 2674-5, *2676*, 2681; **48** 2852, *2866*, 2868-70, *2871*
Ocypode cursor **38** 2231
Ocypodidae **38** *2226-7*, 2230
Ocyptera brassicaria **45** *2658*
Ocypus olens **42** 2472, 2477
Ocythoe tuberculata **48** 2869

Ocythoidae **48** 2868, 2869, 2870
odd-eyed squids **48** *2854*, 2861, 2867
Odobenidae **3** 164, 167, 172
Odobenus rosmarus **3** 172
Odocoileus **7** 418
Odocoilinae **7** 396, 418
Odonata **39** 2311; **40** *2349-62*
Odontaspididae **31** 1839
Odontaspis **31** 1839
Odontoceti **10** 577, 593
Odontomacrurus numax **33** 1951, *1955*
Odontotermes **41** 2416, *2417*
Odonus niger **35** *2083*
Odostomia **46** *2721*
scalaris **46** 2720, *2721*, 2722
Odynerus murarius **43** 2528, 2529
Oeceoptoma thoracicum **42** *2472-3*
Oecophylla smaragdina **43** 2529, 2552-3
Oedipoda germanica **40** *2365*
Oegopsida **48** 2861, 2862
Oeiacus hirundinus **41** 2436, 2437
Oeleacinacea **48** 2825
Oenanthe oenanthe **24** 1388
Oestridae **45** 2659
Ogcocephalus nasutus **33** 1961
Ogcophalidae **33** 1961
Ogilbia **33** 1956
Ogilby's duiker **51** 3020
ogre-faced spiders **39** 2290
Oikopleura **35** 2095, 2098
oil-beetles **42** 2472, *2486-9*
oilbird **21** *1202*, 1203, 1209, *1212*, 1214
classification **21** 1206, 1214
distribution **21** 1204
oilfish **35** 2067
okapi **6** 304, 307; **8** *426-7*, 429, 430; **51** 3024
Okapia johnstoni **8** 430
Okenia aspersa **47** *2787*
Old World flamingo **18** 1022-3, 1024
Old World fly catchers **24** 1399-1400
Old World porcupine **5** 277
Old World tree frogs **30** 1756, 1774, 1779, 1782, 1785
Old World vultures **18** 1056, *1060-4*, 1077-9
classification **18** 1057, 1070
oleander hawk-moth **44** 2621-2, 2624
Oligochaeta **50** 2942, 2945, 2948, 2952, 2956
oligochaetan worms **50** 2945-6
Oligochaetes **45** *2670*; **50** 2952, 2958
Oligohymenophora **50** 2992, 2997
olingo **2** 62-3
Oliva **46** 2755
Oliva porphyria **47** *2762*
olivaceous cormorant **17** 990
olivaceous greenlet **24** 1435
olive black-eye **24** 1417
olive colobus **14** 834, 836
olive fruit fly **45** 2657, 2659
olive ridley turtle **26** 1553, 1554; **51** 3028, 3032
olive shells **46** *2755*, *2762*
olive-bud moth **44** 2603
Olividae **46** 2755
olm **29** 1713; **30** 1742, *1743*, 1745, *1746*
Olocrysa fastuosa **42** *2505*
Olympic salamander **29** 1722
Omalium riparium **42** 2472, 2477
Ommasthrephes bartramii **48** 2867
Ommastrephidae **48** 2861, 2867
Ommatophoca rossi **3** 179; **4** 184
omnivores **1** 27
onager **6** *344*, 345
Onchidiidae **47** 2817
Onchidiids **47** 2803
Onchidium **47** 2817
Onchorcerca volvulus **49** 2925
Oncomelania **47** 2811
Oncorhynchus **33** 1924
Ondontodactylus **37** *2186*, 2187
one-humped camel **7** 381, 388
one-toed amphiuma **30** 1742
one-toed salamander **30** 1745
one-toothed top shell limpet **45** 2700; **46** 2702, *2703*
one-wattled cassowary **16** 925
Oniscoidea **37** 2201
Oniscus **37** *2200*
asellus **37** *2188*, 2201
Onitis **42** 2495
Ontholestes tessellatus **42** *2473*
Onychia caribbaea **48** *2863-5*
Onychophora **36** 2140, 2144; **50** 2960, 2963
onychoporans **45** *2670*; **50** *2959-63*
Onychorhyncus mexicanus **22** 1320
Oopelta micropunctata **48** 2824
opah **34** 1985, *1986-7*, *1996*
opalescent squid **48** 2861-2
Opalia **46** 2721
open-bill stork **17** 1012-3
open-ocean sea cucumber **36** *2117*
Operculina **50** *2986*
Ophelia **49** 2937
Ophicephalus **35** 2071-2
Ophichthidae **32** 1874
Ophidia **28** 1621
Ophidiidae **33** 1956
Ophidiiformes **33** 1956
Ophidiocephalus taeniatus **27** 1570, 1571
Ophioderma longicauda **36** *2132*
Ophiodon elongatus **34** 2007
Ophiophagus hannah **28** 1667
ophiopluteus larva **36** *2113*, 2133
Ophisaurus apodes **27** 1603
Ophiura albida **36** *2132*
Ophiuroidea **36** 2106, 2107, *2127-33*
Ophlitaspongia pennata **47** 2795
Opiliones **38** 2241; **39** 2290
Opisthobranchia **45** 2674, 2680, 2694, 2697; **47** 2766-2801
opisthobranchs **47** *2766*, 2792-3
Opisthocomidae **19** 1102
Opisthocomus hoazin **19** 1102
Opisthoproctidae **33** 1937
Opisthoproctus grimaldi **33** 1937
Opisthoteuthis **48** *2866*, 2868-9
opossum **1** 16; **11** *608*, *611*, *612*, 613-14; **51** 3048
opossum shrimps **37** 2182, *2188*, 2193-4, *2195*
Opsanus tau **33** 1958
ora **27** 1608
orang-utan **13** 757, *760*; **14** 838; **15** *847-8*, *849-56*, 860
classification **13** 728; **14** 839; **15** 852

ABOVE The golden oriole breeds in Europe in the spring.

extinction threat **15** 890
mobility **12** *719*; **13** 723, 756; **15** *834*
orange horseshoe bats **51** 3046
orange snub-nosed monkey **14** 831
orange-cheeked waxbill **25** *1452*, 1453
orb spiders **38** *2257*
orb-shell cockle **48** 2833, 2847
orb-weaver spider **38** 2258 2278, 2279
Orbitilinids **50** 2976
Orbulina **50** *2986*
orca **10** 588, 593
Orchestia **37** 2205
orchid mantid **40** *2398*
Orcinus orca **10** 593
Orctes nasicornis **42** 2499
Oreamnos americanus **10** 550
Orectolobidae **31** 1839
Orectolobus **31** 1839
Oreonympha nobilis **21** 1228
Oreotragus oreotragus **8** 444
'organ grinders' **11** 637
organ-pipe coral **49** *2895*
Orgyia antiqua **44** 2624
oribi **8** *436*, 438-9, *444-6*
oriental barn owl **20** 1195
oriental bay owl **20** 1194, 1195, *1196*
oriental cockroach **40** 2391, 2394-5
oriental dormouse **5** 254, 261-2
oriental fire-bellied toad **30** 1762
oriental rat flea **45** 2665, 2667
oriental water dragon **27** *1588*
oriental white stork **17** 1011
Orinoco crocodile **29** 1692
orioles **25** *1465-7*, 1468
New World **24** 1438, 1440
oriolidae **25** 1465
Oriolus **25** 1465
ornate horned frog **30** *1764*, 1795, *1800*
ornate tinamou **16** 933, 934
ornate umbrellabird **23** 1322, *1323*
Ornithischia **26** *1507*, 1508
Ornithorhynchidae **11** 606
Ornithorhynchus anatinus **11** 606
Ornithoteuthis volatilis **48** 2867
Orohippus **6** 333
Ortalis vertula **19** 1088
Orthegeomys **4** 233
Orthetrum cancellatum **40** *2355*
Orthognatha **38** 2258
Orthonectida **48** 2874
Orthoptera **39** 2311, 2323; **40** 2363-82; **41** 2402
Orthotornus atrogularis **24** 1394
Ortyxelos meiffrenii **19** 1114
Orycteropus afer **6** 304
Oryctes nasicornis **43** 2534
Oryctolagus cuniculus **4** 209
oryx **6** 306, *339*; **9** *484*, 499-502; **51** 3022
classification **8** 434; **9** 485, 490, 502
distribution **9** 486
Oryx **9** 502
Oryzias latipes **33** 1965
Oryziidae **33** 1965
Oryzoryctinae **11** 651
oscines **22** 1303, 1306-7; **23** 1334
Osmeridae **33** 1924
Osmerus eperlanus **33** 1924
Osmia **43** 2540, 2541
Osmius fulvicephalus **43** *2567*, 2570
Osmylidae **43** 2570, 2573
Osphronemidae **35** 2070
Osphronemus goramy **35** 2070
osprey **18** 1055, 1061, 1063, *1073*
classification **18** 1057, 1064
Osteicthyes **31** 1809, 1850
Osteoglossidae **32** 1869
Osteoglossiformes **32** 1869
Osteoglossum bicirrhosum **32** 1869

Osteolaemus tetraspis **29** 1685
Ostraciidae **35** 2082
Ostracion **35** 2082, 2086
Ostracoda **36** 2147, *2160*; **37** 2161
Ostrea **48** 2842
crystagalli **48** *2832*
edulis **48** *2843*
Ostreacea **48** 2837, 2842, 2843
Ostreidae **48** 2842, 2843
ostrich **16** 905, *909*, 911, *917-21*, *922*
classification **16** 925
courtship **16** *919*, 922
ostrich foot shells **46** *2723*, 2724
Ostrinia nubilalis **44** 2609
Ostrom, John **16** 904
Otaria flavescens **3** 172
Otariidae **3** 164, 167
Otarinae **3** 164, 172
Otididae **19** 1107, 1112
Otina otis **47** 2805
Otinidae **47** 2805
Otis tarda **19** 1112
Otocyon **3** 127
Otomyinae **5** 261
Otophidium taylori **33** 1956
otter **1** 26, *38*, 44, *50-1*
classification **1** 55
diet **1** 41-2
distribution **1** 43
national parks **51** 3006, 3013-14, 3023, 3038, 3056
teeth **1** 39
otter cat **3** *148-9*, 158; **51** 3044
otter civet **2** 92, *96*
otter shell **48** *2844*
otter shrew **11** *646*, 648-53, *654*
Otus scops **20** *1199*
ounce **3** 144
Ourebia ourebi **8** 444
ovenbirds **22** 1309-13; **24** 1432-3
classification **22** 1303, 1310
distribution **22** 1308
Ovibonini **10** 550
Ovibos moschatus **10** 550
Ovibovini **8** 434
ovipositor **40** 2366, *2371*
Ovis **10** 570
Ovulidae **46** 2720, 2729
owl butterfly **44** *2596*
owl monkey **13** 774
owl parrot **20** 1168, 1169-70
owl-faced monkey **14** 816
owlet moths **44** 2597, 2615, 2624
owlet-frogmouths **21** 1214
owlet-nightjars **21** *1202*, 1203, 1204, 1206, 1214
owlflies **43** *2565*, *2567*, 2570, 2573, *2574*
owls **16** 914; **18** 1055; **20** *1183-1200*; **51** *3005*, 3007
senses **20** *1185*, 1187, 1190
Owl's rat **5** 289
ox warble fly **45** *2658*, 2659-60
oxpeckers **25** *1462*, 1464
Oxycephalus **37** 2207
Oxychilus allarius **48** 2824
Oxymonachanthus longirostris **35** *2083*
Oxynoidiae **47** 2777
Oxyruncidae **23** 1331
Oxyruncus cristatus **23** 1331
Oxythrips bicolor **41** 2428
Oxyura **18** 1052
Oxyurini **18** 1030, 1052
oyan *see* African linsang
oyster drill **45** 2678; **46** 2746, 2748, *2749*
oyster toadfish **33** *1958*
oyster-leech **49** 2905, 2911
oystercatchers **19** 1121, *1124*, 1125, 1135; **51** 3008
oysters **36** 2103; **45** 2670, 2674, 2676, 2680; **48** *2832*, 2836-7, 2841-3
Ozotocerus bezoarticus **7** 418

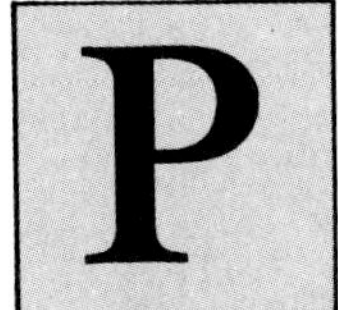

paca **5** 275, 277, 282, *284*, 289
pacarana **5** 277, 281-2, *283*, 289
Pachybrachis **42** 2504
Pachycephala pectoralis **24** 1400
Pachyiscus septmarodensis **48** 2853
Pachyptila **17** 973

ABOVE When disturbed, the porcupine fish inflates its body revealing sharp spines.

Pachypus **42** 2493-4
Pachyrina **45** 2643
Pachytegmentaria **45** 2684, 2689, 2690
Pacific...
ark shell **48** 2834
auklet **20** 1145
baza **18** 1076
diver **16** 954
giant octopus **48** 2852
giant salamander **29** *1712*, 1722
hake **33** 1951
herring **32** 1887, 1890
mole salamander **29** 1713, 1722
monkfish **31** 1841
prickly shark **31** 1837
ridley turtle **26** *1552-3*, 1554
sailfish **35** 2043
salmon **33** *1922*, *1924-7*
sardine **32** 1890
shortbill **35** 2041, 2043
tarpon **32** 1872
tree frog **30** 1792, 1795
walrus **3** 162, 172
white-rumped swift **21** 1218, 1223
white-sided dolphin **10** *592*
yellow angler **33** 1961
pack rat **5** 244
pacu **32** 1909
Padda oryzivora **25** 1453
paddlefishes **31** 1848, *1854-5*, 1856
paddyfield warbler **24** 1395
pademelon **11** 642
Paederus **42** 2477
ruficollis **42** 2472, 2476
Pagellus pagellus **34** 2033
pagoda shells **46** 2746, 2748
Pagodroma nivea **17** 973
Pagophila eburnea **20** 1142
Paguma larvata **2** 89
Paguroidea **38** 2221
Pagurus bernhardus **38** *2224*
paiche **32** 1868
painted bunting **24** *1427*, 1429
painted eel **32** 1880
painted frog **30** 1760, *1762-3*
painted lady **44** *2588*, 2633
painted snipe **19** *1120*, 1121, 1123, *1124*
painted stork **17** 1012, 1015, *1016-7*
painted turtle **26** *1536-7*
painter's mussel **48** 2843
Palaemon serratus **37** *2192*, *2213*
Palaeoheterodonta **48** 2833, 2837, 2843
palaeoniscids **31** 1809
Palaeotaxodonta **48** 2833, 2834, 2837
Palaeotheres **6** 333
pale chanting goshawk **18** 1064-5
pale clouded yellow butterfly **44** 2633
pale flycatcher **24** 1399
pale fox **3** 127, *128*
pale sapphire butterfly **44** *2634*
pale white-eye **24** 1417
pale-headed jacamar **22** 1284
pale-throated three-toed sloth **4** 195
pale-winged trumpeter **19** 1117
pale-yellow robin **51** 3048
Paleocene era **1** 25
Paleodictyoptera **39** 2338
Paleonemertea **49** 2920
Paleosuchus palpebrosus **29** 1685
Palinura **37** 2213
Palinurus **37** 2213, *2214*, *2192*
Pallas' long-tongued bat **12** 705, *708*, 709
Pallas' tube-nosed bat **12** 694, 695
Pallas's cat **3** *142*, 154
Pallas's sandgrouse **20** 1152
pallid bat **12** 712, 716
pallid harrier **18** 1070, 1072
pallid swift **21** 1218, *1219*, *1222*
palm chat **23** *1373*, 1374
palm civet **2** 92, *96*
palm cockatoo **20** *1162*, 1163, *1167*, 1168
palm swift **21** 1218, 1223, *1225*
palm vulture **18** 1058, 1077
palm-nut vulture **18** 1078
palmate newt **29** 1729, *1736*
Palmerston National Park **51** 3048, 3049
Palmotagecko rangei **27** 1569
palolo worms **49** *2936*, 2939-40; **50** 2942
Palpares libelluloides **43** *2567*, 2570
Palpigradi **38** 2241, 2252
pampas cat **3** 158
pampas deer **7** *390*, 398, *411*, 415, 417; **8** 424
classification **7** 418
pampas fox **2** *110*
Pan **15** 852
Panama golden stub-footed frog **30** *1764*
Panaxia dominula **44** 2624
pancake tortoise **26** 1546
Pancarida **37** 2182, 2189, *2192-3*
panchax **33** *1974*, 1978
Pandaka pygmaea **35** 2060
pandas **1** 18, 20, 28, *58*; **2** 62, *66-8*; **51** *3051*, *3058-9*
Pander's ground jay **25** *1488*
Pandinus **38** 2244, 2245
imperator **36** *2143*; **38** *2246*, 2250-1
Pandion haliaetus **18** 1064
Pandionidae **18** 1057, 1064
Pandora albida **48** 2848, 2850
Pandoridae **48** 2848
Pangaea **1** 17
pangolin **4** 197, *198-200*; **10** 598; **51** 3020
Panopea generosa **48** 2849

Panorpa communis **43** *2575*
Panorpidae **43** 2574, 2576
Panthera **3** 144
Pantherinae **3** 144
Pantholops hodgsoni **9** 535
Pantodon buchholzi **32** 1869
Pantodontidae **32** 1869
Panurus biarmicus **24** 1392
Panyptila cayennensis **21** 1218
papal mitre **47** 2761
paper nautilus **48** *2866*, 2869, *2870*
paper wasps **43** 2528, 2529, *2525*
Papilio
  childrenae **44** *2634*
  dehaani **44** *2634*
  karna **44** *2603*
  machaon **44** 2633, *2636*
  ulysses **44** *2634*
Papilionidae **44** 2633, 2635, *2636*
Papilionoidea **44** 2632, 2633
Papio **14** 811
Pappogeomys **4** 233
Papuan frogmouth **21** 1212
Papuan lory **20** 1164
Papuan microeca **24** 1400
Papuan sitella **24** 1409
Papuan spiny stick insect **40** 2385
Paracaudina **36** 2121
Paracentrotus lividus **36** 2125
Paracheirodon innesi **32** 1908
Paraclinus marmoratus **35** 2059
Paradisaea **25** 1480
Paradisaeidae **22** 1303; **25** 1480
paradise duck **51** 3050
paradise flycatcher **24** 1399
paradise flying snake **28** *1649*
paradise jacamar **22** *1280*
paradise kingfisher **21** 1253, 1260
paradise shelduck **18** 1044
paradise tanager **24** *1427-8*, 1429
paradise whydah **25** *1454*, 1459, 1461
paradisefish **35** *2068*, 2069-70
paradoxical frog **30** 1786
Paradoxornis paradoxus **24** 1392
Paradoxornithidae **24** 1392
Paradoxurus **2** 89
Paraechinus aethiopicus **11** 655
Parahippus **6** 333
parakeets **20** 1163, 1165-6, 1168, 1169; **51** 3050
Paralepididae **33** 1946
paramecia **50** *2977*, *2982-3*, *2997-9*
Paramecium **50** 2981, 2988, 2992, *2996-7*
  reproduction **50** *2978*, *2979*, 2998-9
Paramyxine **31** 1818
Paraonyx **1** 55
Parapenaeus longitostris **37** *2219*
parasite catfish **32** 1913, 1920
parasitic caligoids **37** 2163
parasitic copepods **37** 2161, *2165-8*
parasitic cyclopoids **37** 2165-6, *2167*
parasitic eulimid **46** 2720, 2721
parasitic flies **45** 2659
parasitic isopods **37** 2196, 2197, 2199-2200, *2202-3*
parasitic nematodes **49** 2925, *2927-2933*
parasitic river lamprey **31** 1818, *1820-1*
parasitic wasps **39** 2324; **42** 2516
parasitic weaverbird **20** 1175; **25** 1459, 1461
Parasitica **42** 2516
parasol ants **43** 2563
Parastacidae **37** 2220
Paratetranychus pilosus **38** *2242*
Parathemisto **37** 2207, *2208*
Paravespula germanica **43** 2534
Parazca **48** 2880
Parazoanthus axinellae **49** *2897*
parchment worm **49** *2936*; **50** 2942
pardalotes **24** 1416, 1417
Pardalotus punctatus **24** 1417
Pardictis pardicolor **2** 89
Paridae **24** 1403
Parioglossus taenitus **35** 2061
Parnassius apollo **44** *2585*
Parotia lawesii **25** 1480
parrot crossbill **25** 1447
parrot finch **24** 1425
parrotbill **24** 1392, 1393
parrotfishes **31** *1802*; **34** *2012*, 2025-6
  classification **34** 2023
  coral-feeders **34** *1998*, 2013, *2023*
parrots **20** *1163-70*
parsley frog **30** 1768, 1769, *1770*
particoloured bat **12** 712, *714*
Partridge sundial **46** 2716
partridges **16** *913*; **19** 1088, 1096-7, 1098, *1099*
Partulidae **47** 2819
Parulidae **22** 1303; **24** 1431
Parus **24** 1403
Pascolarctidae **11** 612, 633
pasha butterflies **44** 2640
passenger pigeon **20** 1160
Passer **25** 1459
Passeriformes **22** *1301-20*; **23 -25**
Passerina **24** 1429
Passerinae **25** 1459
PASSERINES **22** *1301-20*; **23-5** *1381-1500*
passion-flower butterfly **44** 2639
patagium **11** 626, 630-1
Patagona gigas **21** 1228
Patagonian cavy **5** 273, 278
Patagonian conure **20** 1163
Patagonian hare **5** 278
patas monkey **14** 816, *818*, *820-2*
Patella **46** 2701-2
  aspera **46** 2701
  caerulea **46** 2701
  laticostata **45** 2697; **46** 2701
  mexicana **45** 2697; **46** 2701
  pontica **46** 2701
  vulgata **45** 2697; **46** 2701
Patellacea **45** 2697, 2700
Patellidae **45** 2697, *2700*; **46** 2701-2
Patina pellucida **45** *2700*
Patiria miniata **46** 2715
pauraque **21** 1206
Pauropoda **39** 2302, *2303*
Pavo cristatus **19** 1096
pea crab, host **35** 2061
pea-crabs **37** 2202, *2203*; **38** 2229
pea-shell cockles **48** 2847
peacock **16** 909; **19** *1097*, 1098
peacock butterfly **44** *2606*, 2633
peacock flounder **35** *2078*, 2080
peacock moth **44** 2606
peacock-eyed spiny eel **35** 2072
peafowl **19** 1087, 1096, 1097, 1098; **51** *3026*
pear-tree sawfly **42** 2516
pearl gouramis **32** *1865*; **35** *2064*, *2069*, 2070
pearl mussel **48** *2832*, 2843
pearl oyster **48** 2837
pearlfish **33** *1940*, 1944, *1956*
pearlfishes **36** 2123
pearly nautilus **45** 2674; **48** *2854*, 2855
peccaries **6** 301; **7** 364-6, 370-2; **10** *569*; **51** 3042
Pecten **48** 2833, 2840
  maximus **48** 2837, *2840*
pecten scallop **48** 2841
Pectinacea **48** 2837, 2840
Pectinator spekei **5** 286
Pectinidae **48** 2837
pectoral sandpiper **19** *1130*
Pedetes capensis **4** 233
Pedetidae **4** 233
Pedicellina **49** 2920
Pedicellinidae **49** 2920
Pediculus humanus **41** 2428
Pedionomidae **19** 1107, 1117
Pedionomus torquatus **19** 1117
peewit **19** 1126
Pegasidae **34** 1997
Pegasiformes **34** 1997
Pegasus volitans **34** 1997
Pekin robin **24** 1390
Pelagia noctiluca **49** *2886*
pelagic paper nautilus **48** 2869
pelagic squid **48** *2866*
pelagic tunicates **35** 2090
Pelagothuria ludwigi **36** *2117*
Pelamis platurus **28** 1667
Pelea capreolus **9** 510
Pelecanidae **17** 980
Pelecaniformes **17** *977-94*
Pelecanoides **17** 976
Pelecanoididae **17** 971, 976
Pelecanus **17** 980
Pelecinus polyturator **42** *2519*
pelicans **16** *902-3*; **17** *977-83*, 979, *980-3*; **51** *3014*, 3024
  classification **17** 980
  distribution **17** 984
pelican's foot shells **46** 2720, 2722, 2724, *2726*
Pellorneum capistratum **24** 1390
Pelobates fuscus **30** 1769
Pelobatidae **30** 1769
Pelochys bibroni **26** 1553
Pelodytes punctatus **30** 1769
Pelomedusa subrufa **26** 1530
Pelomedusidae **26** 1530
Pel's fishing owl **20** *1197*, 1199
Peltodoris atromaculata **47** *2793*, 2795-6
Peltohyas australis **19** 1125
Pelusios castaneus **26** 1530
pelycosaurs **26** 1506
pen-tailed tree shrew **13** 730, *744*
Penaeus
  cheraturus **37** *2192*
  duorarum **37** *2212*
pencil catfish **32** 1913, 1920
pencilfish **32** *1906*, 1908
penduline tit **24** 1403, *1407*
Penelope albipennis **19** 1088
penguinfish **32** 1908, 1910
penguins **16** *935-50*
  classification **16** 949
  distribution **16** 944, 948
  national parks **51** 3035, 3050
  nesting sites **16** *942*, 948
  postures **16** *940*, *942*, *945*
Penicillus giganteus **48** *2844*
pennant marten **1** 46
pennant-winged nightjar **21** 1206, 1207, *1208*, *1209*
Pennatula phosphorea **49** *2886*
Pennatulacea **49** 2889, 2900
penshells **48** 2837
Pentalagus furnessi **4** 209
Pentastomida **50** 2963
pentastomids **50** 2963
Pentatomidae **41** 2438, 2442
Pentodon **42** 2500
pepper-shrikes **24** 1435-8
peppered moth **44** *2598*, 2609, 2613-14
Pepsis **43** *2536*
Peracarida **37** 2182, 2189, 2192-3
Peraclidae **47** 2782
Peraclis **47** 2786
Peramelidae **11** 612, 620
Perca **34** 2014; **35** *2064*
perch family **31** 1806, *1860*; **32** *1862*; **35** *2064*
  classification **31** 1858
perch-like fishes **34** *2011-40*; **35** 2041-72
Percheron horse **6** 348
perches **34** *2012-16*
  classification **34** 2013, 2014
  distribution **34** 2022, 2026
perching ducks **18** 1030, 1048-9, 1052
perching geese **18** 1030, 1048-9, 1052
Percichthyidae **34** 2017, 2023
Percidae **34** 2013-14
Perciformes **31** 1858; **34** *2011-40*; **35** *2041-72*
Percopsidae **33** 1948
Percopsiformes **33** 1948
Percopsis **33** 1948, *1996*
Percottus glehni **35** 2060
Perdix perdix **19** 1096
Pere David's deer **7** *405*, 406, 411
peregrine falcon **18** 1055-6, 1058, *1079*, 1080; **19** 1081
  national parks **51** 3013, 3043
perentie **27** 1609, 1614
Pericapritermes **41** 2405
Pericharax heteroraphis **49** *2881*
Pericrocotus divaricatus **23** 1357
Periophalmus **35** *2062-3*
Periophthalmodon **35** 2060, 2062
Periophthalmus **35** 2060, 2062
Peripatidae **50** 2963
Peripatopsidae **50** 2963
Periplaneta americana **40** 2391
Perisoreus infaustus **25** 1489
Perissodactyla **10** 568
periwinkles **45** 2676; **46** *2704*, *2706-11*, 2714; **47** 2801
  classification **46** 2712
Perkinsiella saccharicida **41** 2438, 2447
Perlamantis alliberti **40** 2391, 2400
Perlidae **39** 2338; **40** 2345
Perninae **18** 1070
Pernis apivorus **18** 1070
Perodicticus potto **13** 748
Perognathus **4** 233
Persian fallow deer **7** 398, 406; **8** 421
Persian gazelle **9** 529
Pert **50** 2963
Peruvian blue butterfly **44** *2634*
Peruvian booby **17** 993, 994
Peruvian diving petrel **17** 976
Peruvian huemul **7** 417, 418; **8** 424
Peruvian plantcutter **23** 1325
Peruvian shrew opossum *1* 624

Peruvian vicuna **7** 388
Petauridae **11** 612, 627
Petauroides volans **11** 627
Petaurus breviceps **11** 627
petrels **17** 962, *968*, 971, *972-6*
  classification **17** 973, 976
  distribution **17** 963, 974
Petricola **48** 2847
Petrobius maritimus **39** 2335
Petrochelidon pyrrhonota **23** 1345
Petrodromus tetradactylus **11** 660
Petromyidae **5** 277, 289
Petromys typicus **5** 289
Petromyzon marinus **31** 1818
Petromyzontidae **31** 1818
Petromyzontiformes **31** 1818
petronia **25** 1455
Petronia petronia **25** 1459
Petrosia dura **47** 2796
Peurion black petrel **17** 976
Phacochoerus aethiopicus **7** 370
Phaenus **42** 2492, 2495
Phaeodaria **50** 2991
Phaethon **17** 980
Phaethontidae **17** 980
phainopepla **23** 1369, *1372*
Phainopepla nitens **23** 1372
Phalacrocoracidae **17** 990
Phalacrocorax **17** 980, 990
Phalaenoptilus nuttallii **21** 1206
Phalanger **11** 625
Phalangeridae **11** 612, 625
phalangers **11** *624-6*
Phalangim opilio **38** *2242*
Phalarope lobatus **19** 1135
phalaropes **19** 1126, 1131-2, *1134*, 1135
Phalaropodinae **19** 1135
Phalera bucephala **44** *2604*, 2624
Phaleria cadaverina **42** 2472, 2490
Phalium bandatum **46** *2741*
Phaner furcifer **13** 742
Pharomacrus mocinno **21** 1241
Pharyngobdellae **50** 2958
phascogale **11** 610, *617*, 619
Phascolarctos cinereus **11** 633
Phasianidae **19** 1088, 1096
Phasianus colchicus **19** 1096
Phasmatidae **40** 2385
Phasmatodea **40** 2385
Phasmida **39** 2311; **40** *2383-6*
Phayre's leaf monkey **14** 825
pheasant pigeon **20** *1150*
pheasant-tailed jacana **19** 1123
pheasants **16** 907; **19** *1085*, 1087, 1088, 1096-8
Phidippus **38** *2276*
Philaneus spumarius **41** 2449
Philanthidae **43** 2537, 2540
Philanthus triangulum **43** *2530*, 2537, 2540
Philebopenes longicaudatus **42** *2519*
Philemon corniculatus **24** 1420
Philepitta castanea **22** 1316
Philepittidae **22** 1316
Philesturnus carunculatus **25** 1470
Philine **47** 2768, *2775*
  quadripartita **47** 2775
Philinidae **47** 2767
Philippine colugo **12** *674*, 676
Philippine creepers **24** 1412, 1415
Philippine eagle **18** 1058, 1066, 1070
Philippine fairy bluebird **23** 1360
Philippine falconet **18** 1080
Philippine frogmouth **21** 1213-14
Philippine tarsier **13** 748, 753, 754
Philomachus pugnax **19** 1135
Philomycidae **48** 2822
Phiolophora **50** 2967
Phlaeothripidae **41** 2428
Phlaeothripinae **41** 2428
phlebotomine flies **50** 2988
Phlebotomus papatasi **45** *2644*, 2646-7
Phoca **4** 184
Phocarctos hookeri **3** 172
Phocidae **3** 164, 167, 176, 179; **4** 184
Phocinae **3** 179
Phocoena phocoena **10** 593
Phocoenidae **10** 593
Phocoenoides dalli **10** 593
Phodilus **20** 1194
Phoebetria **17** 971
Phoeniconaias minor **18** 1024
Phoenicoparrus **18** 1024
Phoenicopteridae **17** 999; **18** *1021-6*
Phoenicopterus **18** 1024
Phoeniculidae **21** 1253; **22** 1270
Phoeniculus purpureus **22** 1270, 1271
Phoenicurus **24** 1388
Pholadidae **48** 2848, 2849
Pholadomyoida **48** 2848, 2850
Pholas dactylus **48** 2847-9, *2850*
Pholcidae **39** 2289
Pholidae **35** 2056
PHOLIDOTS **4** *185-200*
Pholis gunnellus **35** 2056
Phoneutria fera **39** 2289
Phoronida **50** 2966, *2968-9*
Phoronis **50** 2966, 2968
  hippocrepia **50** 2966
Phoronopsis **50** 2966, 2968
Photoblepharon palpebratus **34** 1990
Phoxinus phoxinus **32** 1894
Phragmites **47** 2819
Phreatoicoidea **37** 2200
Phrixothrix **42** 2472, 2481
Phronima sedentaria **37** *2188*
Phronis **50** 2966
Phrynelox scaber **33** *1960*
Phrynomeridae **30** 1786
Phrynomerus **30** 1786
Phrynosoma **27** 1579
Phtheirichthys lineatus **35** 2046, 2048
Phthiraptera **41** 2428-9
Phthirius pubis **41** *2428*, *2431*
Phycis blennoides **33** 1951
Phyllastrephus flavostriatus **23** 1359
Phyllidiidae **47** 2796, 2797
Phylliidae **40** 2385
Phylliroe bucephala **47** 2797-8
Phylliroidae **47** 2797
Phyllium grandis **40** *2365*, 2385
Phyllobates bicolor **30** 1785
Phyllobius **42** 2514
Phyllocarida **37** 2182
Phyllodactylus europaeus **27** 1569
Phyllopertha horticola **42** 2499, *2505*
Phyllopteryx taeniolatus **34** 2000
Phylloscopus
  collybita **24** 1394
  trochilus **24** 1394
Phyllostomatidae **12** 681, 709
Phyllostomus hastatus **12** 709
Phyllotreta **42** 2504
Phylloxera vastatrix **41** *2439*, 2452, 2454
Phylloxerinae **41** 2452, 2454
Phyllurus cornatus **27** 1569
Phymateus brunneri **40** *2365*
Physa **47** *2810*
  acuta **47** 2809
  fontinalis **47** *2809-10*
Physalia **47** 2792, 2800; **49** 2889
Physeter macrocephalus **10** 593
Physeteridae **10** 593
Physidae **47** 2805, 2809-10
Physiognathus lesueurii **27** 1585
Physophora **49** *2890*
Phytoecia **42** 2512
phytoflagellates **50** 2976, 2984-5
Phytotoma **23** 1325
Phytotomidae **22** 1303; **23** 1325
piapiac **25** 1489, 1494
Pica pica **25** 1489
Picasso fishes **35** 2082, 2087
Picathartes
  gymnocephalus **24** 1392
  oreas **24** 1392
picathartes or bald crows **24** 1390
Picathartidae **24** 1392
pichi **4** 197
Picidae **22** 1297
Piciformes **22** *1279-1300*
Picinae **22** 1297
pickerel **33** 1937, 1938
Pickfordiateuthidae **48** 2861, 2862
Pickfordiateuthis pulchella **48** 2861, 2862
Picromerus bidens **41** *2442*
piculets **22** *1293*, 1297, 1299-1300
Picumninae **22** 1297
Picumnus exilis **22** 1297
Picus **22** 1297
piddocks **48** 2847, 2848-9, *2850*
pied...
  avocet **19** 1132, *1133*, 1137
  bare-face tamarin **14** 790
  bat **12** 679, 712, 715
  butcherbird **25** 1471
  crow **25** 1489, 1500
  currawong **25** 1470, 1472
  flycatcher **24** *1386*, 1399-1400
  goose **18** 1036
  harrier **18** 1070, 1071
  heron **17** *1004*
  hornbill **22** 1278
  kingfishers **21** *1251*, 1253, 1259; **51** 3026-7
  mannikin **25** *1453*
  wagtail **23** 1347, *1350*, 1352, 1354
  woodpeckers **22** 1300
pied-billed grebe **16** *955*, 956, 960
Pieridae **44** 2633, 2636, *2637*
Pieris brassicae **43** 2526; **44** 2633
pig family **5** 298; **10** *569*; **6** 301, 305, 307; **7** 363-72
pig frog **30** 1773
pig-footed bandicoot **11** 621
pig-nosed softshell turtle **26** 1526, 1553, *1555*
pig-rat **11** 621
pig-tailed macaque **14** *792*, 803, *804*, 805
pig-tailed snub-nosed monkey **14** 827, 830-1
pigeon guillemot **20** 1146, 1148
pigeons **16** *909*; **20** *1150-1*, 1152-3, *1154-60*
pika **4** 203-5, 207, 209; **51** 3036
pike **31** 1855; **32** *1862*; **33** *1992*
  classification **32** 1866; **33** 1923; **34** 1937
  predator **31** *1807*; **32** 1864; **33** *1939*; **34** *1997*
pike conger **32** 1882
pike topminnow **33** *1972*, 1976, 1978
pike-blennies **35** 2059
pikehead **35** 2071-2
pikeperch **34** 2015
Pila **46** 2712
pilchard **32** 1886, 1890
pileated gibbon **15** 842, 846, 848
pill bugs **37** 2201
pill millipedes **39** 2303, 2304, *2306*
pilot fish **34** 2036, 2038
pilot whale **10** 588, *592*
'Piltdown Man' hoax **15** 893-4
Pimelia **42** *2490-1*
Pimelodidae **32** 1913
Pimelodus **32** 1913
Pimpla investigator **43** 2522
pin-tailed parrot-finch **25** 1449
pin-tailed sandgrouse **20** *1150*, 1152
pin-tailed whydah **25** 1459, *1461*
Pinaroloxias inornata **24** 1429
Pinctada margaritifera **48** 2837
pine marten **1** 40, 43, *45-6*; **51** 3010, 3013
pine processionary moths **44** *2591*, 2622-3, *2625*
pine sawfly **42** 2516, *2519*, 2520
pine siskin **25** 1448
pine-tree thrips **41** 2428
pinecone fishes **34** *1988*, 1990
pink conch **46** 2730, *2732-3*
pink Mediterranean top shell **46** *2704*
pink salmon **33** 1924
pink shrimp **37** *2212*
pink-backed pelican **17** 980, 981
pink-footed goose **18** 1033, 1040
pink-footed shearwater **17** 976
pink/orange Mediterranean top shell **46** *2703*, *2704*
Pinna nobilis **48** *2832*, 2836-7
Pinnacea **48** 2837
Pinnidae **48** 2836-7
Pinnipedia **1** 28; **3** 164, 172, 179
PINNIPEDS **3** *161-80*; **4** *181-4*
Pinnixa **38** 2229-30
Pinnotheres pisum **37** *2203*
Pinnotheridae **38** 2229
Pinnotherion vermiforme **37** *2203*
pinon jay **25** 1489, *1490*
pintado petrel **17** *968*, *973*
pintail **18** 1044-5, *1046*, 1047
pinworm **49** 2929
Pinzon tortoise **26** 1544
Piona nodata **38** *2242*
Pipa pipa **30** 1769
pipefishes **34** *1996*, 1998-9, *2000-3*
pipesnakes **28** 1621, *1626-7*
Pipidae **30** 1769
piping guan **19** 1088
pipistrelle **12** *690*, *712*, *713*
Pipistrellus pipistrellus **12** 712
pipits **23** 1347, 1352, *1353-5*
Pipra filicauda **23** 1331
Pipridae **23** 1331
piranhas **32** *1907-9*
pirarucu **32** 1868
pirate bird **17** 993
pirate perch **33** 1948
piratic flycatcher **22** 1320
piraya **32** 1908

Piroplasmea **50** 2991, 2992-3
Pisauridae **39** 2283
Pisidium **48** 2847
pistol shrimp **37** *2211*
pit vipers **28** 1641, 1675, *1678-80*
classification **28** 1669, 1672
Pitangus sulphuratus **22** 1320
Pitar lupanarius **48** *2844*
Pithecanthropus erectus **15** 894, 899
Pithecia pithecia **13** 774
Pithecophaga jefferyi **18** 1070
Pitta **22** 1314
pittas **22** *1314-15*
classification **22** 1303, 1314
distribution **22** 1308
Pittidae **22** 1303, 1314
Pityriasididae **23** 1367
Pityriasis gymnocephala **23** 1367
Placiphorella
atlantica **45** 2684
velata **45** 2684, 2686
placoderm **31** 1807
Placostylus fibratus **48** 2822
Placozoa **48** 2874
Placuna placenta **48** 2842, 2843
Placunidae **48** 2841, 2842, 2843
plague flea **45** 2665, 2667
plaice **31** 1859; **35** 2073, 2075, *2076-8*
plain chachalaca **19** *1087*, 1088
plain xenops **22** 1310, *1313*
plain-brown woodcreeper **22** 1310
plain-headed creeper **24** 1412, 1415
plainfin midshipman **33** 1958
plains bison **8** 469, *477*, *480*
plains rat kangaroo **11** 642
plains spadefoot **30** 1768, 1769
plains viscacha **5** 285-7, 289; **8** 434
plains wanderer **19** 1107, 1117, 1118
plains zebra **6** 334-5, 338, *339*, 340
planarians **49** *2905*, 2909-2910
regeneration **49** *2904*
planigale **11** 617, 619
plankton **32** 1886
planktonic bristleworms **49** 2939; **50** 2942
planktonic larvae **50** 2945
Planorbidae **47** 2805, 2810
Planorbis **47** 2811, 2815
andecolus **47** 2815
carinatus **47** 2811
contortus **47** 2811, 2815
corneus **47** *2804*, *2811*
crista **47** 2811
montanus **47** 2815
planorbis **47** 2807
umbilicatus **47** *2811*
plant hoppers **41** 2438, 2447
plant-feeding beetles **42** *2505*
plant-lice **41** 2437, 2450, 2451
plantcutters **22** 1303, 1304; **23** 1322, 1325, *1330*
plantigrade species **1** 21, 25
Plasmodium **50** 2981, *2994-5*
falciparum **50** 2992, 2994-5
malarie **50** 2994
ovale **50** *2994*
vivax **50** 2981, 2992, 2994
plasmodium protistans **50** *2994-5*
Platacanthomyinae **5** 261
Platalea **17** 1018
Platambus maculatus **42** *2465*
Platanista gangetica **10** 593
Platanistidae **10** 593
plate-billed mountain toucan **22** *1280*, 1290
Platichthys flesus **35** *2080*
platy **34** *1982*
Platyarthrus **37** 2202
Platycephalidae **34** 2007
Platycephalus **34** 2007
Platycercus elegans **20** 1168
Platyctenida **49** 2901, 2902
Platyhelminthes **49** *2903-18*
Platylophus galericulatus **25** 1489
platypus **10** *597-60*; **11** *604-6*
platys **33** 1976, 1978
Platyspsyllus castons **41** 2454-5
Platysternidae **26** 1535
Platysternon megacephalum **26** 1535
Playmenis bigottata **41** *2435*
Plecoptera **39** 2311, 2338; **40** 2344
Plecotus auritus **12** 712
Plectrophenax nivalis **24** 1429
Plegadis falcinellus **17** 1018
Pleocyemata **37** 2212
pleopods **37** *2191*
plesiosaurs **26** *1507*
Plethodon **30** 1750
Plethodontidae **29** 1713; **30** 1750
Pleurobrachia **49** 2902
rhodopis **49** 2901
Pleurobranchidae **47** 2767, 2780
Pleurobranchus **47** *2783*
forskali **47** *2782*
mamillatus **47** 2781
membranaceus **47** 2780, *2781*
Pleurodeles waltl **29** 1729
Pleurodema bibroni **30** 1795
Pleurodira **26** 1530
Pleuronectes **35** 2075
Pleuronectidae **35** 2074-5, 2078
Pleuronectiformes **31** 1858; **35** *2073-80*
Pleuroprocta **47** 2799
Pleurotomaria **45** *2694*
africana **45** 2697, 2698
hirasei **46** *2704*
Pleurotomariacea **45** 2697-8
Pleurotomariidae **45** 2697
Pliny the Elder **15** 859; **32** 1878
Pliocene period **1** 25
Pliohippus **6** 333
Pliotrema **31** 1841
Plisthenes ventralis **41** *2439*
Ploceidae **22** 1303; **25** 1459
Ploceinae **25** 1459
Ploceus **25** 1459
ploughnose chimaera **31** 1846
plovers **16** 914; **19** 1121, *1125-6*, 1127, 1135; **51** 3046
plumbeous kite **18** 1072
plume moths **44** 2604, 2609, *2611-12*
plumed scorpionfish **34** 2007
plunderfishes **35** 2055-6
plush-capped finch **24** 1429, 1431
Pluvialis **19** 1125
Pluvianellidae **19** 1121, 1125
Pluvianellus socialis **19** 1125
Pluvianus aegypticus **19** 1137
Pneumocystis **50** 2993
Pneumoderma atlanticum **47** 2784, 2786
Pneumodermatidae **47** 2784, 2786
Pneumodermopsis ciliata **47** 2784
pochard **18** 1047, 1048
pocket gopher **4** *220-1*, 233, *235*, 238-9
pocket mouse **4** 233
pod razor shell **48** 2848, *2850*
Podarcis muralis **27** 1603
Podargidae **21** 1206, 1214
Podargus strigoides **21** 1214
Podica senegalensis **19** 1114
Podiceps **16** 960
Podicipedidae **16** 960
Podicipediformes **16** *955-60*
Podilymbus podiceps **16** 960
Podocnemis expansa **26** 1530
Podocopa **37** 2161
Podura aquatica **39** *2331*, 2332, 2333
Poecilia **33** 1978
Poecilictis lybica **1** 47
Poeciliidae **33** 1978
Poecilogale albinucha **1** 47
Poecilostomatoida **37** 2163
Poelagus marjorita **4** 209
Poephila guttata **25** 1453
Pogoniulus chrysoconus **22** 1288
Pogonophora **50** *2971-2*
Poiana richardsoni **2** 89
poison-arrow frogs **29** 1701, *1706*; **30** 1776-9, *1780-81*
classification **30** 1756, 1785
Poland, national park **51** 3002, *3006-7*
polar bear **2** *69-70*, *76-7*, 78, 80
distribution **2** 71
polecat **1** *20*, *37*, *45*, 56
classification **1** 46
predator **1** 40, 41, *42*
reproduction **1** 48
Polihierax semitorquatus **18** 1080
Poliocephalus **16** 960
Polioptila caerulea **24** 1392
Polioptilidae **24** 1392
Polish swan **18** 1039
Polistes gallicus **43** 2528, 2529, *2533*
Polistinae **43** 2528, 2529
Pollachius **33** 1951
pollack **33** 1951, 1952
pollan **33** 1934
Polyartemia forcipata **36** 2156
Polyboroides typus **18** 1070
Polyboroidinae **18** 1070
Polyborus plancus **18** 1080
Polybranchia **50** 2971
Polycentropis abbreviata **35** 2044
Polycera **47** *2790-4*
Polyceratidae **47** 2790
Polychaeta **49** 2937; **50** 2941-9
polychaete worms **50** *2941-2*
Polychaetes **45** 2670
POLYCHAETES **50** *2941-56*
Polycladida **49** 2905, *2908*, *2909*, *2910-11*
Polyctenidae **41** 2437
Polycystina **50** 2991
Polydesmidae **39** 2304
Polydon spathula **31** 1856
Polyergus **43** 2529
Polygonia c-album **44** 2633
Polyhymenophora **50** 2992, 2997, 2999
Polyipnus **33** 1944
Polymita picta **47** *2804*
Polyodontidae **31** 1856
Polyorchis **49** *2886*
Polyphaga **41** 2456; **42** 2471-2, 2503, 2506
Polyphylla fullo **42** *2501*, 2503
Polyplacophora **45** *2673*, 2674, 2679, 2684, 2686
Polyprotodonta **11** 612
polyps **49** *2284*, 2888-90, *2897-8*
coral **49** *2884-6*, *2893-5*, *2899-2901*
reproduction **49** 2887, *2892-3*
Polypteridae **31** 1850
Polypteriformes **31** 1850
Polypterus bichir **31** 1850
Polystoma intergerrimum **49** 2912
Polystomella **50** *2980*
Polyzoniidae **39** 2304
Pomacanthidae **34** 2024
Pomacanthus **34** 2024
Pomacentridae **34** 2013, 2024
Pomatia **46** 2708; **47** 2801
Pomatias elegans **46** *2704*, *2708*, 2712
Pomatiasidae **46** 2706
Pomatomidae **34** 2036
Pomatoschistus microps **35** 2060
pompadour cotinga **23** 1322, 1324, *1330*
pompanos **34** 2038
Pompilidae **43** 2537, 2540
Pompilus viaticus **43** 2537, 2540
pond skaters **39** 2322; **41** 2438, *2440*
pond snails **47** 2803, *2804*, 2805, *2807-9*, *2814-15*
Pongidae **14** 839; **15** 852
PONGIDS **14** 837-40; **15** *847-90*
Pongo pygmaeus **15** 852
Pontoporia blainvillei **10** 593
pony **6** 348
pool frog **29** *1700*
poorwill **21** *1203*, 1206, 1207
Pope's tree viper **28** *1680*
porbeagle shark **31** 1832, 1834, 1839
Porcellana platycheles **38** *2224*
Porcellio **37** *2200*
porcupine **5** *272*, 273-8, 283
porcupine fishes **32** 1863; **35** *2081-3*, 2085
Porichthys **33** 1958
Porifera **48** *2875-80*
pork tapeworm **49** 2911, 2917
Porodoridacea **47** 2796
Poromyacea **48** 2848, 2850
Porphyrio **19** 1112
porpoises **10** 572, 584, 588, *589*
classification **10** 593
Port Jackson shark **31** 1828
Portuguese man-of-war **49** 2889, *2890-92*
Portunidae **38** 2225
Portunus pelagicus **38** *2224*
Porzana **19** 1112
possums **11** 624-7
postman butterfly **44** 2633, 2639
Potamidae **38** 2229
Potamochoerus porcus **7** 370
Potamogale velox **11** 651
Potamogalinae **11** 651
Potamon edulis **38** 2229
Potamopyrgus **46** 2713
jenkinsi **46** 2712
Potamotrygon **31** 1844
Potamotrygonidae **31** 1844
potoo **21** *1202*, 1203, *1213*
classification **21** 1206, 1214
distribution **21** 1204
Potoroidae **11** 612, 642
potoroo rat kangaroo **11** *635*, 642
Potosia cuprea **42** 2495
potter wasps **43** 2527-8, 2529, *2532*, *2536*
potto **13** 722, 733, *744*, *751-2*

classification **13** 728, 742, 748; **15** *896*
distribution **13** 739
evolution **13** *727*
pouched animals **11** *607-44*
pouched rat **5** *245*, 248
Pourtalesia jeffreysi **36** 2120
pouter pigeon **20** 1158
powan **33** *1922*
prairie chicken **19** 1092, *1095*, 1096
prairie dog **4** 221, *227-9*, 233, 235
pratincoles **19** 1121, *1136*, 1137-8; **51** 3008
prawns **36** 2147; **37** *2184-5*, *2191*, *2192*, *2213*, 2219
praying mantis **39** 2323; **40** 2391, *2396*, 2397, *2398*
precious wentletrap **46** 2712, 2721, *2726*
predatory snails **48** 2822
prehensile-tail lizard **27** 1587
prehensile-tailed porcupine **5** *276*, 277, 283
Presbytis **14** 826
Priacanthidae **34** 2024
Priacanthus arentus **34** 2024
pricklebacks **35** 2056-7
prickly cockle **48** *2846*
PRIMATES **12-15** *717-900*
classification **13** 728; **15** 896-7
evolution **12** 719-20; **13** 721-2, *726-8*; **15** 892-5, *899-900*
features **13** *723-8*
primitive hexapods **39** 2328
primitive nutshell **48** *2832*, *2835*
primitive snails **47** 2803, 2805
primitive sponges **50** 3000
primitive-looking spiders **39** 2289
Prince Ruspoli's turaco **20** 1173
Princess Stephanie's bird of paradise **25** 1481
Prinotus carolinus **34** 2007
Priodontes maximus **4** 197
Prionace glauca **31** 1839
Prionodon pardicolor **2** 89
Prionodura newtoniana **25** 1476
Prionopidae **23** 1367
Prionops plumata **23** 1367
prions **17** 962, 971-2, 973, 976
Prionus coriarius **42** 2506, 2512
Pristidae **31** 1842
Pristiloma **47** 2816
Pristiophoridae **31** 1841
Pristiophorus **31** 1841
Pristis pectinata **31** 1842
Proboscidea **6** 304, 324
Probosciger atterimus **20** 1168
proboscis bat **12** 697, 704
proboscis monkey **14** 794, *824*, 827, *830*, 831
proboscis worms **49** 2918, *2919-20*
Procambarus **37** 2220
Procapra **9** 529
Procavia **6** 313
Procellaria westlandica **17** 973
Procellariformes **17** *961-76*
Procellariidae **17** 971, 973
Procereae **50** *2942*
processionary moths **44** *2591*, 2622-3, 2624, *2625*
Procnias tricarunculata **23** 1322
Procolobus **14** 836
proctodeal feeding **41** 2408
Proctotrupidae **42** 2516
Proctotrupoidea **43** 2526
proctotrypid wasps **42** 2516; **43** 2526
Procyonidae **1** 28
PROCYONIDS **1-2** *57-68*
Prodotiscus insignis **22** 1288
Progne subis **23** 1345
Promerops cafer **24** 1420
prominent moths **44** 2615, 2624
Proneomenia aglaopheniae **45** *2690*
prong-billed barbet **22** 1287, 1288
pronghorn **6** 305; **8** *431-3*, 434; **10** *568*
Pronolagus **4** 209
Propithecus **13** 742
PROSIMIANS **13** 723, *731-54*; **15** 896
classification **13** 728
distribution **13** 736, 739
evolution **13** 721-2, *727*
Prosimii **13** 728, 742
Prosobranchia **45** 2674, 2680, *2682*, 2694, 2697; **46** 2706, 2712, 2720, 2737
PROSOBRANCHS **45-47** *2693-2766*
Prosopis **43** 2539
Prosthemadera novaeseelandiae **24** 1420
Prostigmata **39** 2295
Protapirus **6** 350
Proteidae **29** 1713; **30** 1745
proteids **30** 1742-3, *1744*, 1745
Proteles cristatus **2** 102
Protelidae **1** 28; **2** 102
PROTELIDS **2** *99-102*
Proterospongiae **50** 3000
Proteus anguinus **30** 1745
Protichneumon pisorius **42** *2519*
Protista **50** 2976
PROTISTANS **50** *2974-3000*
cytoplasm **50** *2988*
evolution **50** 2999-3000
physiology **50** *2976-94*
Proto marina **37** *2207*
Protobranchia **48** 2833
Protopteridae **31** 1850
Protopterus **31** 1850
Protorthoptera **40** 2387
protostomes **50** 2966-7
PROTOZOANS **36** 2103; **50** 2975
Protrocophora **45** *2670*
Protura **39** 2298, 2328, 2333
proturans **39** 2311, *2328-9*, 2333
Prunella **24** 1383
Prunellidae **24** 1383
Prynichus reniformis **38** *2242*
Przewalski (explorer) **8** 477
Przewalski's gazelle **9** 525, 529
Przewalski's horse **6** *331-2*, *345*, 347-8
classificaton **6** 340
distribution **6** 335
Psaltriparus minimus **24** 1403
Psammobates geometricus **26** 1544
Psammostyela delamarei **35** 2094
Psarisomus dalhousiae **22** 1307
Psarocolius montezuma **24** 1440
Pselaphognatha **39** 2302, 2304
Psephurus gladius **31** 1856
Psettodids **35** 2074
Pseudacteon albus **47** 2771
Pseudaletia unipuncta **44** 2591
Pseudemys scripta **26** 1539
pseudid frogs **30** 1785-6
Pseudidae **30** 1786
Pseudis paradoxa **30** 1786
Pseudisidora rubella **47** 2806
Pseudobalistes fuscus **35** *2087*
Pseudobranchus striatus **30** 1754
Pseudocalyptomena graueri **22** 1307
Pseudocarcharias **31** 1839
Pseudocheiridae **11** 612, 627
Pseudocheirus peregrinus **11** 627
Pseudochelidininae **23** 1345
Pseudochelidon **23** 1345
Pseudocordylus microlepidotus **27** 1598
Pseudocreobotra wahlbergi **40** *2398*
Pseudois nayaur **10** 570
pseudophryn frogs **30** 1799-1800
Pseudophyllidae **40** 2369
Pseudopodoces humilis **25** 1489
Pseudorca crassidens **10** 593
Pseudosacculidae **46** 2727
Pseudoscorpiones **38** 2241
pseudoscorpions **38** *2242*, *2250*, *2251-2*
Pseudothecosomata **47** 2782
Pseudotriton **30** 1750
Pseudotropheus
tropheops **35** 2050, *2051*
zebra **35** 2049
Pseudovermidae **47** 2799
Psilorhinus morio **25** 1489
Psittacidae **20** 1168
Psittaciformes **20** *1161-70*
Psittacula krameri **20** 1168
Psittacus erithacus **20** 1168
psocids **41** 2431-2
Psocoptera **39** 2311; **41** *2431-2*
Psolus **36** 2121
Psophia **19** 1117
Psophiidae **19** 1107, 1117
Psychidae **44** 2602, 2609
Psychodidae **45** 2646, 2647; **50** 2985
Psylla pyricola **41** *2450*
Psyllidae **41** 2450
Psylliodes **42** 2504
ptarmigan **19** *1092*, *1093*, 1094; **51** 3011, 3037
Pteraphorus **44** *2604*, 2609
Pteria hirundo **48** *2832*
Pteriidae **48** 2837
Pteriomorpha **48** 2833, 2835, 2837, 2843
Pterobranchia **50** 2971-3
Pterobranchs **50** 2971-3
Pterocles **20** 1152
Pteroclididae **20** 1152
Pteroclidiformes **20** *1149-1152*
Pterocnemia pennata **16** 925
pterodactyls **16** 905
Pterodroma **17** 973
Pteroglossus **22** 1290
Pterois volitans **34** 2007
Pteronarcidae **39** 2338
Pteronura brasiliensis **1** 55
Pterophoroidea **44** 2609
Pterophyllum **35** 2049
Pteropodocys maxima **23** 1357
pteropods **45** 2680
Pteropopidae **12** 681, 694
Pteroptyx malaccae **42** 2472, 2480
Pteropus poliocephalus **12** 694
pterosaurs **16** 905; **26** *1507*, 1508-9; **29** 1682
Pterotracheidae **46** 2735
Pterygota **39** 2311
Pterygotus **38** 2237
Ptilnopus superbus **20** 1156
Ptilocercinae **13** 730
Ptilocercus lowii **13** 730
Ptilogonatidae **23** 1372
Ptilogonys caudatus **23** 1372
Ptilonorhynchidae **25** 1476
Ptilonorhyncus violaceus **25** 1476
Ptiloris magnificus **25** 1480
Ptilostomus afer **25** 1489
Ptychoptera contaminata **45** *2644*
Ptychozoon homalocephalum **27** 1569
Ptynoprogne rupestris **23** 1345
pubic louse **41** 2428, *2431*
pudu **7** *390*, 398, *413*, 417, 418
Pudu **7** 418
Puerto Rican bat **12** 703
Puerto Rican live-bearing frog **30** 1795
Puerto Rican whip-poor-will **21** 1206-7
puff adder **28** 1669, *1672-3*
puffbirds **22** *1280*, 1282, 1283-4
pufferfishes **35** 2081-2, *2083-5*
puffin **20** 1145, 1146, *1147*, 1148
Puffinus **17** 973
puku **9** 510, 514
Pulex irritans **45** 2665, 2666, 2667
Pulicidac **45** 2665
Pulicoidea **45** 2665
pullet carpet shell **48** 2847
Pulmonata **45** 2674, 2680, 2694, 2697; **47** *2800-20*
puma **1** *19*, 20, 60; **3** 134-5, 139, 140-1, *153*; **51** *3040*, 3044
pumpkinseed fish **34** 2014, *2016*, 2017
Puna flamingo **18** 1024
Pungitus pungitus **34** 1993
pupfish **33** 1973
Pupilla **47** *2818*, 2819
pupilloid snail **47** *2818*
purple emperor butterfly **44** *2634*
purple grackle **24** 1440
purple heron **17** 1000, 1007; **51** 3008
purple honeycreeper **24** 1429
purple martin **23** *1345*, 1346
purple swamp hen **19** *1112*, 1115
purple-breasted cotinga **23** *1330*
purple-faced leaf monkey **14** *824*, 826
purple-spotted top shell **46** 2703
purple-throated carib **21** *1236*
purple-throated sunbird **24** *1413*
Purpuricenus **42** 2512
koehleri **39** *2315*
purse-making caddisflies **43** 2580; **44** 2581-2
purse-web spider **39** 2283
puss moth **44** 2594, *2596*, *2600*, *2615*, 2624
Pycnogonida **38** 2234, 2241; **39** 2298
Pycnogyra berendti **47** 2816
Pycnonotidae **23** 1359
Pycnonotus **23** 1359
Pygarrhicas albogularis **22** 1310
Pygathrix **14** 831
pygmy...
antelope **8** 438-9, 444
blue whale **10** 579
chameleon **27** 1592
chimpanzee **14** 838; **15** *847*, 866, 867, 869, *888-90*
classification **15** 852
distribution **15** 848
cormorant **17** 990; **51** 3014
falcon **18** *1055*, 1079, 1080

fox **3** 121-2, 127
geese **18** 1048-9
goby **35** 2060
hippopotamus **7** 374, *377*, 378; **51** 3020
hog **7** 365, 366, 370, 372
marmoset **13** *756*; **14** *783*, 786, 790
mole cricket **40** 2369
moths **44** 2595, 2600
owl **20** *1184*, 1198, *1199*; **51** 3007
parrots **20** 1163, 1168
possums **11** 612, 627
rattlesnake **28** 1669
right whale **10** 577
salamander **30** 1751
scaly-tailed squirrel **4** 233
shark **31** 1839
shrew **1** 8, 9, 11
skunk **1** 55
sperm whale **10** *581*, 592
classification **10** 593
squid **48** *2866*, 2869
sunfish **34** 2014, 2016
white-toothed shrew **11** *648*; **12** *661*, 662
woodpecker **51** 3060
Pygocentrus piraya **32** 1908
Pygopodidae **27** 1570
Pygopus nigriceps **27** 1570
Pygora **42** 2493
Pygoscelis **16** 949
pyralids **44** 2611-13
Pyraloidea **44** 2609, 2611-12
pyramid shells **45** 2678; **46** 2720, 2722
Pyramidella **45** 2678
Pyramidellidae **46** 2720, 2722
Pyrenean brook salamander **29** 1740; **30** *1741*
Pyrenean chamois **10** 543, 548, 549
Pyrenean desman **12** 670, *672*
Pyrenean ibex **10** 553
Pyrocephalus rubinus **22** 1320
Pyrosoma **35** 2099
PYROSOMIDS **35** 2099
Pyrrhococoridae **41** 2438, 2441
Pyrrhocorax pyrrhocorax **25** 1489
Pyrrhocoris apterus **41** 2438, 2441
Pyrrhosoma nymphula **40** *2355*
Pyrrhula pyrrhula **25** 1442
pyrrhuloxia **24** *1426*
Python **28** 1637
Pythoninae **28** 1637
pythons **27** 1618, *1620*; **28** *1624*, 1626, *1628-36*
classification **28** 1621, 1637
distribution **28** 1628-9
PYURIDS **35** 2094
Pyxicephalus adspersus **30** 1778
Pyxis arachnoides **26** 1544

Quadraspidotus perniciosus **42** 2486
quagga (extinct) **6** *338*
quail-thrush **24** 1390
quails **19** *1086*, 1088, 1096-7, 1098, 1099-1100
Queen Alexandra's birdwing **44** *2636*
queen parrotfish **34** *2012*, 2023
queen scallop **48** *2832*, 2834, 2837
queen triggerfish **35** 2082, **36** 2127
queen viana **45** 2700; **46** 2705
Queensland grouper **34** 2022-3
Queensland monitor **27** 1614
Queensland Rain Forest parks **51** 3002, *3048-9*
Quelea quelea **25** 1459, 1460
quetzals **21** *1240*, *1244-5*; **51** 3044
quinnat **33** 1924
Quiscalus quiscula **24** 1440
quokka **11** *636*, 642, 644
quoll **11** *608*, 617, 619

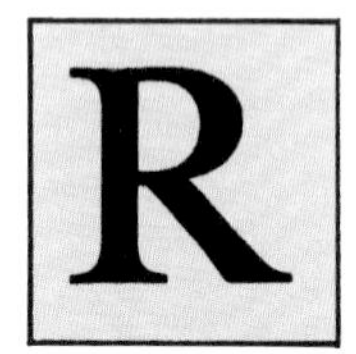

rabbitfishes **31** *1846*; **35** 2066-7
rabbits **1** 39, 40, 50; **4** *202-4*, 205-6, *212-13*, *214*
classification **4** 209
distribution **4** 207
rabudos **5** 289
raccoon **1** *30-1*, *57-8*, 59, *60*; **2** 62, *64-5*
classification **1** 28
raccoon dog **2** *110*; **3** 127, *130-1*
racer snakes **28** 1645, 1658, *1660*
racerunners **27** 1600-1, 1603
Radde's accentor **24** 1383
Radianthus **34** 2029
radiated tortoise **26** 1545
radiolaria **50** *2980*
radiolarians **50** 2988, *2990-1*
raft spiders **38** *2256*, *2275*, *2279*; **39** 2281, 2283
rafter spiders **39** 2289
ragged-tooth sharks **31** 1832
Raggiana bird of paradise **25** *1479*, 1480, 1482-3
ragworms **49** 2939
rail babblers **24** 1390
railroad worm **42** 2481
rails **19** 1105, 1108, *1112*, 1113
classification **19** 1107, 1112
distribution **19** 1106
rain forest butterflies **39** *2326*
rainbow bee-eater **22** *1267*, 1270
rainbow boas **28** 1637, 1639, *1641*
rainbow lorikeet **20** *1162*, 1164, *1168*
rainbow parrotfish **34** 2023
Rainbow Snake **28** 1632
rainbow trout **31** *1821*; **32** 1866; **33** 1931, *1934-5*
classification **33** 1924
rainbow wrasse **34** *2012*, 2023
rainbowfishes **33** 1964; **34** 1982, *1984*
Raja **31** 1842

ABOVE **A resplendent quetzal nesting in the cloud forests of Costa Rica.**

rajah butterflies **44** 2640
Rajidae **31** 1842
Rajiformes **31** 1842
Rallidae **19** 1107, 1112
Rallus aquaticus **19** 1112
ram cichlid **35** *2049*
Ramapithecus **15** 895
Ramphastidae **22** 1290
Ramphastos **22** 1290
Ramphocaerus melanurus **24** 1392
Ramphocinclus brachyurus **23** 1380
ramshorn cuttlefish **48** *2854*, *2857*, 2858
ramshorn snails **47** 2805, *2810-11*, 2815
Rana **30** 1778
Ranatra linearis **41** *2443-4*
Rangifer tarandus **7** 396, 418
Ranidae **30** 1756, 1778
Raphicerus **8** 444
Raphidia notata **43** *2567*, *2568*, 2570
Raphidiidae **43** 2568
Raphidoptera **39** 2311; **43** 2566, *2568*, 2570
raptors **18** 1057
rasbora **32** *1900*
rat fleas **45** 2665, 2667
rat kangaroos **11** 612, 634, 636, 642
rat snake **28** 1645, *1659*, 1661
rat-tail fish **33** 1948, 1951, *1955-6*
rat-tailed maggot **45** 2656-7
ratel **51** 3026
ratfishes **31** 1846
Rathousiidae **47** 2817
RATITES **16** *917-27*
rats **4** 218; **5** 243, *255-8*
classification **5** 254
rattlesnakes **26** *1512*, *1516*, *1518*; **28** *1668*, *1678-80*
classification **28** 1669, 1672
snake prey **28** 1653, 1659
Rattus norvegicus **48** 2827
raven **25** *1484*, 1485, *1488*, 1498, *1499*; **51** 3013
classification **25** 1489
ray-finned fish **31** 1809
rays **31** 1808, *1838*, *1841-6*
cartilaginous fishes **31** 1806
classification **31** 1827, 1842, 1844
lateral line **31** 1828
reproduction **31** 1814, 1843; **32** 1866
razor shell **48** *2844*, 2848
razor-billed curassow **19** *1087*
razorbill **20** 1145, *1146*, 1148
rear-fanged snakes **28** 1641, 1645, 1647-8
Recurvirostra **19** 1137
Recurvirostridae **19** 1121, 1137
red...
admiral butterfly **39** *2309*; **44** *2591*, 2633, *2638*; **51** 3056
ants **43** 2555-6
avadavat **25** 1452-3, *1454*
bat **12** 688, *690*
beetle **42** 2504
bird of paradise **25** 1478
bishop **25** *1454*, *1459*
boarfish **34** 1990
brocket **7** 418
buffalo **8** 467
bugs **39** 2297

colobus **14** 830, 834, 836; **51** 3020
comb starfish **36** *2132*
coral **49** 2900
cornetfish **34** 1999-2000
crossbill **51** 3056
deer **6** 308; **7** *389*, 396, *397*, *399-400*, 405-7, 411; **8** 421
deer, national parks **51** 3010, *3011*, 3013, 3050
dhole **3** *129-30*
fox **2** 111, 119; **3** 121, *124-5*, 127, 128
goral **9** 538; **10** 550
goshawk **18** 1065
grouse **19** 1092, 1093, 1094
guenon **14** 821
gurnard **34** 2007
hartebeest **9** 486-7
hawk-moth **44** *2604*
howler monkey **13** *766-7*, 774, *775*, 780; **51** 3038-9
junglefowl **19** 1096, 1098
kangaroo **11** *607*, 609, 635, *638-9*, *642*, 644; **51** 3046, 3048
kite **18** 1070, 1072
knot **19** 1135
lechwe **9** 512
lizardfish **33** 1946
lynx **3** *142*, 143
mites **39** *2296*, 2298
mullet **34** *2012*, *2032*, 2033
munia **25** 1453
nose **48** *2844*
oak roller **42** 2506, *2508-9*
panda **1** 28, *58*; **2** 62, *67-8*
piranha **32** *1908*
poplar leaf beetle **42** 2506, *2507*
rockhare **4** 209
salamander **29** 1704, *1712*; **30** 1750, 1751
salmon **33** 1924
sea bream **34** 2033
sea squirt **35** 2094, *2095*
shiner **32** 1892
slug **47** *2804*
squirrel **4** *215-16*, *220*, *222-3*, 234; **51** 3010
distribution **4** 221
tailed pipesnake **28** 1626-7
titi monkey **13** 774
uakari **13** *768-9*, 772, 774
underwing butterfly **44** *2596*
underwing moth **44** 2617, 2624
velvet mites **39** *2293*
wolf **2** 117
Red River hog **7** 367, 370
Red Sea butterfly fish **31** *1857*
red-and-blue poison-arrow frog **30** 1779, 1785
red-back spider **38** 2277; **39** *2282*
red-backed mousebird **21** 1246
red-backed salamander **30** 1750
red-backed shrike **22** *1303*; **23** *1363*, *1366*, 1367
red-backed squirrel monkey **13** 768, *771*
red-bellied lemur **13** 742, 745
red-bellied newt **29** 1739, *1740*
red-bellied sureli **14** 826
red-bellied toad **30** 1760, 1762
red-billed chough **25** 1489
red-billed dwarf hornbill **22** 1274, *1276-7*, 1278
red-billed oxpecker **25** 1462
red-billed quelea **25** 1459, 1460
red-billed scythebill **22** 1308, 1310, *1311*
red-billed tropicbird **17** *979-80*
red-billed woodcreeper **22** 1310
red-blooded annelids **50** 2948
red-blotched shieldtail snake **28** 1626
red-breasted flycatcher **24** 1400
red-breasted meadowlark **24** 1440
red-breasted merganser **18** *1050*, 1051, 1052
red-breasted plantcutter **23** 1325, *1330*
red-breasted pygmy parrot **20** 1168
red-breasted wryneck **22** 1297, 1299
red-browed treecreeper **24** 1415
red-cheeked cordon-bleu **25** *1453*
red-chested buttonquail **19** 1114
red-collared widow **25** 1460
red-cowled cardinal **24** *1428*
red-crested cardinal **24** *1426*
red-crested pochard **18** 1047, *1048*; **51** 3008
red-crested turaco **20** 1174, 1178
red-crowned crane **19** 1107
red-eared turtle **26** 1538, 1539
red-eyed dove **20** 1156
red-eyed tree frog **26** *1502*; **30** *1794*
red-eyed vireo **24** *1435*
red-faced banana spider **38** 2277
red-faced lovebird **20** 1163
red-faced mousebird **21** 1246, 1247, *1248*
red-footed booby **17** 992, 994
red-footed falcon **18** 1080; **19** 1081, 1083; **51** 3014
red-footed tortoise **26** *1542*
red-fronted bombardier beetles **42** 2462
red-fronted gazelle **9** *524*, 529
red-fronted lemur **13** *736*
red-fronted thornbird **22** 1312-3
red-handed howler monkey **13** *762*
red-handed tamarin **14** 790
red-headed barbet **22** 1287
red-headed finch **25** 1453
red-headed krait **28** *1668*
red-headed rockfowl **24** 1392
red-headed weaver **25** 1455, 1458, 1459
red-headed woodpecker **22** *1297*, *1298*, 1300
red-hills salamander **30** 1751
red-jawed spider **38** 2272
red-knobbed coot **19** 1112, *1113*
red-legged cormorant **17** *978*
red-legged falconet **18** *1054*
red-legged honeycreeper **24** *1429*
red-legged partridge **19** 1096, 1097, *1099*
red-legged seriema **19** 1117
red-naped trogon **21** *1240*, 1241
red-necked grebe **16** *956*, 960
red-necked nightjar **21** 1206
red-necked phalarope **19** 1131, *1134*, 1135
red-rumped jumping spider **38** *2261*
red-rumped swallow **23** *1343*, 1345, 1346
red-shanked douc **14** *824*, *827*, 831
red-spotted newt **29** *1712*
red-striped ribbon snake **28** *1642*
red-tailed comet **21** *1231*
red-tailed greenbul **23** *1358*
red-tailed phascogale **11** 617
red-tailed shark **31** *1808*
red-tailed tropicbird **17** *978*, 980
red-throated diver **16** 952-3, 955
classification **16** 954
red-throated loon **16** 955
red-vented bulbul **23** 1359
red-whiskered bubul **23** *1358*, 1359
red-winged blackbird **24** 1440
red-winged crested cuckoo **20** *1172*
red-winged tinamou **16** 934
redbellied batfish **33** *1961*
redfin parrotfish **34** 2026
redfin pickerel **33** 1938
redfish (*Sciaena*) **34** 2032, 2033
redfish (*Sebastes*) **34** 2007
redia **49** *2911*
redmouth whalefishes **34** 1988, 1990
redpoll **25** 1446
redshank **19** *1128*, 1135; **51** 3008
redstart **24** 1382, *1384-5*, 1387-8
redtail monkey **14** 816
Redunca **9** 510
Reduncini **8** 434; **9** 490, 503-16
Reduviidae **41** 2437-8
redwing **51** 3007
reed bunting **24** *1422*
reed snake **28** 1644
reed warbler **20** *1177*; **22** 1305; **24** *1392*, 1394, 1395
reedbuck **9** 490, 503-5, 508, 515-16; **51** 3022
classification **8** 434; **9** 510; **10** *569*
reedfish **31** 1850, *1852*, 1853
reef building coral **49** *2894-5*
reef shark **31** 1839
reef squid **48** 2861, *2862*
Reeve's muntjac **7** 395, 396
Reeve's sundial **46** 2712, 2716
Reeve's turtle **26** 1540
regal horned lizard **27** 1573
Regalecidae **34** 1987
Regalecus glesne **34** 1987
regent bowerbird **16** *910*; **25** *1473*, 1475, 1476; **51** 3049
Regulus regulus **24** 1394
Reichenow's weaver **25** 1458
reindeer **1** 41, 46; **6** 307; **7** 394, *416*, 419, *420*; **8** *421-4*
classification **7** 396, 418
distribution **7** 414
national parks **51** 3036, 3052
Remiropsis pallidus **35** 2046-7
Remiz pendulinus **24** 1403
Remizidae **24** 1403
Remora **31** *1830*
australis **35** 2046, 2048
osteochir **35** 2048
remora **53** 2046
remoras **31** *1830*; **34** 2013; **35** *2046-8*
reproduction
birds **16** *912-14*
mammals **1** 14-16
reptiles **26** 1514-17
sex change fishes **34** 2023
viviparous fish **34** 1982
REPTILES **1** 11, 14, 16; **26-29** *1501-1695*
classification **26** 1510
defence techniques **26** 1520-2
diet/feeding habits **26** 1517-19
eye and vision **26** 1513-14
heart and breathing **26** 1514
intelligence **26** 1511-12
lizard features **27** 1562-5
nervous system **26** 1510-11
origin/evolution **26** 1506-9
reproduction **26** 1514-17
scales and skin **26** 1509-10
senses and smell **26** 1512-13
skeleton **26** 1509-10

ABOVE A black rhino collects foliage using its prehensile upper lip.

  temperature **26** 1519-20
requiem sharks **31** 1835, 1839
resplendent quetzal **21** *1240*, 1241 *1244-5*; **51** 3044
reticulated gecko **51** 3043
reticulated giraffe **8** *425*, 428, 430
reticulated python **27** 1618, *1620*; **28** 1629, *1630-1*, 1633
  classification **28** 1637
Rhabditia **49** 2925
Rhabdopleura **50** 2971-2
Rhabdornis inornatus **24** 1412
Rhabdosoma **37** *2206*, 2207
Rhacophoridae **30** 1756, 1785
Rhacophorus nigropalmatus **30** 1785
Rhamphichthyidae **32** 1920
Rhamphichthys rostratus **32** 1920
Rhamphochromis longiceps **35** *2049*, 2050
Rhamphotyphlops braminus **28** 1625
Rhea americana **16** 925
rheas **16** 918, *923-4*, 925, *926-7*
Rheidae **16** 925
Rheiformes **16** 925
rhesus macaque **12** *718*; **14** 793, 801, 803; **51** 3028
rhesus monkey **14** *800-1*, 802-5
rhim **9** 529
Rhincodon typus **31** 1839
Rhincodontidae **31** 1839
Rhinecanthus **35** 2082, 2087
Rhineuridae **27** 1616
Rhinobatidae **31** 1842
Rhinobatus rhinobatus **31** 1842
Rhinoceros **7** 361
rhinoceros beetles **42** *2498*, 2499-2501, 2503
rhinoceros iguana **27** 1579
rhinoceroses **5** 298-9, *300*; **6** 353-60; **7** 361-2; **10** *568*
  national parks **51** 3022, *3026-7*, 3032
Rhinocerotidae **7** 361
RHINOCEROTIDS **6** *353-60*; **7** *361-2*
Rhinochimaeridae **31** 1846
Rhinocryptidae **22** 1314
Rhinoderma darwini **30** 1799
Rhinodermatidae **30** 1799
Rhinolophidae **12** 681, 704
Rhinolophus **12** 704
Rhinophrynidae **30** 1769
Rhinophyrnus dorsalis **30** 1769
Rhinopoma microphyllum **12** 704
Rhinopomastus cyanomelas **22** 1270
Rhinopomatidae **12** 681, 704
Rhinotermitidae **41** 2405, 2406
Rhinura floridana **27** 1616
Rhipidodendron splendidum **50** *2980*
Rhipidura javanica **24** 1400
Rhizocephala **37** 2174, 2177-8
Rhizocrinus lofotensis **36** *2117*
Rhizomastigida **50** *2974*
Rhizomyinae **5** 254, 255
Rhizopoda **50** 2991
Rhodeus sericeus **32** 1894
Rhodinocicla rosea **24** 1429
Rhodostethia rosea **20** 1142
rhombic egg-eating snake **28** 1644, 1645, 1646
Rhomboidella columbiana **48** 2840
Rhomborrhina **42** 2495, 2503
Rhopalodina lageniformis **36** *2117*, 2121
Rhyacophilidae **43** 2580; **44** 2581
Rhyacophiloidea **43** 2580; **44** 2581
Rhyacotriton olympicus **29** 1722
Rhynchites auratus **42** 2506, 2514
Rhynchobdellae **50** 2958
Rhynchocephalia **26** 1510, 1557-60
Rhynchocyon chrysopygus **11** 660
Rhyncholestes raphanurus **11** 624
Rhynchomeles prattorum **11** 620
Rhynchonycteris naso **12** 704
Rhyncophtherina **41** 2428
Rhyncota **41** 2434
Rhyniella praecursor **39** *2330*
Rhynochetidae **19** 1107, 1117
Rhynochetos jubatus **19** 1117
Rhyssa persuasoria **42** 2516; **43** *2521*, 2522, *2523*
ribbon seal **4** *182*, 184
ribbon-tailed bird of paradise **25** 1480, 1483
ribbonfishes **34** 1986-8, *1996*
ribbontail ray **31** *1843*, 1844
rice eel **34** 2006
rice tenrec **11** 651, 652
rice-field salamander **29** 1723
'ricebird' **24** 1440
ricefishes **33** 1965
Ricinoides **39** 2290
Ricinulei **38** 2241, 2252; **39** 2290
ricinuleids **38** 2241; **39** 2289-90
Rictaxis punctolacteus **47** 2771
ridley turtles **26** *1553*, 1554-5
rifleman **22** *1316*, 1317
Riftia **50** 2971-2
right whale **10** 574, 575, *576-8*
ring dove **20** *1155*
ring ouzel **24** 1388
ring-necked parakeet **20** 1168
ring-necked pheasant **19** *1085*, 1096, 1097, 1098
ring-tailed cat **2** 66-7
ring-tailed lemur **13** *724-5*, *732*, 735, 743, 748
  distribution **13** 739
  diurnal **13** 733, *738*
  social behaviour **13** *740-1*, *742*
ring-tailed mongoose **2** *84*, 92
ring-tailed rock wallaby **11** *616*
ringed china-mark moth **44** 2612
ringed plover **19** 1125
ringed seal **3** *180*; **4** *182*, 183, 184; **51** 3056
Ringiculidae **47** 2767, 2771
ringtail possums **11** 612, *631-2*, 627
Rio Grande beavers **51** 3042
Riparia riparia **23** 1345
Ripistes parasita **50** 2947, 2952
Rippon Falls barbel **32** 1899
Rissa tridactyla **20** 1142
Rissoacea **46** 2712, 2713
Risso's dolphin **10** 588, 589
river dolphins **10** 584, 586, 593
river lamprey **31** 1818, *1820-1*
river limpet **47** 2816-17
river martins **23** 1343, 1345
river stingray **31** 1844
Rivomarginella **47** 2763
rivulines **33** 1968, 1976, 1978
Rivulus marmoratus **33** 1976, 1978
roach **32** 1893, 1895, *1901-2*
  classification **32** 1894
roadrunner **20** 1175, 1178, *1180*, 1181
roan antelope **9** 495, *498*, 502
robber crab **38** 2223, *2224*
robber flies **45** 2652, *2653-5*, *2658*
robber frog **30** 1795, *1798*
robin **16** *911*; **22** *1306*; **24** 1382, *1383*, 1388
Robulus calcar **50** *2980*
rock...
  cod **34** *2020-1*, 2023
  dove **20** 1155, 1156-7, *1158*
  goby **35** *2060*
  gunnel **35** 2056-7
  hyrax **1** 18; **6** *309*, 311-12, 313, 316
  lizard **27** 1599
  lobsters **37** *2214*
  mantids **40** 2400
  parrot **20** 1163
  partridge **51** 3013
  petronia **25** 1455, *1458*, 1459
  pigeon **20** 1158
  pipit **23** 1355
  ptarmigan **51** 3052
  shells **46** 2745
  shrimps **37** *2191*
  sparrow **25** 1455, *1458*, 1459
  thrushes **24** *1387*, 1388-9
  urchin **36** *2124*
  wallabies **11** *635-7*, 642
  wren **22** 1316
rock-rat **5** 273, 289, 294
rockfishes **34** 2006-7
rockfowl **24** 1390, 1392
rockhopper penguin **16** *935-6*, *940*, 948, 949; **17** *964-5*
rockling **33** *1947*, 1951, *1953-4*
Rocky Mountain goat **6** 307
rodent louse **41** 2428
RODENTS **4** *215-18*; **5** *241-296*
  primate evolution **12** 719-20
Rodolia cardinalis **42** 2486, *2487*
roe deer **7** *402-3*, 404, 414-13; **51** 3013
  classification **7** 396, 418
roker **31** 1842, 1844
Rollandia microptera **16** 960
rollers **21** 1251-2; **22** *1261-3*, *1266-7*; **51** 3008
  classification **21** 1253; **22** 1261
  distribution **22** 1262
Rollulus roulroul **19** 1096
Roman mole **12** 670
Romerolagus diazi **4** 209
Romney Marsh frog **30** 1771
Rondeletidae **34** 1990
roof rat **5** 243, *254-7*, 255
roofed oyster **48** *2832*
rook **22** *1304*; **25** 1485, 1489, 1498, *1500*
Roosevelt's hartebeest **9** 486
Roosevelt's muntjac **7** 396
rooster tail conch **46** *2726*
ropefish **31** 1850
rorquals **10** 576, *578*, 579-84
  classification **10** 577
  spout **10** *573-4*
Rosalia alpina **42** 2506, 2507-12
rose aphid **41** *2439*, *2451*, *2460*
rose chafers **42** 2495, *2499*, 2503
rose gall wasp **42** 2516, *2519-20*
rose-breasted thrush-tanager **24** 1428, 1429
rose-coloured starling **25** 1462
rose-ringed parakeet **20** 1166, 1168
rose-thorn tree-hopper **41** 2449
roseate spoonbill **17** *996*, 1018, 1020
rosefinches **25** 1447-8
rosellas **20** *1162*, 1165, 1166, 1168
Ross seal **3** 179; **4** 184
Ross's goose **18** 1040
Ross's gull **20** 1142
Rostanga **47** *2794-5*
Rostangidae **47** 2795
Rostratula benghalensis **19** 1123
Rostratulidae **19** 1121, 1123
Rostrhamus sociabilis **18** 1070
rosy barb **32** 1899
rosy boa **28** 1637
rosy pastor **51** 3054
rosy underwing moth **44** 2617
Rothschild's giraffe **8** 430
Rotifera **49** *2921-25*
rotten-stump termites **41** 2405
rough periwinkles **46** *2709*
rough-legged buzzard **18** 1060, *1065*, 1070
rough-scaled sand boa **28** 1637
rough-skinned newt **29** 1739
roughshark **31** *1838*
roughsnout rat-tail **33** 1951
roughtail goby **35** 2060-1
roulroul **19** 1096, 1099
Round Island boa **28** 1637, 1639-40
roundworms **49** 2925, 2928, 2929
rousette flying fox **12** *680*, *690*, *696*, *697*
Rousettus aegyptiacus **12** 694
rove beetles **42** 2472, *2473*, *2476-8*; **41** 2454
royal antelope **8** 438, *439*, 444
Royal Chitwan National Park **51** *3026-7*
royal penguin **16** 938, 948, 949
royal python **28** *1629*, 1633, 1637
royal tern **19** *1122*
Royle's pika **4** 209
rubber boa **28** 1635, 1636-7
'rubber eel' **32** 1882
rubber frogs **30** 1785, 1786
ruby-tailed wasps **43** *2527*, 2529, *2536*
ruby-throated hummingbird **21** *1237*, 1238
rudd **32** 1894-5, *1901-2*
ruddy duck **18** 1052
ruddy shelduck **51** 3054
ruddy turnstone **19** 1135
ruff **16** *911*; **19** *1120*, 1127-8, *1131* 1135
ruffed grouse **19** 1092, 1096
ruffed lemur **13** *736*, 742
rufous...
  elephant-shrew **11** *657*, 660
  grasshopper **40** *2372-3*
  hornero **22** 1310
  hummingbird **21** 1237
  night heron **17** 1006
  ovenbird **22** *1309*, 1310, *1312*
  piculet **22** 1297
  rat kangaroo **11** 642
  scrub-bird **23** 1328, *1329*
  shrike-thrush **24** 1400
  Simen fox **51** 3017
  tiger heron **17** 1007
  treecreeper **24** *1414*
  vanga **23** 1368
rufous-banded miner **22** 1310
rufous-breasted hermit **21** *1226*
rufous-breasted leafscraper **22** 1310
rufous-browed pepper-shrike **24** 1435

rufous-checked nightjar **21** 1206
rufous-necked snow finch **25** 1455
rufous-tailed jacamar **22** 1281, *1283*, 1284
rufous-tailed weaver **51** 3023
rufous-throated dipper **23** 1374, *1376*
Rumina **48** 2821
Ruminantia **10** 568-9
ruminants **6** 301, *304-6*
Runcina coronata **47** 2767, 2775
Runcinoidea **47** 2767, 2775
running centipedes **39** 2308
running coua **20** 1178, 1181
running frog **30** 1782, *1784*, 1785
running jays **25** 1494
Rupicapra rupicapra **10** 550
Rupicaprini **8** 434; **10** 550
Rupicola **23** 1322
Ruppell's fox **3** 127
Ruppell's vulture **18** 1070
Rusa deer **7** 406
Russell's viper **28** 1674
Russian desman **12** 670, *672*
Russian saiga **9** 536
Russian sturgeon **31** *1808*, *1851*, 1856
rusty blackbird **24** 1440
rusty-spotted cat **3** 154
Rutela lineola **42** 2499
Rutelinae **42** 2503
Rutilus rutilus **32** 1894
Ruvettus pretiosus **35** 2067
Ruwenzori least otter shrew **11** 649, 651, 653
Rynchopidae **19** 1121; **20** 1145
Rynchops **20** 1145
Ryukyu island sika **7** 404

S

Sabella
pavonina **49** *2935*, *2936*
spallanzanii **49** 2939
Sabellastarte indica **50** *2945*
Sabellidae **50** 2942
sable **51** 3056
sable antelope **8** 434; **9** *484*, 486, 495, *498*, 502
sac-spider **38** *2256*, 2277
Saccoglossus **50** 2971, 2973
Saccopharyngidae **32** 1874
Saccopharynx **32** 1874
Sacculina **37** *2180*
carcini **37** 2178
Sacoglossa **47** 2767, 2775, 2776, 2777
sacred ibis **17** 1018, *1020*
sacred kingfisher **21** 1253
sacred scarab beetle **42** 2491-2, *2494*, 2496-7, 2503
Sacrophilus harrisii **11** 619
saddle oysters **48** 2842, 2843
saddle-back tamarin **14** 790
saddle-bill stork **17** 1011, 1012, *1014*
saddle-case makers **43** 2580
saddle-case-making caddisflies **44** 2581
saddleback **25** *1469*, 1470
saddleback toad **30** 1795
saffron dragonfly **40** *2355*, *2358*
sage grouse **19** *1089*, 1092, 1093, 1095, 1096
Sagittariidae **18** 1057, 1080
Sagittarius serpentarius **18** 1080
Sago pedo **40** 2369
Saguinus **14** 790
saiga **8** 434; **9** 535, *536-7*, 538
Saiga tatarica **9** 535
Saigini **8** 434; **9** 535
sail-fin lizard **27** *1563*
sailfin black molly **33** *1963*, *1978*
sailfin molly **33** *1972*, *1978-9*
salt toad **30** 1789-90
salt-marsh harvest mouse **5** 266
Salticidae **38** 2258, 2263; **39** 2289
saltwater crocodile **29** 1685, *1690*, 1691, 1693
Salvelinus **33** 1924
Salvin's barbet **22** 1287
sambar **7** 400-1, 404, 406, *416*
Samoan palolo worm **49** 2939
San Jose scale insect **42** 2486
sand...
boas **28** *1635*, 1637
cat **3** *138*
crabs **37** 2220

ABOVE Tube sponges attached permanently at their bases to a reef.

sailfishes **35** 2041, 2043; **51** 3032
Saimiri sciureus **13** 774
St Mark's hairfly **45** 2646-7
St Peter's fish **34** 1990
saithe **33** 1951-2
saki **13** *765*, 768, *769*, 772; **51** 3038
classification **13** 763, 774
salamanders **29** 1698, *1702*, 1703, 1704, *1712-30*; **30** *1741-54*
classification **29** 1701, 1713; **30** 1745, 1750, 1754
distribution **29** 1715
Salamandra **29** 1729
Salamandridae **29** 1713, 1729
Salanoia unicolor **2** 92
Salmo **33** 1924
salmon **31** *1812*, 1814; **32** 1895; **33** *1921-32*
classification **31** 1858
salmon trout **33** 1932
Salmonidae **33** 1924
Salmoniformes **31** 1858; **32** 1866; **33** *1921-42*
Salpa maxima **35** *2099*
Salpids **35** 2099
salps **35** 2090, *2099-2100*, **37** *2188*
dollars **36** 2115, *2117*, 2124
dusted cone shell **47** 2764
eels **34** 2033, *2035-8*
gaper **48** 2848
gazelle **9** 529
lances **34** 2033
lizards **27** *1594*, 1600
classification **27** 1562, 1603
distribution **27** 1595
martin **22** *1303*; **23** 1340, 1343, 1344, 1345, 1346-7
monitor **27** 1609
partridge **19** 1097
sharks **31** *1826*, 1832, 1839; **35** 2048
shrimps **36** 2147; **37** 2169, *2211*
skink **27** *1593-5*, *1596*, 1598
stargazer **35** 2059
tiger sharks **31** 1832, 1835, 1839
vipers **28** 1673-4
wasps **43** *2529*, 2535, 2540
sand-dusted cone **46** 2746
sand-dwelling darkling beetles **42** 2472, 2490-1
sand flies **45** *2644*, 2646, 2647
sand-smelts **34** 1982-4, *2037*
sanderling **19** 1127, 1135
sandfishes **27** 1593
sandgrouse **20** *1150-2*, 1158
sandhill crane **19** 1105, 1106, 1107
sandhoppers **37** 2203, *2205*
sandpipers **19** 1121, 1126-9, *1130*, 1135
sandwich tern **20** *1143*, 1144, 1145
sangai **7** 404; **8** 421
Sanopus splendidus **33** 1958
Santa Gertrudi cattle **8** 476
sapphire-bellied hummingbird **21** 1238
saratoga **51** 3047
sarcastic fringehead **35** 2059
Sarcodina **50** 2976, 2991
Sarcodines **50** *2991*
sarcodinians **50** 2988, 2990-1
Sarcomastigophora **50** 2974, 2976, 2991
Sarcophaga carnaria **45** 2659
Sarcoptidae **39** 2295
Sarcoramphus papa **18** 1064
sardinc **32** 1886, 1890
Sardinian brook salamander **29** 1729, 1740
Sardinian red deer **7** 405
Sardinian salamander **30** 1747
Sardinops sagax **32** 1890
sargassum anglerfish **33** *1961*
Sarkidiornis melanotus **18** 1052
Sarotheradon galileus **35** *2049*
sarus crane **17** *1016-17*; **19** *1105*, 1107
Sasia abnormis **22** 1297
sassaby **9** 488-9
Satan **32** 1913
satin bowerbird **25** *1473*, *1475*, 1476; **51** 3049
satinfin shiner **32** 1892
Saturnia pavonia **44** 2624
Saturniidae **44** 2623-4
satyr tragopan **19** *1086*, 1096
Satyridae **44** 2633, 2640
saucer bugs **41** 2438, 2442
Sauer, E. and F. **16** 920
Sauria **27** 1562
Saurischia **26** *1507*, 1508
saury **33** 1965, 1966
savannah baboon **14** *792*, *805-7*, 808, *809*, 813
classification **14** 811
savannah elephant **6** 321, 324
Savi's pine vole **5** *251* -2
Savi's pipistrelle **12** *712*
saw sharks **31** 1839-40
saw-billed mergansers **18** 1052
sawbills **18** 1030, 1049-51, 1052
sawfishes **31** 1841-2
sawflies **42** 2516, *2518-20*; **43** *2521*
sawtooth eels **32** 1884
sawtooth termites **41** 2403, 2405
Saxicola **24** 1388
scabies mite **39** 2295
scad **34** 2036, 2038
Scaergus unicirrhus **48** 2852
Scala communis **45** *2682*
scald fish **35** 2080
scale insects **42** 2483, 2486; **41** 2438, 2452
scaled blennies **35** 2058-9
scaled carp **32** 1896
scaled piculet **22** *1298*
scaled squid **48** 2861, 2862

scaleless blennies **35** 2058
scallops **45** 2674, 2675; **48** *2831, 2837-9*, 2840-1
scaly anteater **4** 197-8, 200; **51** 3020
scaly dragonfish **33** *1940*
scaly ground roller **22** 1261
scaly-breasted ground dove **20** *1150*
scaly-fronted weaver **25** 1459, 1460
scaly-tailed flying squirrel **12** *674*
scaly-tailed possum **11** 624-5, 626
scaly-tailed squirrel **4** 233
scaly-throated honeyguide **22** 1288-9
scalyfoots **27** 1569, 1570
scampi **37** *2214*
Scandentia **13** 730
Scaphander lignarius **45** 2692; **47** *2775*
Scaphandridae **47** 2767, *2770*
Scapharca inaequivalvis **48** 2834
Scaphiopus bombifrons **30** 1769
Scaphirhynchus platorhynchus **31** 1856
Scaphopoda **45** *2673*, 2674, 2684, 2691-2
scarab beetles **39** 2325; **40** *2364*; **41** 2456; **42** *2491-4, 2496-7*, 2503
Scarabacinus termitophilus **42** 2503
Scarabaeidae **41** 2456; **42** 2491-4, 2497-8, 2503
Scarabaeinus **42** 2494, 2495
Scarabaeoidea **42** 2491-2, 2499, 2501, 2503
Scarabaeus sacer **42** 2503
Scardinius erythrophthalmus **32** 1894
Scaridae **34** 2023
scarlet ibis **17** *996*, 1018, 1020
scarlet king snake **28** *1658*
scarlet macaw **20** *1161*, 1168, 1170
scarlet rosefinch **25** 1442, 1447
scarlet tiger-moths **44** 2617, *2618-19*, 2624
scarlet-backed flowerpecker **24** 1417
Scartelaos **35** 2060, 2062
Scarus **34** 2023
Scatophagidae **35** 2044, 2046
Scatophagus **35** 2044
scats **35** 2044, *2045-6*
Sceloporus **27** 1579
Scenopoeetes dentirostris **25** 1476
Schaller, George B. **3** 146
Schaller, George and Kay **15** 859-60
Schetba rufa **23** 1368
Schiffornis major **23** 1331
Schiphozoa **49** *2892* -3
Schistocerca gregaria **40** *2363, 2365*, 2369
Schistosoma **47** 2810
haematobium **49** *2913*; **47** 2810
japonicum **49** *2913*; **47** 2811
mansoni **49** 2911, *2913*, 2914; **47** 2810
Schistosomatidae **49** 2913
Schizodactyloidea **40** 2369, 2371-4
Schlegel's asity **22** 1315
Schmidt, Johannes **32** 1878
Schoeniophylax phryganophila **22** 1310
Schomberg's deer **7** 401
school bass **34** 2022
Schreiber's bent-winged bat **12** 712, 715
Schweigger's hinge-backed tortoise **26** 1546
Sciaena aquila **34** 2033
Sciaenidae **34** 2033
scimitar oryx **9** 499, 500-1, 502
scimitar-bill **22** 1270, 1271
Scincus scincus **27** 1598
Scinicidae **27** 1562, 1598
scissor-tailed flycatcher **22** 1317, 1320; **23** 1321
scissor-tailed swift **21** 1225
SCIURIDS **4** *219-40*
Sciuromorpha **4** 221, 233; **5** 277
Sciurus vulgaris **4** 233
Scleopspongiae **48** 2880
Scleractinia **49** 2889, 2897
Scolia **43** 2534, *2536*
scoliid wasps **43** 2534, *2536*
Scoliidae **43** 2529, 2534
Scolopacidae **19** 1121, 1135
Scolopacinae **19** 1135
Scolopax rusticola **19** 1135
Scolopendra **39** 2307
gigantea **39** 2306, 2307
Scolopendromorpha **39** 2307
Scolytidae **41** 2456
Scolytus scolytus **42** *2505*; **41** 2456
Scomberesocidae **33** 1965
Scomberesox saurus **33** 1965
Scombridae **34** 2036
Scombrus scombrus **34** 2036
Scophthalmus **35** 2075
Scopidae **17** 999, 1011
scops owl **20** *1183*, 1199
Scopus umbretta **17** 1011
Scorpaena grandicornis **34** 2007
Scorpaenidae **34** 2007
Scorpaeniformes **34** *2005-10*
Scorpio maurus **38** 2244
scorpion flies **39** 2311; **42** 2516; **43** *2574-6*;
Scorpiones **38** 2241, 2244, 2250
scorpionfishes **34** 2005-7
scorpions **36** 2103, 2140, *2143*; **38** 2240, 2241, *2242, 2244-51*
classification **38** 2241, 2244, 2252
sting **38** *2239*, 2247-8
scoters **18** *1050*, 1051, 1052
Scotland, nature reserve **51** 3002, *3010-11*
Scotopelia Peli **20** 1199
Scottish Highland cattle **8** 476
scrawled filefish **35** 2082
screamers **18** *1028, 1029*, 1030-1
scrub hen **19** 1088, *1090*
scrub jay **25** *1484*
scrub python **28** 1633
scrub wallaby **11** 642
scrub warbler **24** 1395
scrub-birds **22** 1303; **23** 1322, 1328, *1329*
scrub-fowl **19** 1088
scrub-robin **24** 1390
sculpins **34** 2007-8
Scutigera **39** 2307
Scutigerella **39** 2303
Scutigeromorpha **39** 2307, 2308
Scutisorex somereni **12** 662
Scyliorhinidae **31** 1839
Scyliorhinus **31** 1839
Scyllaeidae **47** 2797
Scyllaridae **37** 2213
Scyllea pelagica **47** 2797
Scyphozoa **49** 2887, 2889, 2892-3
scyphozoan jellyfish **49** *2886*
Scytalopus macropus **22** 1314
scythebills **22** 1308
Scytodes thoracica **39** 2283
Scytodidae **38** 2258; **39** 2283
sea...
anemones **34** *2028-9*, 2031; **36** 2103, *2154-5*; **48** *2879*; **49** 2883-4, *2886, 2893, 2896-7*
bass **34** 2013, 2017, 2022-3
biscuits **36** 2115
bream **34** 2033, *2034*
butterflies **45** 2677, 2680; **47** *2774*
canary **10** *586*
catfish **32** 1911, 1913-14
cow **5** 298; **6** 304, 310, 312-16
cucumbers **36** *2106, 2117-19, 2121-4*
anatomy **36** 2107, *2108*, 2109
classification **36** 2107
diet **36** 2114
evolution **36** 2115
larva **36** *2113*
movement **36** 2113
regeneration **36** 2110-11
daisies **36** 2106, 2107, 2114, 2115, 2137
eagles **18** 1070, 1072; **51** 3014
egg **35** 2094
fan **49** *2883*, 2884, *2886*, 2889, 2900
hares **45** 2677-8; **47** 2767-9, 2771, *2774, 2778-80, 2793*; **50** *2941*
hedgehogs **36** *2119*
hen **31** *1804-5*
krait **28** *1667-9, 1672*
lamprey **31** *1816*, 1818, 1821, 1823-4
lemons **45** 2678
lilies **36** 2106, 2113, *2115-17*
anatomy **36** 2107, *2108*, 2109
classification **36** 2107
defence **36** 2118
regeneration **36** 2110, 2120
lions **1** 24, 32, *34*; **3** 163, *170-1*, 174-5; **51** 3035
classification **1** 28; **3** 164, 172
moths **34** 1997, *1998*
mouse **49** *2936*; **50** *2941*, 2942
otter **1** *38*, 44, 53, *54*, 55
diet **1** 41-2
distribution **1** 43
endangered species **1** 56
reproduction **1** 44-5, 52
pansies **47** *2797*; **49** 2889, 2900
pens **49** *2886*, 2889, 2900
plumes **49** 2884, 2889, 2900
scorpion **34** *2008*
slugs **36** 2103; **45** *2668-9, 2677*, 2680, 2694; **47** *2766-802*
classification **45** 2674, 2697
food **45** *2674*, 2677, 2678
snails **34** 2007, 2010; **45** 2694; **46** *2719-21*, 2727, *2729*, 2735, *2737*
snakes **28** 1640, 1641, 1661, *1667-9*
distribution **28** 1644
migration **28** 1672
spiders **36** 2140; **38** 2234; **39** *2298-2300*
squirts **31** *1803*; **35** *2088-2098*; **45** 2678
swallows **20** 1143
trout **33** 1923-4, 1930, 1932-3
turtles **26** *1527*, 1547, *1553*, 1554-5
urchins **36** *2101-2, 2105-6, 2117, 2124-7*
anatomy **36** *2108, 2109*
classification **36** 2107
defence **36** *2118-19*
distribution **36** 2120-1
egg development **36** *2112*
evolution **36** 2115
movement **36** 2109, 2113
spines **36** *2107*
walnuts **49** 2901
whip **49** 2889, 2900; **51** 3032
sea-dragon **34** *2003*
sea-ducks **18** 1030, 1049-50, 1052
sea-mites **39** 2294
sea-shore jumping spider **38** *2279*
sea-slaters **37** *2199*, 2201
seagulls *see* gulls
seahorses **34** *1991-2, 1996*, 1998
classification **34** 2000
general features **34** *2001-4*
seal family **1** 24, 32; **3** *161-80*; **4** *181-4*; **51** 3035, 3053, 3056
classification **1** 28; **3** 164, 172, 179
distribution **3** 164
seal louse **41** 2428
searobin **34** 2007
Searsiidae **33** 1937
searsiids **33** 1937, 1942
seashore isopod **37** *2188*
Sebastes marinus **34** 2007
Secernentea **49** 2925
secretary bird **18** 1056, 1058, 1059, 1061; **19** *1083, 1084*
classification **18** 1057, 1080
Sedentaria **50** 2942
sedge frogs **30** 1756, 1782, *1783*, 1785
sedge warbler **22** 1305
seed bugs **41** 2441
seedeater **24** 1422-3
seedsnipe **19** 1121, 1137, *1138*
Segestriidae **38** 2258; **39** 2283
Segisaurus **1** 8
segmented worms **36** 2140; **50** 2945
sei whale **10** 577
Seirus novoboracensis **24** 1431
seladang **8** 468
Selevinia betpakdalensis **5** 254
Seleviniidae **5** 254
Selous, Frederick **6** 359
Semaeostomeae **49** 2889
Semeiophorus vexillarius **21** 1206
Semioptera wallacei **25** 1480
Semirossia tenera **48** *2860*
Semnornis **22** 1288
Senegal coucal **20** 1178, *1181*, 1182
Senegal softshell turtle **26** 1526, 1553, 1556
Sepia **48** 2855, *2863*

elegans **48** 2855
officinalis **48** *2851-2, 2854,* 2855, 2858
orbignyana **48** 2855
typica **48** 2855
Sepiidae **48** 2858
Sepioidea **48** 2855, 2857
Sepiola **48** 2855, 2858, *2859-61*
Sepiolidae **48** 2855
Sepioteuthis sepioidea **48** 2861, *2862*
Septibranchia **48** 2850
septibranchs **45** 2677
Serengeti National Park **51** 3002, *3022-3*
Sergeant Baker **33** 1943, 1946
Sericulus chrysocephalus **25** 1476
seriema **19** 1106, 1107, *1117*, 1118
Serinus canaria **25** 1442
serotine **12** *681-2, 690, 706-7*, 712, 714
serow **9** *534*, 535, 539-40
serpent eagle **18** 1071
Serpentes **27** *1617-20*; **28** *1621-80*
Serpula **49** *2936*; **50** *2947*
Serpulidae **50** 2942
Serpulorbis arenaria **46** 2712, 2716
Serranidae **34** 2013, 2023
Serranus **34** 2023
Serrasalmus nattereri **32** 1908
Serritemitidae **41** 2405
Serritermes serrifer **41** 2405
serval **3** *137, 142, 143*; **51** *3016*
Sesia apiformis **44** 2609
Sesiidae **44** 2609
Sesioidea **44** 2609
Setifer setosus **11** 651
Setonix brachyurus **11** 642
Setonophrys euphilium **50** *2991*
Setophaga ruticilla **24** 1431
Seurat (zoologist) **37** 2193
Seven islands thrush **51** 3060
seven-gilled shark **31** 1829
seven-spotted ladybird **42** 2472, *2483-4, 2486*
seven-striped whiptail **27** *1602*, 1603
seventeen-year cicada **41** 2438, 2448
Severtzov's argali **10** 563, 566
sexton beetles **42** 2471, 2472, *2473-5*
Seychelles frog **30** 1783, 1785
Seychelles Islands tree frog **30** 1785
shads **32** 1886, 1889-90
shag **16** *911*; **17** 984, 990
shaketails **22** 1309
shanny **35** 2058
sharks **31** *1825-41*; **35** *2047-8*; **51** 3032
classification **31** 1809, 1827-8, 1839, 1841
evolution **31** 1806, 1808
reproduction **31** 1814; **32** 1866
senses **31** 1828, *1831*
sharksuckers **35** *2046-8*
sharp-nosed puffers **35** 2082
sharp-ribbed salamander **29** *1723-4*, 1729
sharp-tailed grouse **19** 1092
sharp-tailed streamcreeper **22** *1311*
sharpbill **23** *1331*
Sharpe's grysbok **8** 444, 446
sharptail sunfish **35** 2087
shearwaters **16** *908*; **17** 962, *968, 972*, 976
appearance/habits **17** 974
classification **17** 973
distribution **17** 963
sheatfish **32** 1913
sheath-tailed bat **12** 696, 704, 681; **51** 3046
sheathbills **19** 1121, 1137, *1138*, 1139
sheep **5** 298; **6** 301, 304-5, 308; **10** 561-70
sheep chewing louse **41** 2428
sheep frog **30** 1784
sheep liver fluke **49** *2911, 2912*
sheet-web spiders **39** 2283, *2289*
sheldgeese **18** 1030, 1041, 1044
shelducks **18** 1031, 1033, 1041, *1045*; **51** 3008
classification **18** 1030, 1044
shelled amoebas **50** 2989, 2991
shelled sea butterflies **47** 2780-3, 2786
Shepherd's beaked whale **10** 585
shield bugs **41** *2433*, 2438, *2439, 2442*
shieldtail snakes **28** *1627-8*
classification **28** 1626
distribution **28** 1621, 1628
shining cuckoo **20** 1181; **51** 3050
shining monarch **24** 1400
shining starling **25** 1461-2
shining sunbeam **21** 1228
Shinisaurus crocodilurus **27** 1609
shiny cowbird **24** *1436*, 1440
shiny pufferfish **35** 2082
ship rat **5** 243, 256
shipworm **48** *2844*, 2848, 2850
Shire horse **6** 348
shoe-billed stork **17** 1009, *1010*, 1011
shoebills **17** *996*, 1009, *1010*; **51** 3024
classification **17** 999, 1011
distribution **17** 1005
shore clingfish **33** *1962*
shore crab **37** *2180*
shore lark **23** 1334, *1335*, 1339
short-beaked echidna **11** 606
short-billed dowitcher **19** 1135
short-eared dog **3** 126-7
short-eared elephant shrew **11** 660
short-eared owl **20** 1185, *1191*, 1194, 1199
short-horned flies **45** 2652
short-horned grasshopper **40** 2364, 2366, 2376, *2382*
short-horned lizard **27** *1572*
short-nosed bandicoot **11** 620
short-nosed echidna **11** *601-4*
short-nosed fruit bat **12** 693, 694
short-nosed rat kangaroo **11** 642
short-snouted elephant shrew **11** *660*
short-tailed albatross **17** 971
short-tailed bats **12** 679, 681, 716
short-tailed opossum **11** 615
short-tailed pygmy monitor lizard **27** 1609, 1614
short-tailed pygmy tyrant flycatcher **22** 1317, 1320
short-tailed shrew **11** *646*
short-toed eagle **18** *1059*, 1070; **51** 3014
short-toed lark **22** *1303*; **23** 1334, *1338*; **51** 3008
short-toed treecreeper **24** 1412, *1413*
short-winged grasshopper **40** *2365*
short-winged grebe **16** 956, 960
Shorthorn cattle **8** 476
shorthorn sculpin **34** 2007-8
shortnose chimaera **31** 1846
Shou **7** 405
shovel-billed kingfisher **21** 1260
shovel-nosed lobsters **37** 2213-14
shovel-nosed salamander **30** 1750, 1751
shoveler **18** 1045, *1046*, 1047
shovelnose sturgeon **31** *1852*, 1856
shrew mouse **5** 262
shrew opossum **11** 612, 624
shrew rat **5** 262
shrew-hedgehog **11** 655
shrews **1** *8*; **11** *646, 648*; **12** *661-3, 666-7*
classification **11** 651
distribution **11** 647
shrike-vireo **24** 1435-8
shrikes **22** 1303, 1305; **23** *1362-8*, 1374
shrimp/goby symbiosis **35** 2061
shrimpfish **34** 2000
shrimps **36** 2140, 2146, 2147, *2153*; **37** 2169, 2190, *2192*, 2211-12
classification **37** 2182
mantis shrimp predator **37** 2183
shrinking frogs **30** 1785-6
Sialia sialis **24** 1388
Sialidae **43** 2570
siamang **14** *838-40*; **15** 841-2, 846, *847*, 848
Siamese crocodile **29** 1685, *1691*
Siamese fighting fish **35** *2064*, 2069, *2070*
Siberian bighorn **10** 570
Siberian chipmunk **4** *230-1*, 233; **51** 3052
Siberian flying squirrel **12** *674*
Siberian jay **25** 1489, 1491
Siberian roe deer **7** 412, 413
Siberian salamander **29** *1712*, 1713, 1715-16
Siberian tiger **51** 3004, 3056, *3057*
Siberian weasel **51** 3052
Siberian white crane **19** 1105, 1106
Siberian wild dog **2** 111
sickle-crested bird of paradise **25** 1480
sicklebills **21** 1228, 1236; **23** 1368
Sicyases sanguineus **33** 1962
side-necked turtles **26** 1528, 1530
side-striped jackal **2** 118
sidewinder rattlesnake **26** *1520*; **28** *1668*, 1669, 1679
sifakas **12** *720*; **13** *732-3, 738, 742-3*, 748-9; **15** *896*
classification **13** 728, 735, 742
distribution **13** 739
Siganidae **35** 2067
Siganus **35** 2066-7
signature spider **38** *2240, 2261, 2263*; **39** *2288*
sika deer **7** 398, 404, *410*; **8** 421; **51** 3060
classification **7** 396, 406
Sikhote-Alin State Nature Reserve **51** 3002, 3004, *3056-7*
silk-moths **44** 2606, 2623-5, *2626, 2627, 2628*
feeding **44** 2588, 2590
silkworm moth **44** 2624, 2625-6
silkworms **36** 2140; **44** 2593, 2625-6, *2628*
silky anteater **4** *186*, 188, *192-3*, 195
silky cuscus **11** 625
silky flycatchers **23** *1369*, 1372
Silpha **42** 2472
Silphidae **42** 2471-2, 2474
Siluridae **32** 1913
Siluriformes **31** 1858; **32** 1913
Silurus glanis **32** 1913
Silva laevigata **42** *2471*
silver barramundi **51** 3047
silver bream **32** *1903*; **34** *2034*
silver conch **46** *2722*
silver dollar **32** 1909
'silver eel' **32** 1875, 1877
silver hake **33** 1955
silver hatchetfish **32** 1908
silver salmon **33** 1924, *1929*
silver sea bass **34** 2013
silver 'Y' moth **44** *2588, 2604, 2621*, 2624
silver-backed fox **3** 127
silver-backed jackal **2** *117-18*
silver-eared mesia **24** *1390*
silver-eye **51** 3050
silver-spotted ghost moth **44** 2600
silverback gorilla **15** 859, 860-1, 864
silvered leaf monkey **14** 825, *826*, 836
silverfish **39** 2311, *2327*, 2335, *2336*
silversides **33** 1964; **34** *1982-4*
silvery mole-rat **5** 284
Simen fox **51** 3017
Simen Mountains National Park **51** 3002, *3016-17*
Simenchelys parasiticus **32** 1874
Simien jackal **2** 118
Simnia **46** *2729*
patula **46** *2734*
purpurea **45** *2681*
spelta **46** 2729
Simuliidae **45** 2651-2
Simulium equinum **45** *2644*, 2651-2
Sinai rosefinch **25** 1447-8
singing bush-lark **23** 1334
singing honeyeater **24** 1420
single cirri octopus **48** 2852
single-celled algae **37** *2209*
singleslits **33** 1962
Sinhalese frogmouth **21** 1213
sinistral miniature horn shells **46** 2712, 2718
Sinodontis **32** 1913
Siphlonuridae **40** 2343
Siphonalia **46** 2750, 2751
Siphonaptera **39** 2311; **45** *2664-7*
Siphonaria **47** 2805
Siphonariacea **47** 2805
Siphonariidae **47** 2805
Siphonodentaiidae **45** 2692
Siphonophora **49** *2890-2*
Siphonosomatoida **37** 2163
Siren **30** 1754
Sirenia **6** 304, 314
sirenians **5** 298; **6** *312-16*
Sirenidae **29** 1713; **30** 1754
sirens **30** *1753-4*
classification **29** 1713

Siricidae **42** 2516-17
siskin **25** 1442, 1446; **51** 3056
Sistrurus catenatus **28** 1669
Sisyridae **43** 2570, 2571
sitatunga **8** *448*, 450, *452-3*, 456; **51** 3022
sitella **24** 1409, 1412
Sitta **24** 1409
Sittidae **24** 1409
six-gilled shark **31** *1828*, 1829
six-lined racerunner **27** 1603
six-spot burnet moth **44** *2604*, 2609, *2610*, 2611
six-wired bird of paradise **25** 1482
skates **31** 1808, 1843-4
  see also rays
skeleton shrimps **37** *2188*, 2207
skelly **33** 1934
skimmers **19** 1121, 1138; **20** 1144-5
skinks **27** 1565, *1592-6*
  classification **27** 1562, 1598
  distribution **27** 1595
skipjack **34** 2040
skippers **33** 1965-6; **44** 2629, *2630*, 2633
skuas **18** 1058; **19** 1121, 1138, *1139*, 1140; **20** 1142
skunk **1** *38*, 42, 45, *56*
  classification **1** 55
  distribution **1** 43
  reproduction **1** 48, 52
skylark **23** 1334, *1336-7*, 1338, *1356*
slaty bristlefront **22** 1314
slaty gnateater **22** 1314
slave-maker ants **43** 2529, *2562*, 2564
Slavonian grebe **16** *957*, 960
sleeper fishes **35** 2060, 2065
sleepy lizard **27** 1593
slender loris **13** *731*, *744*, *748-9*, 752, 754
slender salamanders **30** 1750, *1753*
slender-billed kite **18** 1072
slender-horned gazelle **9** 529
slender-snouted crocodile **29** *1683*, 1685, 1687, 1693
slickheads **33** 1937, 1941-2
slider turtle **26** 1539
slimy salamander **30** 1750
slipper animalcule **50** 2971, 2992, *2997*
slipper limpet **46** *2714*, 2720, *2724*, 2727
slipper lobster **37** 2214, *2215*
slipper shells **45** 2676
slipper snail **45** 2677
slit limpets **45** 2698
slit-faced bats **12** 681, *690*, 699, 704
slit-shells **45** 2697, 2698
Sloane's viperfish **33** *1940*, 1944
sloe bug **41** *2440*
Sloenodontidae **11** 651
sloth **4** *185-6*, 187, 189, *193-4*
sloth bear **2** *70*, 80-1, *82*
slow loris **13** *746-7*, 748, *750*, 752, 754
slow-worm **27** 1601, 1603, *1604-5*, 1606, *1607*
slugs **45** 2670, 2680; **47** *2800-4*, 2817; **48** *2822-6*
  see also sea slugs
  classification **45** 2674, 2697
  courtship **47** *2812-13*
small cats **3** 139
small copper butterfly **44** *2635*
small kingfishers **21** 1253, 1256
small postman butterfly **44** 2633, 2639
small tortoiseshell butterfly **36** *2103*; **44** *2592*, 2633, *2634*
small turret shells **46** 2712
small white butterfly **44** 2633
small-billed false sunbird **22** 1316
small-horned octopus **48** 2869
small-scaled tree pangolin **4** *198*, *199*, 200
small-toothed saw shark **31** 1839
smallmouth bass **34** *2014*, 2016
smallmouth buffalo fish **32** 1894
smalltooth sawfish **31** *1838*, 1842
smelts **33** 1923-4, 1936-7
smew **18** *1050*, 1052
Smilogobius **35** 2061
Sminthurides **39** 2331
Sminthuroides aquaticus **39** *2330*, 2332
Sminthurus viridis **39** 2330, 2333
smoky bat **12** 709
smooth butterfly ray **31** 1844
smooth coated otter **1** *38*
smooth dogfish **31** 1839
smooth hound shark **31** 1835, 1839
smooth newt **29** *1714*, 1729, *1731-3*, 1737; **30** *1746*
smooth snake **28** 1645, *1656-7*
smooth-billed ani **20** *1172*
smooth-fronted dwarf caiman **29** *1686*
snail kite **18** 1070, 1072
snail limpet **46** 2701
snail-eating snakes **28** 1641, 1643-4, 1645
snailfishes **34** 2007, 2010
snails **36** 2103; **45** 2670, *2675*, 2676, 2680, 2694; **46** *2704*, *2708*, **47** 2761-2820; **48** *2821-2*, *2826-8*
  classification **45** 2674, 2697
  courtship **47** *2812-13*
  fluke hosts **49** 2913
snake eagles **18** 1058, 1067, 1070, 1071
snake eels **32** 1874, 1883
snake lizards **27** *1563*, 1565, 1569, *1570*, 1571
snake mackerels **35** 2067
snake pipefish **34** 2000, *2001*
snake worm **49** *2936*
snake-eating turtle **26** 1539
snake-necked turtle **26** *1524*, 1530, *1531-2*
snakebirds **17** 990, *991*
snakefish **35** 2066-7
snakeflies **39** 2311; **43** 2565, 2566, *2567*, *2568-70*
snakehead fish **34** 2026-7; **35** 2071-2
snakes **26** 1513-14; **27** 1562, 1564, *1617-20*; **28** *1621-80*
  classification **26** 1510; **28** 1621
  distribution **28** 1628
  evolution **26** *1507*, 1509
  feeding habits **26** *1516-17*
snapping shrimp **37** *2211*
snapping turtle **26** 1526, *1533-5*
Snares Island penguin **16** 948, 949
snipe **19** 1126, *1129*, 1130-1, 1135; **51** 3008
snipe eels **32** 1874, *1884*
snipefishes **34** *1996*, *2000*
snouted termite **41** *2404*
snow bunting **24** *1421*, 1429
snow finch **25** 1455, 1459; **51** 3013
snow goose **16** *906-7*; **18** *1039*, 1040, *1042-3*, 1044
snow leopard **1** 24, 35; **3** 134, 144, 148-9; **51** *3058-9*
snow petrel **17** 971, *973*
snow scorpion flies **43** 2575, 2576
snow sheep **10** 561, 566, 570
snow vole **5** 250; **51** 3013
snowshoe hare **4** 210
snowy owl **20** 1185, *1188-9*, 1194, 1199, 1200
snowy sheathbill **19** *1122*, 1137, *1138*, 1139
snub-nosed monkeys **14** 796, 822, *824*, 827, 831
snubnose parasitic eel **32** 1874, 1884
Soay sheep **10** *567*
social comb-footed spider **38** *2278*
social weaver **25** 1458, *1460*
sockeye salmon **33** 1924-5
Socotra cormorant **17** 985
Soemmerring's gazelle **9** 519, 529
soft corals **49** *2885*, *2886*, 2889, *2898*, *2900-1*
soft ticks **39** *2294*, 2295
soft-tails **22** 1310
softshell turtles **26** 1553, 1556
soil mites **39** 2289
soldier-fish **34** *1990*
sole **31** *1859*
Solea solea **35** 2075
Soleidae **35** 2075
Solemya **45** 2677; **48** 2835, 2837
Solemyidae **48** 2835, 2837
Solen arcuata **48** 2848
Solenidae **48** 2849
Solenodon **11** 651
solenodons **11** 647, 648, *650-1*
solenogasters **45** 2674, 2684, *2689-90*
Solenostomide **34** 2000
soles **35** *2073-5*, 2080
Solidula solidula **47** *2771*
Solifugae **38** 2241, 2252-4
solitary bees **43** 2540-1, *2542*
solitary sandpiper **19** 1129
solitary vireo **24** 1435
solitary wasp **43** *2532*
Solpuga **38** 2252-3
Somali edge-snouted worm-lizard **27** 1616
Somali ostrich **16** 919, 925
Somalian ass **6** 335, *341*, 344
Somateria mollissima **18** 1052
Somniosus microcephalus **31** 1841
song babblers **24** 1389-90
song sparrow **24** 1422, 1429
song thrush **24** 1388-9
songbirds (oscines) **22** 1307; **23** 1334
Sonoran deer **51** 3042
Sooglossidae **30** 1785
Sooglossus seychellensis **30** 1785
sooty albatross **17** *963*, 969, 971
sooty boubou **23** 1367
sooty falcon **19** 1083
sooty mangabey **51** 3020
sooty oystercatcher **19** 1125
sooty shearwaters **17** *969*
sooty tern **20** 1144, 1145
Sorex **12** 662
Soricidae **11** 651; **12** 662
Soriculus **12** 662
Sotalia fluviatilis **10** 593
soupfin shark **31** 1839
souslik **4** *220*
South African coiled nerite **46** 2705
South African rock sucker **33** 1962
South America, national parks **51** *3034-5*, *3038-9*
South American...
  army ants **43** *2558*
  bullfrog **30** 1793, 1795, *1799*
  cloud swift **21** *1218*
  jumping metalmark **44** *2634*
  nymphalid **44** *2634*
southern...
  alligator lizard **27** 1601-2, 1603
  banded snake eagle **18** 1070
  black tit **24** *1413*
  cassowary **16** 925, 928
  cavefish **33** 1948
  elephant seal **4** *183*, 184
  fer-de-lance **28** 1644, *1668*, 1669, 1675, *1678*
  flying squirrel **4** *216*, *220*, 233
  fulmar **17** 973
  fur seal **3** 164
  ground hornbill **22** *1275*, 1278
  hairy-nosed wombat **11** 633-4
  hawker dragonfly **40** *2355*
  lapwing **19** 1125
  mole viper **28** 1643
  pudu **7** *390*, *413*, 417; **8** 424
    classification **7** 418
  red salamander **30** 1751
  reedbuck **9** 510, *515-16*
  right whale **10** 575, *576*
  sea lion **3** 172
  smooth snake **28** *1657*
  tamandua **4** *186*, 195
  three-banded armadillo **4** *197*
  tree hyrax **6** 311, 313
  white rhino **7** 361
Sowerby's beaked whale **10** 593
spadefoot toads **30** 1765, 1768, *1769*, *1722*
Spadella **50** 2971
Spalacinae **5** 254
Spalacopus cyanus **5** 289
Spallanzani, Lazzaro **32** 1878
Spanish crescent-horned beetle **42** *2497*
Spanish dancer sea slug **47** *2786*, *2800*
Spanish fighting bull **8** 476
Spanish goat **10** 553, 556-7, 570
Spanish ibex **10** 553, 556-7, 570
Spanish killifish **33** *1973*, 1978
Spanish lobsters **37** 2213-14
Spanish mackerel **34** 2040
Spanish sparrow **25** 1455, 1459
Spanish turtle **26** 1539
Spantagus pupurens **36** 2120
Sparidae **34** 2033
sparkling violetear **21** *1227*, 1230
sparling **33** 1924, 1937
sparrow weaver **25** 1459
sparrowhawk **18** 1057, 1059-60, *1061*, 1063-4, 1070; **51** 3046
sparrows **16** 911; **24** 1381, 1422-3; **25** *1454*, 1455
  classification **24** 1429; **25** 1459
  distribution **25** 1452
spear-nosed bats **12** 684, 703, 705, *708*
  classification **12** 681, 709

spearfishes **35** 2041, 2043
speckle-fronted weaver **25** 1459
speckled mousebird **21** 1247
spectacled bear **2** *70*, 71, 82
spectacled caiman **29** 1685, *1686*
spectacled guillemot **20** 1146, 1148
spectacled leaf monkey **14** *825*, 826
spectacled owl **20** *1184*
spectacled salamander **29** *1728-30*; **30** *1746*
spectacled weaver **25** 1455
spectral tarsier **13** 748, 753
Speke's gazelle **9** 529
Speke's gundi **5** 286
Speotyto cunicularia **20** 1199
sperm whale **10** *572*, *575*, *580*, 584-5
 classification **10** 593
 spout **10** *573-4*, 584
spet **35** 2042-3
Sphaerechinus granularis **36** 2117
Sphaeriacea **48** 2847
Sphaeriidae **48** 2845, 2847
Sphaerium
 corneum **48** 2833, 2847
 lacustre **48** 2845
Sphaeroma **37** *2188*
Sphaerularia bombi **49** *2930-1*
Sphecidae **43** 2534, 2540
Sphecidae wasp, bug predator **41** 2449
Sphecoidea **43** 2534, 2537, 2540
Sphecotheres flaviventris **25** 1465
Spheniscidae **16** 949
Sphenisciformes **16** *935-50*
Spheniscus **16** 949
Sphenodon punctatus **26** 1560
Sphenodontidae **26** 1560
Sphenurus sphenurus **20** 1156
Spheriacea **48** 2845
Sphex rufocinctus **43** 2535, 2540
Sphiggurus mexicanus **5** 283
Sphincterochila **47** 2802
Sphingidae **44** 2617, 2624
Sphingoidea **44** 2624
sphinx-moths **44** 2617
Sphyraena **35** 2043
Sphyraenidae **35** 2043
Sphyrapicus varius **22** 1297
Sphyrna **31** 1839
Sphyrnidae **31** 1839
spider crabs **38** 2223, *2224*, 2232
spider mites **39** 2295, 2298
spider monkeys **13** 722, *729*, *762*, 763-4, 780; **14** *781-2*
 classification **13** 728, 774
spider shell **46** 2720, *2723*, *2726*
spider tortoise **26** 1544, 1546
spider-hunters (sunbirds) **24** 1418
spider-hunting wasps **43** 2537-8, 2540
spiders **36** 2103, 2140, 2141, *2143*; **38** 2240, 2241, *2255-80*; **39** *2281-90*
 poison **38** 2270-2
 reproduction **38** 2274-6
 webs **38** *2264-5*, *2267*, 2272-4
Spilogale **1** 55
Spilornis cheela **18** 1070
Spinachia spinachia **34** 1993
spindle shell **46** *2726*
spined loach **32** 1894, 1905
spinefoots **35** 2066
spinetails **22** 1312
spinner dolphin **10** 588
'spinning tops' **46** 2702-3
spiny...
 anteater **10** 598
 bandicoot **11** 620
 boa **28** 1639
 cockle **48** *2844*
 dogfishes **31** 1836-7, 1839, 1841
 dormouse **5** 261-2
 eels **32** 1872; **35** *2072*, *2083*
 lizards **26** *1518*; **27** 1572, 1573, 1576, 1579
 lobsters **37** 2178, 2181, *2192*, 2213, *2214*, 2216-17
 mouse **5** 261
 pocket mouse **4** 233
 rat **5** 273, 277, 289, 295
 rays **34** 1989
 sand shrimps **36** 2147
 shells **48** 2841
 softshell turtle **26** *1524*, 1526, 1553, *1556*
 spider crab **38** *2230*, 2232
 starfish **36** *2130*
 stick insect **40** 2385
 turtle **26** 1540
spiny-bodied orb-weaver **38** *2261*
spiny-headed worm **49** 2934
spiny-tailed lizard **27** 1565, 1583, *1585*, 1586
spiral-horned antelopes **8** 434, 449, 452, 456, 458; **10** *569*
spire shells **46** 2712, 2713
Spirobranchus giganteus **50** 2942, *2946*
Spirographis **49** *2936*; **50** *2944-5*
Spirorbidae **50** 2942
Spirorbis **50** *2944*
Spirostomum **50** 2976
Spirotricha **50** 2992, 2999
Spirula **48** *2854-5*, *2857-8*
Spirulidae **48** 2855, 2858
Spiruria **49** 2925
spitting spiders **38** 2258, 2270; **39** 2283
spittlebugs **39** 2321; **41** *2448-9*
splashing tetra **32** 1908, *1909*, 1910
splay-footed crickets **40** 2369, 2371, 2374
splendid fairy wren **24** *1398*
split shell **46** *2704*
split-lure frogfish **33** 1961
Spondylidae **48** 2837, 2841
Spondylus **48** *2832*, 2837
sponge crab **38** 2223-5
sponges **36** 2103; **46** *2719*; **48** *2875-80*; **49** *2881-2*
Spongia officinalis **48** 2880
Spongicola **48** 2878
Spongilla **48** 2878, *2879*, 2880
spongillaflies **43** 2570, 2571
Spongillidae **49** 2881
spookfishes **33** 1937, *1941*
spoon-winged lacewings **43** 2570, 2574
spoonbills **17** *996*, 997, *1020*; **51** 3014
 classification **17** 999, 1018
 distribution **17** 1019
Sporopipes frontalis **25** 1459
SPOROZOANS **36** 2103; **50** *2990-3*
sportive lemur **13** 738-9, 742
spot-billed pelican **17** 981, 982
spot-breasted oriole **24** *1426*
spot-nosed monkeys **14** *795*, 816
spot-winged monarch **24** *1399*
spotted...
 bowerbird **25** *1474*, 1476
 crake **19** 1112
 creeper **24** 1412, 1414
 cuscus **11** *616*, *625*
 cusk eel **33** 1956
 damselfish **34** 2024, 2030
 dikkop **19** 1136
 dogfishes **31** *1826*, *1831*, 1834, 1839
 eagle **18** 1067, 1070; **51** 3007
 eagle ray **31** *1827*
 flycatcher **24** *1396-7*, 1399, 1400
 fritillary **44** *2602*
 hyena **2** *100*, *104-8*; **51** 3019, 3023
 leopard seal **4** 181
 longhorn beetle **42** 2506, *2512-3*
 mouse deer **7** 391, 392
 pardalote **24** *1415*
 platys **33** 1980
 salamander **29** 1718, *1719-20*, 1722
 sandgrouse **20** *1151*
 seahorse **34** 2000
 seal **4** 184
 water snake **28** 1643
 wolf-fish **35** 2056, *2057*
spotted linsang **51** 3026
spotted-backed weaver **25** 1458
spotted-sided finch **25** 1453
spotted-tailed quoll **11** *608*
sprat **32** 1886, 1890
spring salamanders **30** 1750, 1751
springbok **9** *518*, 520, *530*, 531-2; **51** 3018
 classification **9** 529
springhare **4** 233
springtails **39** 2303, 2311, 2320, 2328, *2329-33*; **40** 2364
spruce grouse **19** *1086*, 1092
spur-winged goose **18** 1048
spur-winged lapwing **19** 1125
spur-winged plover **19** 1125
spurdog shark **31** 1837, 1841
Spurilla neapolitana **47** 2800, *2801*
squacco heron **17** *999*, 1000, 1004, 1007; **51** 3008
Squalidae **31** 1841
Squaliformes **31** 1841
Squalus acanthias **31** 1841
Squamata **26** 1510; **27** 1562, 1616; **28** 1621
square-lipped rhino **6** 357
square-marked toad **30** 1789, 1790
squat lobster **37** *2220*
Squatina **31** 1841
Squatinidae **31** 1841
squid, swordfish prey **35** 2041
squids **36** 2103; **45** 2670, 2674-5, 2681; **48** 2852, *2854*, *2860-8*
Squilla **37** *2188*; **47** 2797
squirrel family **1** *15*; **4** *219-40*; **51** 3010
squirrel monkey **13** *757*, *762*, 763-4, *770-2*, 773
 classification **13** 774
 distribution **13** 768
 national parks **51** 3038, 3044
squirrelfishes **34** *1985*, 1986, *1988-9*
 classification **34** 1990
 distribution **34** 1988
Sri Lanka blue magpie **25** *1488*
Sri Lanka prehensile-tail lizard **27** 1585
stable flies **45** 2659, *2660*, 2662-3
Stachyris chrysaea **24** 1390
stag beetles **41** 2456; **42** 2491-2, *2501-3*
Stagnicola **47** 2808-9
stalk-eyed squid **48** *2854*, 2861
stalked barnacle **37** *2170*, 2171
standard-winged nightjar **21** *1202*, 1206, 1207, *1208*
Staphylinidae **42** 2472, 2476
Staphylinus
 caesareus **42** *2473*, *2477*
 olens **42** 2472
star sea squirt **35** 2094, *2095*
star-nosed mole **11** *646*, 649; **12** 670, 672
starfishes **36** 2103, *2104-6*, 2107, *2111*, *2130-2*, *2133-7*
 body parts **36** *2108*, 2109
 classification **36** 2107
 diet **36** 2114
 digestive system **36** 2134-5
 distribution **36** 2121
 larvae **36** *2113*, 2114
 movement **36** 2113, *2135-6*
 origins **36** 2115
 predators **36** 2127, *2134*
stargazers **34** 2033, *2034-5*
starlings **25** 1452, *1461-4*
 classification **22** 1303; **25** 1462
 distribution **25** 1452
starry flounder **35** 2074
statocysts **37** 2194
Staurotypidae **26** 1535
Staurotypus triporcatus **26** 1535
steamer ducks **18** 1030, 1041, 1044
Steatornis caripensis **21** 1214
Steatornithidae *22* 1214, 1206
steelhead trout **33** 1931, *1935*
steenbok **8** 441, *442-4*, 446
Steller's sea cow **6** 314, 316
Steller's sea eagle **18** 1072
Steller's sea lion **3** *162*, *165*, 174; **51** 3056
 classification **3** 172
 distribution **3** 164
Stellula calliope **21** 1228
Stenochoteres egregius **37** *2168*
Stenopelmatidea **40** 2369
Stentor **50** 2992, *3000*
 coruleus **50** 2999
 polymorphus **50** *2980*
Stephanorrhina guttata **42** 2495
Stephenitis pyri **41** 2439
Stephens Island wren **22** 1317
steppe fox **2** 119; **3** 127, *128*
steppe pika **4** 209
steppe polecat **51** 3052
Stercorariidae **19** 1121; **20** 1142
Stercorarius **20** 1142
Sterna **20** 1145
Sternidae **19** 1121; **20** 1145
Sternoptychidae **33** 1944
Sternotherus odoratus **26** 1535
Sternotomis **42** 2513
Stichaeidae **35** 2056
stick insects **39** 2311; **40** *2383-7*
stickleback, tapeworm host **49** *2915*
sticklebacks **34** *1991-7*
 classification **34** 1993
 distribution **34** 1999
 nests **34** *1992*-3
sticky caecilian **29** 1710
Stictonetta naevosa **18** 1044
Stictonettini **18** 1030, 1044

stifftails **18** 1030, 1051, 1052
Stigmella ridiculosa **44** 2600
Stilbum cyanurum **43** *2536*
Stilifer **46** 2720, *2758*
Stiliferidae **46** 2720, 2721-2
Stiliger **47** *2777-8*
Stiligerae **47** 2777
stilts **19** 1121, 1129, 1132, 1137; **51** 3046
stingless bees **43** 2540, 2543
stingray **31** *1838*, 1844-5
stink beetle **41** 2457
'stinking jim' **26** 1533
stinkpot turtle **26** *1533*, 1535
Stipiturus malachurus **24** 1398
Stizostedion **34** 2014
stoat **1** *39*, *40*, 48, 56
territories **1** 43, 44
stock dove **20** 1152, 1155, 1156, 1158
stock fish **33** 1951, 1954-5
Stomatopoda **37** 2182
Stomiiformes **33** 1944
Stomoxys calcitrans **45** 2659
stone curlews **19** *1122*, 1129, *1134*, 1136; **51** 3008
classification **19** 1121, 1137
stone loach **32** *1864*, 1894, 1905
stone marten **1** 40, *44*, 46, *47*
stonechat **24** 1387, 1388
stonefishes **34** 2006-7
stoneflies **39** 2311, 2322-3, 2338; **40** *2344-7*
Stone's sheep **10** 566-7
stony corals **49** 2889, *2895*, 2897-9
storks **16** *902-3*; **17** 997, *1009-17*; **51** 3027
classification **17** 999, 1012
distribution **17** 1019
nesting **17** *1010*, 1011
'storm cock' **24** *1388*
storm petrels **17** 962, *968*, *972*
classification **17** 971, 976
distribution **17** 974
Strangalia maculata **42** 2506, *2512-3*
straw-coloured flying fox **12** *681*, 694, 695, *702*
streamertail **21** *1216*, 1228, *1232*, 1237
Strepaxea **48** 2822
Strepaxidae **48** 2822
Strepera graculina **25** 1470
Strepsicerotini **8** 434, 447-60
Strepsiptera **39** 2311; **43** 2575, 2576
Streptopelia **20** 1156
Stresemann's bush-crow **25** 1494
striated heron **17** 1005
Strigidae **20** 1194, 1199
Strigiformes **20** *1183-1200*
Strigops habroptilus **20** 1168
stripe-headed creeper **24** 1415
striped...
barb **32** 1894, *1897*, 1899
bass **34** 2023
burrfish **35** 2082, 2085
hyena **2** *100*, *103*, 104-7; **51** 3054
manakin **23** 1332
mongoose **2** 92, *93*, *96*
mouse **5** *242*
mousebird **21** 1246
mullet **35** 2043
possum **11** 627
rat **5** 262
scat **35** 2044
serranid **34** 2023
skink **27** 1595
skunk **1** 55, *56*
squirrelfish **34** *1989*, 1990
stripeless tree frog **29** *1698*
Strix aluco **20** 1199
Strombacea **46** 2720, 2722
Strombidae **46** 2714, 2720
Strombus **46** 2720, 2723
gallus **46** *2726*
gigas **45** 2696; **46** *2732-3*
goliath **46** 2720, 2722
lentiginosus **46** *2722*
Strongylida **49** 2925
Strongylocentrotus propuratus **36** 2126
Struthidea cinerea **25** 1470
Struthio camelus **16** 925
Struthionidae **16** 925
Struthioniformes **16** 925
stump-tailed chameleon **27** 1592
stump-tailed macaque **14** *796*, 803, 805
stump-tailed skink **27** 1593, *1594*, 1598
sturgeons **31** *1806*, *1808*, 1848, *1851-4*
classification **31** 1809, 1856
Sturnidae **22** 1303; **25** 1462
Sturnira lilium **12** 709
Sturnus **25** 1462
Stylochus frontalis **49** 2905, 2911
Stylommatophora **47** 2803, 2805, *2810*, 2817-18; **48** *2821-30*
Stylonicha **50** *2993*
Stylopidae **43** 2576
sub-ungulates **5** 298
subantarctic fur seal **3** *168*
subcylindrical truncatella **46** 2716
Suberites domuncula **46** 2719
suboscines **22** 1303, 1306-7
Succinea **47** *2819*, 2820
Succineacea **47** 2817, 2818, 2820
Succinedae **47** 2820
Succinia putris **47** *2804*
sucker-footed bat **12** 681, 708, 709
suckerfish **31** *1830*; **35** 2046, 2048
suckermouth armoured catfish **32** 1913
suckers **32** 1894, 1904, 1910
sucking lice **39** 2311; **41** 2428, 2429-30
suction disc **35** *2046-7*
Suctoria **50** 2971, 2992
suctorians **50** *2998-9*
Sudan golden sparrow **25** *1454*, 1455
sugar glider **11** *616*, *622-3*, *627*, 630; **12** *674*; **51** 3048
sugarbirds **24** 1419, 1420
sugarcane plant hopper **41** 2438
Suidae **7** 370
SUIDS **7** *363-72*
Suillotaxus marchei **1** 55
Suina **10** 569
Sula **17** 994
Sulawesi cuscus **11** 625
Sulawesi swordtail butterfly **44** *2634*
Sulidae **17** 994
sulphur-crested cockatoo **20** 1163, 1168
sultan tit **24** 1402
Sumatran elephant **6** 324, 326
Sumatran hare **4** 209, 214
Sumatran orang-utan **15** 852, 853
Sumatran rhino **6** *354*, 356-7, 358; **7** 361, 362
Sumatran umbrella octopus **48** *2866*
summer flounder **35** 2075, *2078*
sun animalcules **50** 2990-1
sun bears **2** *70*, 71, 81
sun bittern **19** *1104*, 1107, 1115, *1117*, 1118
sun grebe **19** 1114
sun skink **27** *1593*
sun spiders **38** *2238*, 2241, *2242*, *2252-4*, *2260*
sun stars **36** *2132*, 2134, *2135*, *2136*
sunbeam python **28** 1626
sunbeam snake **28** 1621, *1624*, *1626*, 1628
classification **28** 1626
distribution **28** 1628
sunbirds **22** 1304, *1305*; **24** *1416-18*
classification **22** 1303; **24** 1417
distribution **24** 1408
Suncus **1** *8*; **12** 662
Sunderbans Tiger Reserve **51** 3002, *3028-9*
sundial **46** *2704*, 2712, *2716-17*
sunfishes **34** 2014, 2015-7; **35** 2082, 2087
sungazer **27** *1594*, *1597*, 1598
suni **8** 438-9, 444
superb bird of paradise **25** *1477*, 1480, 1483
superb fairy wren **24** 1399
superb fruit dove **20** 1156
superb lyrebird **23** 1325, *1326-7*, *1328*, *1356*
surelis **14** 796, 826
surgeon fish **31** *1858*; **34** *2019*; **35** *2065-6*, 2067
Suricata suricatta **2** 98
suricate **2** 86, *90-1*, *96*, *98*
Surinam toad **30** 1763, *1764*, *1765*, 1768, 1769
Surnia ulula **20** 1199
Sus **7** 370
swallow tanager **24** *1426*, 1429, 1430
swallow-tailed bee-eater **22** 1267
swallow-tailed gull **19** *1122*
swallow-tailed manakin **23** 1331, *1332*, 1333
swallow-tailed swift **21** 1225
swallow-winged puffbird **22** 1284
swallower fishes **32** 1874, 1884
swallows **16** 912; **22** *1302*, 1304, 1306; **23** *1340-7*
classification **22** 1303; **23** 1345
distribution **23** 1322
nests **23** *1343*
swallowtail butterfly **39** *2319*; **44** 2594, *2603*, 2633, *2635-6*
swamp deer **7** *397*, 401, 404, *406*, *410*; **8** 421
swamp eel **34** *1996*, *2005-6*
swamp rabbit **4** 209, 212
swamp rat **5** 261
swamp wallaby **11** 642
swan goose **18** 1040; **51** 3052
swan mussel **48** 2843
swans **18** *1028*, 1029, *1030*, 1031-4, *1036-9*
body parts **16** 905, 906
classification **18** 1030, 1044
distribution **18** 1031
Swayne's dik-dik **8** *436*, *440*, 444
Swayne's hartebeest **9** 486
swee waxbill **25** 1453
sweepslang **27** 1597, 1598
swift fox 121-3, *128*
classification **3** 127
swift moths **44** 2595, 2599
swiftlets **21** 1218, *1223*, 1224
swifts **16** 912; **21** *1217-27*
classification **21** 1218
distribution **21** 1217, 1219, 1222-3
swim bladder **31** 1859; **32** *1861-3*
swimming crab **38** *2224*, 2225-9
sword-billed hummingbird **21** *1216*, 1228, 1229, *1230*, 1232
swordfish **31** 1859; **34** *2037*; **35** 2041, 2043, 2047
swordtail **33** *1972*, 1976-8, 1980; **34** *1981*
swordtail characin **32** 1908, 1910, *1911*
Sydney funnel-web spider **38** 2258; **39** *2281*, *2282*, 2283, 2285
Sygnathus **34** 2000
syllid **49** *2936*
Syllidae **50** 2942
Syllis ramosa **49** 2939; **50** 2942
Sylvia **24** 1394
Sylvicapra grimmia **8** 440
Sylviidae **24** 1394
Sylvilagus **4** 206, 209
Sympetrum pedemontanum **40** *2355*
Symphosodon **35** 2049, 2054
Symphurus arawak **35** 2075
Symphyla **39** 2302, 2303
Symphyta **42** 2516, 2518
Synanceiidae **34** 2007
Synaphobranchidae **32** 1874
Synapis **42** 2495
Synbranchidae **34** 2006
Synbranchiformes **34** *1996*, 2006
Synbranchus marmoratus **34** 2006
Syncarida **37** 2182, 2189, 2192, *2193*
Syncerus caffer **8** 468
Syngnathidae **34** 2000
Syngnathiformes **34** *1996*, 1998, 2000
Synodontidae **33** 1946
Synodus synodus **33** 1946
Synthliboramphus craveri **20** 1148
Syntomis phegea **39** *2322*
Syrian ostrich **16** 918-19
Syrian wild ass **6** 345
Syrphidae **45** 2655, 2659
Syrphus ribesii **45** 2656
Syrrhaptes **20** 1152
Syrski (biologist) **32** 1878
Systellommatophora **47** 2803, 2805, 2817
Sysyridae **43** 2570, 2571

tabanid fly **45** *2654*
Tabanidae **45** 2652
Tabanus bovinus **45** 2652, *2458*
Table Mountain ghost frog **30**

1799
table-top coral **51** 3032
Tacazze sunbird **24** *1417*
Tachina larvarum **45** 2662
tachinid flies **45** 2660-2
Tachinidae **45** 2659-60
Tachybaptus ruficollis **16** 960
Tachycineta bicolor **23** 1345
Tachycnemis seychellensis **30** 1785
Tachyeres **18** 1044
Tachyerini **18** 1030, 1044
Tachyglossidae **11** 606
Tachyglossus aculeatus **11** 606
Tachypleus gigas **38** 2235
Tacicha torosa **29** 1729
Taczanowski's snow finch **25** 1455
Tadarida **12** 716
Tadorna **18** 1044
Tadornini **18** 1030, 1044
tadpole clingfish **33** 1962
tadpole shrimp **36** 2149, *2150-1, 2156*
tadpole-fish **33** *1952*
tadpoles **29** *1698*, 1703, 1706; **30** *1758-9*
Taenia **49** 2911
solium **49** 2911, 2917
Taeniura lymma **31** 1844
tahr **9** *534*, 535; **10** 552, 554-5, 570
Tai National Park **51** 3002, *3020-1*
taiko **17** 976
tailed amphibians **29** 1713
tailed frog **30** 1759, 1760, *1764*, 1768
tailless whip scorpions **38** 2241, *2242*, 2252, *2254-5*
tailorbird **24** *1392*
taipan **28** 1640, 1641, 1667
taira **1** 41, 46
Taiwan sika **7** 404
Taiwan turtle **26** 1540
Taiwanese serow **10** 541, 550
takahe **19** *1104*, 1112, 1113, 1115; **51** 3050
takin **8** 434; **9** *534*, 535; **10** *545*, 549-50
talapoin monkey **14** 793-4, *795*, 816, 819-20, *821*
Talitrus **37** 2205-6
saltator **37** *2205*
Talpa **12** 670
Talpidae **11** 651; **12** 670
taltuza **4** 233
tamandua **4** *187*, 188, 195
Tamandua **4** 195
tamarau **8** 466, 468
tamaraw **8** 463, 468
tamarins **12** 720; **13** *758*, 763-4; **14** 782, *783*, 786-7, 790; **51** 3038
classification **13** 728; **14** 790
distribution **13** 768
primate order **12** 719; **15** *897*
Tamias sibiricus **4** 233
tammar wallaby **11** *637*, 642
tanagers **22** 1303; **24** *1426, 1427-8*, 1429
Tanaidacea **37** 2195-6
Tangara chilensis **24** 1429
tangled web spiders **39** 2283
tangs **35** 2065-7
tank goby **35** 2060
tanner beetle **42** 2506, 2512
Tanyptera atrata **45** *2644*
Tanysiptera galatea **21** 1253
Tanzania, national park **51** 3002, *3022-3*
tapaculos **22** 1308, 1314
Tapes decussatus **48** 2850
tapestry turban shell **45** 2700; **46** 2703
tapeworms **49** *2903-20*
Taphozous perforatus **12** 704
tapir **5** 299-300; **6** *301*, 319, 349-52; **10** *568*; **51** 3041
Tapiridae **6** 352
TAPIRIDS **6** *349-52*
Tapirus **6** 352
tarantula hawk-wasp **43** *2536*, 2537
tarantula-eating wasp **43** 2538, 2540
tarantulas **38** 2257, 2258, 2263; **39** 2283
Tardigrada **50** 2961, 2963
TARDIGRADES **45** *2670*; **50** *2963, 2964*
Tarentola mauritanica **27** 1569
tarpan **6** 347, 348; **51** 3006-7
Tarpon atlanticus **32** 1872
tarpons **32** 1868, *1872*; **33** *1940*
tarsiers **13** 722, 727, 739, *744, 753-4*
classification **13** 728, 742, 748
eyes **13** 721, 733-4
primate order **12** 718, 719; **15** *896*
Tarsiidae **13** 742, 748
Tarsipedidae **11** 612, 633
Tarsipes rostratus **11** 633
Tarsius **13** 748
Tasaday people **15** *892-3*
Tasmanian devil **11** *608*, 610, *617-18*, 619
Tasmanian devil flea **45** 2665
Tasmanian tiger **11** 618, *619*
Tasmanian wallaby **11** 635
Tasmanian wolf **11** 618, *619*
tasselled wobbegong **31** *1829*
tassle-eared marmoset **14** 782, 787, 790
Tate's shrew opossum **11** 624
Tatra chamois **10** 548
Tauraco **20** 1178
Taurotragus **8** 452
tawny cockroach **40** *2394*
tawny eagle **18** 1058
tawny frogmouth **21** *1202, 1210-11*, 1214
tawny owl **20** *1195*, 1199, *1200*
tawny pipit **23** 1352, *1353*, 1354
tawny prominent moth **44** 2625
Taxidea taxus **1** 55
Taxomyia taxi **45** 2645, 2647
Tayassu **7** 370
Tayassuidae **7** 370
TAYASSUIDS **7** *364-6, 370-2*
teal **18** 1044, 1045, *1046*, 1047
teeth, mammals **1** 11-12, 20-1, *22*
Tegeneria domestica **38** *2261*
Tegeticula yuccasella **44** 2595
tegu **27** *1594, 1601*, 1603
Teiidae **27** 1603
Teleonomus lopicida **41** 2437
TELEOSTS **31** *1808, 1857-60*; **32** *1861-6*
classification **31** 1809; **34** 2013
evolution **31** *1806*, 1809
swim bladder **31** 1858; **32** *1861-3*
Telescopus fallax **28** 1645
Telespyza cantans **24** 1435
Tellinacea fabuloides **48** 2847
Tellinidae **48** 2847
Telmatherina ladigesi **34** 1982
Telmatobius culeus **30** 1795
Telmatochromis vittatus **35** *2049*
Temminck's pangolin **4** 200
temple turtle **26** 1540
ten-spot ladybird **42** 2484
tench **32** 1893, *1895-6*, 1897-8
classification **32** 1894
Tenebrio molitor **42** 2472, *2492*
tenebrionid beetles **41** 2456, *2457*
Tenebrionidae **41** 2456; **42** 2472, 2490
Tengmalm's owl **20** *1184*, 1199
tenpounders **32** 1872
Tenrec ecaudatus **11** 651
Tenrecidae **11** 651
Tenrecinae **11** 651
tenrecs **11** *646-7*, 648-9, *651-3*
tent-building bat **12** 703
tentacled snake **28** *1642*, 1645, 1648-9
tentacleless squid **48** 2861
Tentaculata **49** 2901, 2902
Tenthredinidae **42** 2516, 2518
Tenthredopsis **42** *2518*
Tephritidae **45** 2657, 2659
Terathopius ecaudatus **18** 1070
Teratornis **18** 1062
Terebra
staminea **47** 2766
subulata **47** *2762*
triseriata **47** 2766
Terebrantia **41** 2428
Terebratulida **50** 2966
Terebridae **46** 2746; **47** 2766
Teredinidae **48** 2848-50
Teredo **48** *2844*, 2848, 2850
termite beetles **42** 2472
termites **39** 2311, 2319-20, 2323, 2326; **40** 2390; **41** *2401-26*
aardvark food **6** 310
aardwolf food **2** 101
elephant-shrew food **11** 660
nests **41** 2403, 2418-19, *2422-3*
sloth bear food **2** 81-2
soldiers **41** 2404-7
Termitidae **41** 2403, 2405, 2408, 2411
Termitomyces **41** 2423
termitophiles **41** 2423
Termopsidae **41** 2405
terns **19** 1121, 1139; **20** *1143-4*, 1145; **51** 3008
Terpsiphone viridis **24** 1400
Terrapene **26** 1539
terrapins **26** 1527, 1536, 1538-9
classification **26** 1510
terrestrial leeches **50** 2958
terrestrial tree shrew **13** 730
Tersiinae **24** 1429
Tersina viridis **24** 1429
Tertiary period **1** 28
tessellate nerite **46** 2705
Testacealobosa **50** 2989, 2991
Testacella **48** 2825
Testacellidae **48** 2825
Testudinae **26** 1544
Testudinata **26** 1530
Testudo **26** 1544
Tethyidae **47** 2797
Tethys **47** 2797
Tetracerus quadricornis **8** 460
Tetragonopterus **32** 1909
Tetranychidae **39** 2295
Tetrao **19** 1093
Tetraodon fluviatilis **35** 2082
Tetraodontidae **35** 2082
Tetraodontiformes **35** *2081-7*
Tetraogallus tibetanus **19** 1096
Tetraonidae **19** 1088, 1093
Tetrapterus angustirostris **35** 2043
tetras **32** *1906*, 1908, *1909*
Tetrax tetrax **19** 1112
Tetrigidae **40** 2369
Tettigonia viridissima **40** 2369-70
Tettigoniidea **40** 2369
Teuthidea **48** 2867
Teuthoidea **48** 2855, 2857-8, 2860-1
Texas alligator lizards **51** 3043
Texas banded gecko **27** 1568
Texas blind salamander **29** *1712*; **30** 1750, 1752
Texas blind snake **28** *1622*, 1623, 1625
Texas horned lizard **27** 1572
Texas peccary **51** 3042
Thailand, national park **51** 3002, 3004, *3030-1*
Thailand brow-antlered deer **7** 404; **8** 421
Thalassicola nucleata **50** *2890*
Thalassinoidea **37** 2220
Thalassoma bifasciatum **34** 2023
Thaliacea **35** 2090
thaliceans **35** *2099-2100*
thamin **7** 404
Thamnophilus doliatus **22** 1310
Thamnophis sirtalis **28** 1645
Thanatophilus sinuatus **42** *2473*
Thaumetopoeidae **44** 2622-3, 2624
Thayeria obliquua **32** 1908
Thea **42** 2472, *2482*, 2484
Thecalia concamerata **48** 2845
Thecla **44** *2596*
thecodonts **26** 1506, *1507*
Thecosomata **47** 2767, *2784*, 2786
thecosome mollusc **47** *2774*
Theileria **50** 2992, 2997
Thelyphonus **38** 2255
Theodoxus **46** 2705
fluviatilis **46** *2704-5*
longispina **45** 2700
Theraphosa leblondii **39** *2282*, 2283
Theraphosidae **38** 2258, *2261*, 2263; **39** 2283
therapsids **26** 1506, *1507*
Theridiidae **38** 2257, 2258; **39** 2283
Thermobia **39** 2335
Thermosbaena mirabilis **37** 2193
Thermosbaenacea **37** 2193
Theropithecus gelada **14** 811
Thiara amurua **46** *2704*
thick-billed lark **23** 1334
thick-billed murre **20** 1148
thick-billed prion **17** 973
thick-knees **19** 1134, 1137
thick-lipped dog whelk **46** 2746, *2751*
thick-tailed bush baby **13** 739, 748, 752
thick-tailed opossum **11** 615
thickheads **24** 1400
thin-lipped mullet **35** 2043
thin-spined porcupine **5** 283
thinhorn sheep **10** 566-7, 570
Thinocoridae **19** 1121, 1137
Thinocorus rumicivorus **19** 1137
Thomisidae **38** 2257; **39** 2289
Thomomys **4** 233
Thompson, J. V. **37** 2169
Thomson's gazelle **9** *522-3*, 524, 529; **51** 3022-3

Thoracica **37** 2169, 2174
thornback ray **31** 1842, 1844
thornbirds **22** 1309
thorny corals **49** 2889, 2899
thorny devil **27** 1585, *1587*
thorny leaf cricket **40** *2365*
thorny oyster **48** *2832*, 2837, 2841
Thorold's deer **7** 406
thrashers **23** 1378, 1380
Thraupinae **24** 1429
thread herring **32** *1888*
thread snakes **28** 1621, *1622*, 1623, 1625
thread-horned flies **45** 2647
thread-waisted wasps **43** *2529*, 2534-5, *2536*, 2540
thread-winged lacewings **43** 2570, 2574
three spot gourami **32** *1865*
three-banded armadillo **4** 189, *197*
three-bearded rockling **33** *1953-4*
three-pronged bristletails **39** *2328*, *2334*, 2335
three-spined stickleback **34** 1992-3, *1994-5*
three-striped damselfish **34** 2024, 2030-1
three-toed amphiuma **30** 1742
three-toed parrotbill **24** 1392
three-toed salamander **30** 1745
three-toed skink **27** 1595, *1596*, 1598
three-toed sloth **4** 193, 195
three-toed woodpecker **51** 3007
three-wattled bellbird **23** 1322, 1323, *1324*
threefin blenny **35** 2059
Threkiornis aethiopica **17** 1018
thresher shark **31** *1826*, 1834, 1839
Threskiornithidae **17** 999, 1018
thrips **39** 2311; **41** 2428, *2430-1*
thrush-like wren **23** 1377, 1379
thrushes **16** 916; **22** 1303; **24** 1382, *1388-9*
Thryonomyidae **5** 277, 289
Thryonomys
gregorianus **5** 289
swinderianus **5** 289
Thryothorus ludovicianus **23** 1379
thumbless bats **12** 681, 708, 709
thunderfly **41** 2428, *2431*
Thunnus thynnus **34** 2036
Thyca **46** 2727
thylacine **11** *608*, 609, 610, 612, 618, 619
Thylacinidae **11** 612, 619
Thylacinus cynocephalus **11** 619
Thylacomyidae **11** 612, 620
Thymallus thymallus **33** 1924
Thyroptera discifera **12** 709
Thyropteridae **12** 681, 709
Thysamia agrippina **44** *2596*, 2624
Thysanoptera **39** 2311; **41** *2428-31*
Thysanura **39** 2311, 2335, 2336
tiang **9** 488
Tibetan antelope **9** 535
Tibetan gazelle **9** 520, 525, 529
Tibetan sand fox **3** 127
Tibetan sandgrouse **20** 1152
Tibetan snowcock **19** 1096, 1097
Tibetan takin **10** 550
Tibetan water shrew **12** 662, 663
Tibia fusus **46** *2726*
Tichodroma muraria **24** 14
tick spiders **38** 2252
ticks **36** 2103, 2140; **38** 2241; **39** 2293-8
tiger...
barb **32** *1906*
beetles **39** 2324; **41** 2456, 2458, *2459-60*; **42** 2461
bittern **17** 1007
butterflies **44** 2607
cat **3** 158; **51** 3044, 3048
cowrie **46** 2720, *2725*, 2730, 2736
heron **17** *996*, 997, 1007, 1008
moths **44** *2604*, 2616, 2617 *2620*, 2624
defence **44** *2618-19*
salamander **29** *1712*, *1718-19*, 1722
scallop **48** 2837
shark **31** 1835, *1836*, 1839
snake **28** *1667*
tigerfishes **32** 1907, 1908
tigers **1** *17*, 22, 32; **3** *134*, 137, *144-5*, 152
classification **3** 144
distribution **1** 17; **3** 135, 140, 152
national parks **51** 3004, *3026*, *3028-9*, *3056-7*
tigrillo **3** 158
Tigriornis leucolophus **17** 1007
Tigrisoma lineatum **17** 1007
Tijuca atra **23** 1322
Tilapia **35** 2049-50, *2056*
andersoni **35** *2056*
karomo **35** 2054
macrochir **35** 2054, *2056*
rendalli **35** 2050
variabilis **35** *2056*
zillii **35** 2050
Tiliqua rugosa **27** 1598
Timaliidae **24** 1390
timber wolf **51** 3036, 3041
timberman beetle **42** 2506, *2512*
Timematodea **40** 2385
Timor deer **7** 406
Tinamidae **16** 933
Tinamiformes **16** 918, *932-4*
tinamous **16** 918, *932*, *933*, 934; **19** 1097
Tinamus major **16** 933
Tinbergen, Niko **16** 903; **20** 1141
Tinca tinca **32** 1894
Tinea **44** 2609
Tineidae **44** 2600, 2609
Tineoidea **44** 2600, 2602, 2609
Tingidae **41** 2438, 2441
tinkerbird **22** 1286, 1287, 1288
tiny ladybird **42** 2484, 2486
Tipula oleracea **45** *2641*, 2643, *2645*, 2647
Tipulidae **45** 2643, 2647
tit babblers **24** 1389
titan **34** 2040
Titan mussel shrimp **36** 2160
Titanolabis collossea **40** 2389
titi monkeys **13** *764-5*, 768-9, 774; **15** 846
tits **24** 1382, *1401-7*
Tmetothylacus tenellus **23** 1352
toad-eater snake **28** 1644
toadfish **33** *1958-9*
toads **29** 1698, 1702, 1703, 1704, *1706*; **30** *1755-1800*
classification **29** 1701; **30** 1756
distribution **30** 1768, 1790
Tockus **22** 1278
toco toucan **22** *1280*, 1290
tococos **22** 1309, 1310, 1312
Todidae **21** 1253; **22** 1270
todies **21** 1252, 1253; **22** *1268-9*, 1270
Todus **22** 1270

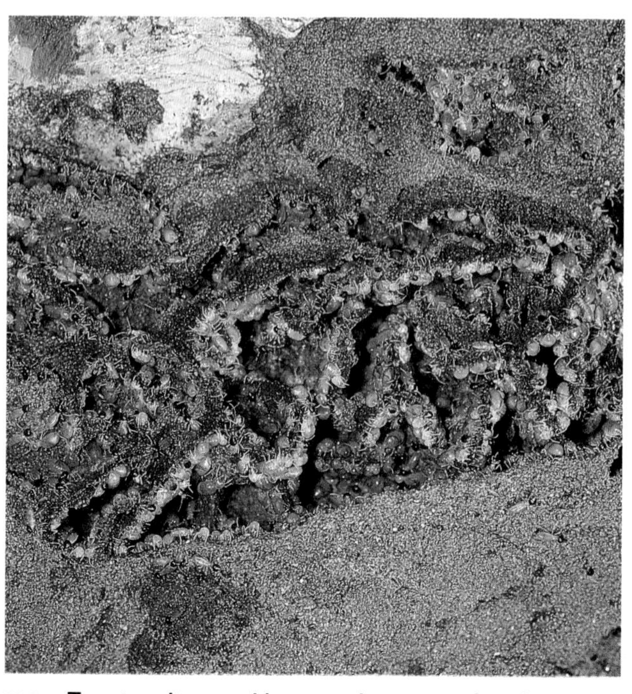

ABOVE Tree termites working together to repair a damaged nest.

tody motmot **22** 1269, 1270
toe-biter bugs **41** 2443
tokay gecko **27** *1563*, 1565, 1566, *1567*, 1569
Tolypeutes **4** 197
tomb bat **12** *690*, 696-7, *703*
Tomistoma schlegelii **29** 1685
Tomopteridae **49** 2939; **50** 2942
Tomopteris hegolandica **49** *2940*
tompot blenny **35** 2059
tongue worms **50** 2960, 2963-4
tongue-fishes **35** 2075
tongue-soles **35** 2075, 2080
Tonicella lineata **45** *2684*
Tonna
galea **46** 2737, **47** *2762*
perdrix **46** *2745*
Tonnacea **46** 2737, 2740
Tonnidae **46** 2737, 2743
tooth-billed bowerbird **25** 1472-3, 1474, 1476
tooth-billed pigeon **20** 1156, 1158
tooth-shelled molluscs **45** 2691
toothcarps **33** 1964, *1970-80*; **34** 1981-2
classification **33** 1968, 1978
distribution **33** 1976
toothed whales **10** 577, *584-96*
top shells **45** 2700; **46** *2702-3*
tope **31** 1814, 1834, 1839
topi **9** 486, 488-9, 490; **51** 3024
topknot **35** *2073*, 2074-5
toque macaque **14** 803, 805, 808
tora hartebeest **9** 486
Torgos tracheliotus **18** 1070
Torina variegata **46** 2717
Torpedinidae **31** 1842
Torpedo
marmorata **31** 1842
nobiliana **31** 1842
torpedo **31** 1842
torrent catfish **32** 1912-13
torrent duck **18** 1047
torrent dwelling caddisflies **44** *2581-2*
torrent lark **25** 1469, 1470
torsk **33** 1954
Torticidae **44** 2603
tortoise beetles **42** 2504, *2506-7*
tortoise-shell butterfly **44** *2592*, 2633, *2634*
tortoises **1** 14; **26** *1523-4*, 1525, *1540-6*; **51** 3034
classification **26** 1510, 1544
evolution **26** *1507*
Tortricidae **44** 2609
Tortricoidea **44** 2609
Tortrix viridiana **44** *2604*, 2609
toucan barbet **22** *1287*, 1288
toucanets **22** 1290, 1291
toucans **22** 1274, *1280-1*, 1282, *1290-2*
classification **22** 1284, 1290
distribution **22** 1282
Toxoplasma gondii **50** 2993
Toxostoma rufum **23** 1380
Toxotes jaculata **35** 2044
Toxotidae **35** 2044, *2064*
Trachinidae **34** 2033
Trachinus draco **34** 2033
Trachipteridae **34** 1987
Trachipterus **34** 1987
trachura stickleback **34** 1992
Trachurus trachurus **34** 2036
Trachyphonus darnaudii **22** 1288
Trachyrhynchus trachyrincus **33** 1951

Tragelaphus **8** 452
Tragopan satyra **19** 1096
tragopans **19** 1096, 1098
Tragulidae **7** 392
TRAGULIDS **7** *389-92*, 414
Tragulus **7** 392
transparent goby **35** 2065
Transvaal sweepslang **27** 1598
trap-door spiders **38** 2258, 2279-80; **39** 2281
tree...
babbler **24** 1389
boas **28** 1635, 1636
cricket **40** *2366*
ducks **18** 1030, 1036
finch **24** 1425
fox **3** 126
frogs **26** *1501-3*; **30** *1772*, *1764*, 1791-2, *1793*, *1796-7*
classification **30** 1756, 1785, 1795
distribution **30** 1774, 1790
Old World **30** 1756, 1774, 1779, 1782, 1785
hyrax **6** *311-12*, 313, 316
kangaroo **11** *616*, 634, 636, 642; **51** 3048
lizard **27** 1573
mantids **40** 2391, 2400
monitor **27** *1607*, 1609, 1614
mouse **5** 261
pangolin **4** *198*; **51** 3020
pies **25** 1490
pipit **23** 1352, 1354
porcupine **5** *276*, 277, 283
shrews **12** *718*, 719-20; **13** 721, *730*, 739, *744*
snails **47** *2804*, 2817
snake **27** 1618
sparrow **25** 1455, 1459
squirrels **4** 223, 226, 232-3, 234
swallow **23** 1345, 1346
termite **41** *2424*
warbler **24** 1395
tree-climbing salamander **30** 1752
tree-dwelling ant **43** 2529, *2556*
tree-hoppers **40** *2364*; **41** *2439*, *2448*, 2449-50
tree-of-heaven silk-moths **44** 2624
treecreepers **16** 905, 909; **24** 1408, *1412-14*
treerunners **22** 1309; **24** 1409, 1412
Trematoda **49** 2911, 2912-3
trematode fluke **47** 2820
tremblers **23** 1380
Triakis semifasciata **31** 1839
Triatoma
infestans **41** *2437*
megista **41** 2438
Tribolonotus **27** 1598
Triceratops **26** 1508
Trichechus **6** 314
Trichinella spiralis **49** 2925, *2928*, 2929
Trichiuridae **35** 2067
Trichiurus lepturus **35** 2067
Trichius **42** 2503
fasciatus **42** 2495
zonatus **42** *2499*
Trichobatrachus robustus **30** 1785
Trichodectes canis **41** 2428
Trichogaster leeri **35** 2070
Trichoglossus haematodus **20** 1168
Trichomonas **50** 2976
dubosqui **50** *2980*
Trichomycteridae **32** 1913
Trichonympha corbula **50** 2976
Trichoplax adhaerans **48** 2874
Trichoptera **39** 2311; **43** *2577-80*; **44** 2582
Trichosurus **11** 625
Trichuris trichiura **49** 2925, 2929
Tricladida **49** 2905, 2909
Tridacna **48** *2844*, *2847*
Tridacnidae **48** 2846, 2847
Tridacttyloidea **40** 2369
triggerfishes **35** 2082, *2083*, *2086-7*
Trigla lucerna **34** 2007
Triglidae **34** 2007
Trigoniidae **48** 2843
Trigonoida **48** 2843
Trigonopsis cameronni **43** 2525
Trigonopterygoidea **40** 2369
trillers **23** 1357
trilobites **36** 2140, *2141*
Trimeresurus **28** 1669
Trimmatom nanus **35** 2060
Trinectes maculatus **35** 2075
Tringa **19** 1135
Tringinae **19** 1135
Trionychidae **26** 1553
Trionyx spinifer **26** 1553
Triops cancriformis **36** *2156*
Triphoridae **46** 2712
Triplax aenea **42** *2505*
tripod fish **33** 1944, *1946*
Tripoxylon figulus **43** 2537
Tripterygiidae **35** 2059
triton shells **46** 2737, *2738-9*, *2742-3*, 2744; **47** *2762*
Tritonalia nodifer **46** *2738-9*
Tritonia
festiva **47** *2792*, 2796-7
hombergi **47** 2796
plebeia **47** *2795*, 2797
Tritoniidae **47** 2796
Triton's trumpet **46** 2737, 2743, *2744*
Triturus **29** 1729
Trivia **46** 2720, 2727
arctica **46** *2728*
Trividae **46** 2720
Trochacea **45** 2700; **46** 2702
Trochidae **45** 2700; **46** 2702-3
Trochilidae **21** 1218, 1228
Trochiloectes **41** 2428
Trochilus polytmus **21** 1228
Trochomorpha trochiformis **47** 2816
Trochus niloticus **45** 2700
trocophores **50** 2945
Trogidae **42** 2503
Troglocaris inermis **37** *2213*
Troglodytes **23** 1379
Troglodytidae **22** 1303; **23** 1379
Trogloglanis **32** 1913
Trogon **21** 1241
Trogonidae **21** 1241
Trogoniformes **21** *1239-45*, 1246
Trogonophidae **27** 1616
trogons **21** *1239-45*, 1246
Trombidiidae **39** 2295
Trombidioidea **39** 2295, 2298
Trophidae **47** 2790
tropical centipedes **39** *2302*
tropical damselfly **40** 2362
tropical flying fish **33** 1965
tropical rain forests **4** 200
tropical slugs **47** 2803
tropicbirds **17** 973, *978-80*
Tropicorbis **47** 2810
Tropidophis **28** 1637
trout **31** 1806, 1824; **32** 1895; **33** *1923-4*, *1930-6*; **51** 3041
tapeworm host **49** 2915
trout-perches **33** 1948; **34** *1996*
Trox **42** 2503
true cattle **8** 468
true deer **7** *389-91*, *393-420*; **10** *569*
true eagles **18** 1070
true eel **34** 2006
true flies **39** 2311, 2323, **45** *2641-64*
true geese **18** 1030, 1039, 1040, 1044
true lemurs **13** 735, 739, 743
true seal **3** 167, 176, 180; **4** 183, 184
classification **3** 179
distribution **3** 172, 180
true shrikes **23** *1362-7*
true soles **35** 2075
trumpet manucode **25** 1480
trumpet shells **46** 2722
trumpetbird **25** 1480
trumpeter finch **25** 1448
trumpeter hornbill **22** 1278
trumpeter swans **51** 3041
trumpeters **19** 1107, 1115, 1117-8
trumpetfishes **34** *1998-2000*
Truncatella **46** 2716
subscylindrica **46** 2712
Truncatellidae **46** 2712, 2716
trunk barb **32** *1861*
trunkfishes **35** 2082, 2085-6
Trypanosoma
gambiense **50** 2976, 2981, *2985*
rhodesiense **50** 2976, 2981, 2985
Trypanosomatidae **50** 2985
trypanosomatids **50** *2985*
trypanosomids **36** 2103
Trypetesa lampas **37** 2177, *2179*
tsaine **8** 468, 474
tsessebe **9** 488-9
tsetse flies **39** 2310; **45** *2658*, 2659, 2662-3; **50** 2976
tuan **11** 617
tuatara **26** 1513, 1515, *1557-60*
classification **26** 1510, 1560
evolution **26** *1507*
tub gurnard **34** 2007, *2010*, *2037*
tube anemone **49** *2886*, *2897*
tube-blenny **35** 2059
tube-making caddisflies **43** 2580; **44** 2583-4
tube-mouth pencilfish **32** *1906*, 1908
tube-nose seabirds **17** 962
tube-web spiders **38** 2258; **39** 2283
Tubifex **50** 2947, 2952
Tubificidae **50** 2952
Tubulanus annulatus **49** *2918*, 2920
tubular sponge **35** 2059
Tubulidentata **6** 304
Tubulifera **41** 2428
tuco-tuco **5** *272*, 277, 289, *294*
tucuxi **10** *588*, 593
tufted bat **12** 697
tufted deer **7** 396, 414
tufted duck **18** 1047, 1048
tufted puffin **19** *1122*; **20** 1148
tufted-ear marmoset **14** 787, 790
tui **24** *1413*, *1420*
tulip shells **46** *2754-5*
tun shells **46** 2737, 2743, *2745*; **47** *2762*
tuna **31** 1959; **32** *1863*; **34** *2037*, 2039; **35** *2041*, 2047
classification **34** 2036
tundra swan **18** 1044
Tunga penetrans **45** 2665
Tunicata **35** 2090
tunicates **50** 2966
tunny **34** 2036, 2040
tuntong **26** 1539, 1540
tupaia **13** *730*
Tupaia glis **13** 730
Tupaiidae **13** 730
Tupaiinae **13** 730
Tupinambis teguixin **27** 1603
turacos **20** *1172-4*, 1178, 1179
turban shells **45** 2700; **46** 2703
Turbanella **49** 2923
Turbellaria **49** 2904, 2905, *2908*, 2910
Turbinella pyrum **46** 2746
Turbinidae **45** 2700; **46** 2703
Turbo **45** 2700; **46** 2703
turbots **35** 2075, 2080, *2083*
Turdidae **24** 1388
Turdus
merula **24** 1388
migratorius **24** 1388
philomelos **24** 1388
pilaris **24** 1388
viscivorus **24** 1388
turkey vulture **16** 912; **18** 1062-3, 1064
turkeyfish **34** 2007
turkeys **19** 1087, 1088, 1098, *1100*, 1101-2
Turkish gecko **27** *1569*
Turnicidae **19** 1107, 1114
turnip moth **44** 2617, 2624
Turnix **19** 1114
turnstone **19** 1126, 1131, *1132*, 1135; **51** 3046
turquoise jay **25** *1488*
turquoise poison arrow frog **29** *1706*
turret shells **46** *2704*, 2712, *2716-17*, *2724*, 2746; **47** 2765-6
Turridae **46** 2746; **47** 2765
Turritella **46** 2717
communis **46** *2704*, 2712
Turritellidae **45** 2680
Tursiops truncatus **10** 593
turtle dove **20** *1153*, 1156, 1159
turtles **26** *1524-40*, *1547-56*; **35** 2047; **51** 3028
see also terrapins; tortoises
classification **26** 1510, 1530, 1535, 1539, 1553
evolution **26** *1507*
tusk shells **45** 2674, 2684, *2691-2*
tusk-shelled caecid **46** 2712
tussock moths **42** 2461; **44** 2591, 2616, 2624
twaite shad **32** 1889-90; **33** *1922*
twelve-wired bird of paradise **25** 1482
twig snake **28** 1649
twinspot wrasse **34** *2018*, 2019
twisted-winged parasites **43** 2575-6
twite **25** 1446
two-banded bream **34** *2034*
two-humped camel **7** 381, 388
two-legged worm lizard **27** *1615*, 1616
two-pronged bristletails **39** *2329*,

2333
two-spotted ladybird **42** 2472, *2483-4*
two-tailed pasha butterfly **44** 2633, 2640
two-toed amphiuma **30** *1741-2, 1743*, 1745
two-toed sloth **4** 189, 193, *195*
two-winged flies **39** 2311, 2323; **45** 2647
two-winged flying fishes **33** 1966-7
Tylenchida **49** 2925
Tylodidinae **47** 2767
Tylodina **47** 2767
perversa **47** *2780*
Tylodinella **47** 2767
Tylodinidae **47** 2780
TYLOPODS **6** 301, 304
Tylos **37** 2202
Tylototriton andersoni **29** 1729
Tympanuchus cupido **19** 1093
Typhaeus typhoeus **42** 2492, 2497
Typhlichthys subterranus **33** 1948
Typhlogobius californiensis **35** 2060
Typhlomolge rathbuni **30** 1750
Typhlophis **28** 1625
Typhlopidae **28** 1621, 1625

ABOVE Exposure to the sun turns the bald Uakari's face red.

Typhlops vermicularis **28** 1625
Typhlotriton spelaeus **30** 1750
Tyranni **22** 1303
Tyrannidae **22** 1303, 1320
Tyrannosaurus **26** 1508
rex **1** 8
Tyrannus tyrannus **22** 1320
tyrant flycatchers **22** *1317-20*; **23** 1321-2
classification **22** 1303, 1320
distribution **22** 1308
Tyroglyphidae **39** 2295
Tyto **20** 1194
Tytonidae **20** 1194

uakari **13** 763, *768-9*, 772, 774; **51** 3038
Uca **38** *2226-7*
Uganda kob **9** 509-11, *512*
Ugandan lubber locust **40** *2365*
Ujong Kulon National Park **51** 3002, *3032*
Uloboridae **39** 2284
Ulobridae **39** 2290
Umbonia spinosa **41** *2439*, 2449
Umbra kraemeri **33** 1937
Umbraculidae **47** 2767, 2779
Umbraculum mediterraneum **47** 2767, 2779-80
umbrella octopuses **48** *2866*, 2868, 2869
umbrella shells **47** 2767
umbrella termite **41** *2424*
umbrellabirds **23** 1322, *1323, 1330*
Umbridae **33** 1937
Ummidia aouduini **38** *2261*
Ungud (Rainbow Snake) **28** 1632
UNGULATES **5-6** *297-316*
classification **10** 568-9
unicorn fishes **35** 2065-7
Unio pictorum **48** 2843
Unionicola ypsilophora **38** *2242*
Unionoida **48** 2843
Uniramia **36** 2140; **39** 2303, 2311
upland goose **18** *1032*, 1044
Upper Amazonian porcupine **5** 283
Upright Man **15** 899
upside-down catfish **32** *1906*, 1913, *1915*, 1920
Upupa epops **22** 1270
Upupidae **21** 1253; **22** 1270
Uraeginthus bengalus **25** 1453
Uranoscopidae **34** 2033
Uratelornis chimaera **22** 1261
Uria aalge **20** 1148
urial **10** 561, *562*, 563, 570
Urnatella **49** 2920
Urnatellidae **49** 2920
Uroceros gigas **42** *2516-17*
UROCHORDATES **35** *2090-2*, 2094
Urocyon **3** 127
Urodela **29** 1701, *1711-40*; **30** *1741-54*
Uromastyx aegyptius **27** 1585
Uropeltidae **28** 1621, 1626
Uropeltis biomaculatus **28** 1626
Uropsilus soricipes **12** 670
Uropygi **38** 2241, 2252
Urosalpinx **45** 2678
cinerea **46** 2745-6
Urotriorchis macrourus **18** 1070
Ursidae **1** 28
URSIDS **2** *69-82*
urus **8** 468, 475
USA, national parks **51** 3002-4, *3040-3*
USSR, national parks **51** 3002-4, *3051-7*
Utomeris io **44** *2596*

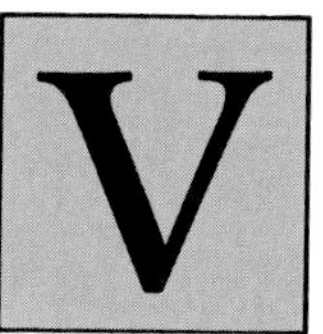

Vaal rhebok **9** 510, 516
Vallonia costata **47** *2818*, 2819
Valvifera **37** 2200
vampire bats **1** 11; **12** *678*, 684, *690*
blood eaters **12** *685*, 708, *710-11*
classification **12** 681, 709
distribution **12** 679
vampire moth **44** 2598
vampire squid **48** 2855, 2861, *2866*, 2867-8
Vampyromorpha **48** 2855, 2861, 2867
Vampyroteuthis infernalis **48** *2861, 2866*, 2867-8
Vampyrum spectrum **12** 709
Van Dam's vanga **23** 1368
vancho spider **38** 2277
Vandellia **32** 1913
Vanellinae **19** 1125
Vanellus vanellus **19** 1125
Vanessa atalanta **44** 2633
vanga shrikes **23** *1356*, 1368, 1374
Vangidae **23** 1368
vapourer moth **44** *2616-17*, 2624
Varanidae **27** 1609
Varanus **27** 1609
Vardiacea **48** 2846
variable grove snail **47** *2804*
Varieca variegata **13** 742
varied sitella **24** 1409
variegated fairy wren **24** *1386*
variegated tinamou **16** 933, 934
vase shells **46** 2746, 2755
Vasidae **46** 2746, 2755
vegetarian finch **24** 1424
veiled octopus **48** *2866*
veiltail guppy **33** *1972, 1980*
Vejdovsky, F. **37** 2189
vejovids **38** 2245
Velella **47** 2792, 2799, 2800
Veliidae **41** 2438, 2440
Velodona togata **48** *2866*
velvet ants **43** *2526*, 2529, 2533, *2536*
velvet asity **22** 1315, 1316
velvet belly dogfish **31** 1837, 1839
velvet mites **39** *2293*, 2295
velvet scoter **18** 1051
velvet worms **36** 2140, 2144; **50** 2960-1, 2963
velvet-fronted nuthatch **24** *1413*
vendace **33** 1934
Veneracea **48** 2847
Veneridae **48** 2847
Veneroida **48** 2845, 2847
Venerupis pullastra **48** 2847
Venus **48** 2847, *2848*, 2849
Venus clam **48** 2847
Venus shells **48** 2849
verdin **24** 1403, 1407
nest **22** *1305*
Vermetidae **46** 2712, 2717
Vermetus adansoni **45** *2680*
Vermetus arenarius **46** *2704*
vermiform blind snake **28** 1622
vermilion flycatcher **22** *1320*
vermitids **46** 2717
Verongia fistularis **35** 2059
Veronicellidae **47** 2817
Verreaux's eagle **6** 312; **18** 1060, 1067; **51** 3017
Verreaux's eagle owl **20** *1184, 1198*
Verreaux's sifaka **12** *720*; **13** *732-3*, 739, *742*, 748-9
verruca barnacle **37** 2174
Verrucomorpha **37** 2174
Vertiginacea **47** 2817, 2818, 2819
Vertigo **47** 2817, 2819
alpestris **47** *2818*
moulisiana **47** 2819
vervet monkey **14** *791*, 793, *795*, 816, *818-19*; **51** 3023
Vespa crabro **43** 2529, 2530, *2536*
vesper bat **12** 712-16
Vespertilio murinus **12** 712
Vespertilionidae **12** 681, 712
Vespinae **43** 2528-30
Vespoidea **43** 2527, 2529
Vespula vulgaris **43** 2529, 2532-3
Vestalis luctuosa **40** 2362
Vestiaria coccinea **24** 1435
Viana regina **45** 2700
Victoria crowned pigeon **20** *1150*, 1156, *1157*
Vicugna vicugna **7** 388
vicuna **7** *380, 382-5*, 387, 388
Vidua **25** 1459
Viduninae **25** 1459
Vieillot's black weaver **25** 1455, 1459

village weaver **25** 1458
vine bell-moth **44** 2603, *2608*
vine phylloxera **41** *2439*, 2452
vine snakes **26** *1517*; **28** 1641-3, 1645, *1650*, 1651
Vinsomella caeca **42** 2502
violaceous trogon **21** *1239*, 1241,

viscacha **5** 275, 283, 285-6, *287*
classification **5** 277, 289
viscacha rat **5** 294
Vitrina pellucida **48** 2824
Viverra **2** 89
Viverricula **2** 89
Viverridae **1** 28; **2** 89, 92, 98

ABOVE A short-tailed field vole climbs over vegetation searching for food.

1242, 1243
violet sea slug **47** 2787
violet sea urchins **36** *2117*
violet snails **45** 2675; **46** *2704*, 2712, *2719-20*, 2736, 2758-9
violet turaco **20** *1172*
violet-backed starling **25** 1462
violet-cheeked waxbill **25** 1453
violet-crested turaco **20** *1174*, 1178
violin spider **38** 2272; **39** *2282*
viper **26** *1516*
Vipera **28** 1669
viperfish **33** *1940*, 1943-4
Viperidae **28** 1621, 1669
Viperinae **28** 1669
vipers **28** 1640, 1641, *1668*, *1672-80*
classification **28** 1621, 1669
distribution **28** 1644
vireo family **24** 1434-8
Vireo olivaceus **24** 1435
Vireolanius melitophrys **24** 1435
Vireonidae **24** 1435
Virginia nightingale **24** *1423*
Virginia opossum **11** *608*, *611*, *613-14*
classification **11** 615
distribution **11** 610
Virginian deer **7** *408-10*, 414
Virunga National Park **51** *3001*, 3002, *3024*
VIVERRIDS **2** *83-98*
Viviparacea **46** 2706, 2712
viviparous blenny **35** *2056*, 2057, 2059
viviparous brotulids **33** 1956
viviparous lizard **26** *1515*, 1517, 1520; **27** 1598-9, 1603
Viviparus **46** *2712*
vlei rat **5** 261
Vogelkop gardener **25** *1473*, 1475-6
volcano rabbit **4** 209, 214
volcano sponge **49** *2881*
vole **4** 218; **5** 243, 249, *250*, 251, 254
Voluta musica **46** 2746; **47** 2761
volute shell **47** *2762*
volutes **46** 2746, 2760
Volutidae **46** 2746, 2760; **47** 2761
Volva volva **46** *2726*, 2729
Volvocales **50** 3000
Volvox **50** *3000*
Vombatidae **11** 612, 633
Vombatus ursinus **11** 633
Vormela peregusna **1** 46
Vorticella **50** *2999*
Vulpes **3** 121, 124-5, 127
vulpine **51** 3050
Vulsella rugosa **48** 2837
Vultur **18** 1064
vultures **1** *25*; **18** *1054*, 1059, 1060, *1061-4*, 1077-9; **51** 3017
birds of prey **18** 1055, 1056, *1058*
classification **18** 1057, 1064, 1070
distribution **18** 1056
vulturine guineafowl **19** *1100*, 1101

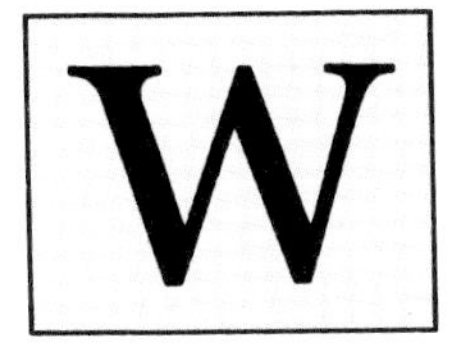

waders **19** *1120-39*; **51** 3008, 3027
wagtails **23** 1347, *1348-52*, 1353-4, *1356*
waldrapp **17** 1018, 1020
walia ibex **9** *534*; **10** 553, 555; **51** 3016-17
walking catfish **32** *1906*, 1913
walking fishes **35** 2070
walking-worm **50** *2960*
wall lizards **27** *1594*, *1598-1600*
classification **27** 1562, 1603
distribution **27** 1595
Wallabia bicolor **11** 642
wallabies **11** 612, *616*, *634-44*; **51** 3046, 3048
classification **11** 612, 642
distribution **11** 634
Wallace, Alfred Russel **15** 892; **25** 1483
Wallace's flying frog **30** 1779, 1785
Wallace's standardwing **25** 1480, 1483
wallaroo **11** 642; **51** 3046
wallcreeper **24** 1408, *1409*
Waller's gazelle **9** 529
walleye **34** 2014-15
walrus **1** *36*; **3** *162*, 167, *172-4*, *175*, 178-9
classification **1** 28; **3** 172
distribution **3** 164, 174
wambenger **11** 617
wandering albatross **17** *966-70*
classification **17** 971
wandering spiders **39** 2284
wandering whistling duck **18** *1028*
wapiti **7** *400-1*, 404, *416*, *419*
classification **7** 406; **51** *3041*, 3050
warble flies **45** *2658*, 2659-60
warbler finch **24** 1425
warblers **16** 909; **24** *1393-5*
warbling silverbill **25** *1449*, 1453
wart hog louse **4** 2428
wart snakes **28** *1624*, *1625-8*
wart-biter bush-cricket **40** *2370*, 2371
warthog **6** 301; **7** *364*, 365, 367, *368-9*; **51** 3022, 3024
classification **7** 370
distribution **7** 366
warty newt **29** 1729
warty venus shell **48** *2848*, 2849
wasp beetles **42** 2513
wasp flies **45** *2658*
wasps **39** 2311, *2312*, *2319*, 2324, 2326; **42** *2515-20*; **43** *2521-38*
classification **43** 2540
social behaviour **43** *2524-5*
water...
bears **50** 2960-1, *2963*
beetles **41** 2454, 2458; **42** 2463, 2468, *2481-2*
buffalo **8** *463*, 466-7, 468
bugs **41** 2438, 2442
chevrotain **7** *391*, 392
cobra **28** 1661
fleas **36** 2152-3, *2156-8*
body parts **36** 2160
classification **36** 2147, 2149
mites **38** *2242*
moccasin **28** 1669, 1680
monitor **27** *1609*
opossum **11** 614, *615*
pipit **23** 1354, *1355*
rail **19** *1112*, 1115
rat **5** 252, 262
scorpions **41** 2438, 2442, 2443
shrews **11** *649*; **12** 662, *663*, *668*
slaters **37** *2188*, 2200
snails **47** 2810
snakes **28** 1641, 1645, 1648, *1653-4*
spider **39** 2281
stick insect **41** *2443-4*
striders **41** 2438, 2439, 2440-1
vole **5** *251*, 252-3
worms **50** 2960, 2961
'water-bottle bird' **20** 1182
water-deer **7** *390*, 394, *405*, 411
classification **7** 396
distribution **7** 398
waterboatmen **39** 2321; **41** 2438, 2444, *2445*
waterbuck **9** 490, *503-10*, *516*; **10** *569*; **51** 3022
waterdogs **29** 1713; **30** 1742, 1743, 1745
waterfowl **18** 1027-52
watering-pot shell **48** 2848
wattle eye **24** 1399
wattle-billed bird of paradise **25** 1480
wattlebirds **25** 1468, *1469*, 1470
wattled crane **19** 1106, 1107
wattled false sunbird **22** *1311*, 1316
wattled ibis **17** 1018
wattled starling **25** 1462, 1463
watussi **8** 476
waved albatross **17** 969, 971
wax moth **44** *2613*
waxbills **25** *1452*, 1453
waxwings **23** 1368-9, *1370-1*, 1372, 1374
weasel **1** *38*, 39, *40-1*, 52, 56; **51** 3052
classification **1** 28, 46
reproduction **1** 35, 52
territories **1** 43-4
weasel lemur **13** 728
weaver ants **43** 2529, *2552-3*
weavers **18** 1080; **25** 1455, *1458-61*; **51** 3023
classification **22** 1303; **25** 1459
distribution **25** 1452
web-footed gecko **27** 1567, 1569
web-footed salamander **30** 1745, 1750
webspinners **39** 2311, 2338; **40** *2347-8*
Weddell seal **3** 179; **4** 184
wedge-billed woodcreeper **22** 1308, 1310
wedge-tailed eagle **18** 1066-7; **51** 3046

wedge-tailed green pigeon **20** *1150*, 1156
weedy seadragon **34** 2000, *2003*
weeper capuchin **13** 773
weevers **34** *2012*, 2013, 2033,
2035, *2036*
weevils **36** *2141*; **39** 2311, 2326; **42** *2505*, *2508-9*, *2513-14*; **41** 2455-7
classification **42** 2506
weka **51** 3050
wels **32** 1892-3, *1914-15*
wentletraps **46** 2712, 2719, 2720-1, *2726*
West African cockle **48** 2846
West African live-bearing toad **30** 1789, 1790, *1791*
West African manatee **6** 314
West African mud turtle **26** *1528*, 1530
West African serpent eagle **18** 1071
West African tongue-sole **35** 2075
West Caucasian tur **10** 570
West Indian manatee **6** 313-14, *316*
West Indian palolo worm **49** 2939
western...
baboon **14** 811
banded gecko **27** 1569
banjo frog **30** 1799, *1800*
barbastelle **12** 712
black and white colobus **14** 836
blind snake **28** *1622*
classification **28** 1623, 1625
distribution **28** 1628
diamondback rattlesnake **28** *1668*, 1669
fence lizard **27** 1573
grebe **16** *955*, 956, 960
grey kangaroo **11** 644
hartebeest **9** 486
hognosed snake **28** 1645
hyrax **6** 313
korrigum **9** *488*
lowland gorilla **15** 848, 852, 856, 864, 890
parotia **25** *1477*
pocket gopher **4** 233
red colobus **14** *824*, 836
reef heron **17** *996*, 1000
spadefoot toad **30** 1768, *1769*
spotted skunk **1** 55
swamp turtle **26** 1530-1
tarsier **13** 734, *744*, 748, *753*
toad **30** *1789*
tree hyrax **6** *305*, 311, 313
whip snake **28** 1645, 1658, *1659*, 1660
Westland black petrel **17** 973, 976
weta **40** 2368, 2369
whale lice **37** 2207-8

ABOVE A male warthog frequently battles with other males for dominance.

whale shark **31** 1813, *1826-7*, 1829-30
classification **31** 1809, 1839
whale-headed stork **17** 1009, 1011; **51** 3024
whalebirds **17** 971-2
whalefishes **34** 1988, 1990
whales **10** *571-88*; **51** 3035
krill predators **37** *2209*, 2211
whalesucker **35** 2046, 2048
wheat thrip **41** 2428
wheatear **24** 1382, *1387-8*
wheel-bearers **49** *2921*
whelks **45** 2678, *2696*; **46** 2714-15, 2748, *2750-4*, *2756-7*, 2759
classification **46** 2746
whinchat **24** *1387*, 1388
whip scorpions **38** 2240, 2241, 2252, 2254-5
whip snakes **28** 1645, 1649, 1658, *1659*, 1660
whip-poor-will **21** 1206
whiplash squid **48** *2854*
whiptail catfish **32** 1913
whiptail lizards **26** 1515; **27** 1600-1, *1602*, 1603
whiptail tetra **32** *1906*
whipworms **49** 2929
whirligig beetles **39** 2322; **41** *2441*, *2455*, 2456; **42** *2468-71*
whiskered tree swift **21** 1224, 1227
whistlers **24** 1400
whistling ducks **18** 1030, 1036
whistling swan **18** 1044
white...
bellbird **23** 1323
booby **17** 994
butterflies **44** 2633, 2636-8, *2639*
cattle **8** *473*
mangebey **14** 814, *815*, 816
mulberry scale **42** 2486
oryx **9** 500-2
pelican **16** *902-3*; **51** 3041
plume moth **44** *2604*, 2609, *2612*
rhino **5** *300*; **6** *354*, 356, 357-8, *359-60*; **7** 361-2
spoonbill **17** 1018, *1019*, 1020
stork **17** 1011-2, *1013*
sturgeon **31** 1853-4, 1856
sucker **32** 1894
tamarin **14** *783*
wagtail **23** *1351*, 1352, *1356*
whales **10** 584, 587, 593
white-backed night heron **17** 1006
white-backed woodpecker **51** 3013
white-bearded manakin **23** *1330*, 1331, *1332-3*, 1334
white-bellied bustard **19** *1104*
white-bellied dacnis **24** 1429
white-bellied plumed pigeon **20** *1150*
white-bellied sea eagle **18** *1054*
white-bellied stork **17** 1012
white-bellied tree pangolin **4** 200
white-bellied worm-lizard **27** 1616
white-billed diver **16** 952, 954-5
white-breasted go-away bird **20** 1173
white-breasted kingfisher **21** *1250*
white-breasted mesite **19** 1114, 1116
white-breasted nuthatch **24** *1409*
white-breasted trembler **23** 1380
white-breasted whistler **51** 3047
white-browed coucal **20** *1171*, 1178, *1182*
white-capped dipper **23** 1374, *1376*
white-cheeked otter **1** 55, 56
white-cheeked spinetail **22** 1310
white-cheeked turaco **20** 1173
white-coated harp seal **4** *184*
white-collared kingfisher **21** 1252, 1253, *1259*, 1260
white-crested laughing thrush **24** *1386*, *1389*, 1390
white-crested tiger heron **17** *996*, 1007
white-eared catbird **25** *1474*
white-eared hummingbird **21** 1238
white-eared kob **9** 509
white-eyed buzzard-eagle **18** 1070
white-eyed river martin **23** 1343, 1345
white-eyes **24** 1417, 1418-19
white-faced capuchin **13** 773, 774
white-faced hornet **43** 2530
white-faced saki **13** *765*, 772, 774
white-faced whistling duck **18** 1036
white-flippered penguin **16** 948, 950
white-footed mouse **5** *243*, 244
white-fronted capuchin **13** 773
white-fronted goose **18** *1028*, *1040*, 1044; **51** 3038
white-handed gibbon **15** 842, 848; **51** 3031
white-headed buffalo weaver **25** 1459
white-headed duck **18** 1052
white-headed flightless steamer duck **18** 1044
white-headed mousebird **21** *1247*
white-headed vulture **18** 1078
white-lipped pecarry **7** *364*, 366, 370-1, *372*
white-necked nighthawk **21** 1206
white-necked puffbird **22** 1283, 1284
white-necked rockfowl **24** *1390*, 1392
white-necked zorilla **1** 41, 42, 47
white-nosed coati **2** *62*
white-nosed monkey **51** 3020
white-plumed antbird **22** 1313-4
white-rumped swift **21** 1218, 1223
white-spotted octopus **48** 2852, 2869
white-striped sheathtail bat **51** 3046
white-tailed deer **7** 398, *408-10*, 414, 418; **8** 424
white-tailed gnu **9** *484*, 490, 492, *495*
white-tailed kingfisher **21** *1254-5*
white-tailed kites **18** 1070, 1076
white-tailed prairie dog **4** 227
white-tailed sea eagle **18** 1060, 1070
white-tailed trogon **21** *1240*, 1241, 1243
white-tailed tropicbird **17** 980
white-throated cachalote **22** 1313
white-throated grass wren **51** 3047
white-throated swift **21** 1218, 1224
white-throated treerunner **22** 1310, 1312
white-tipped reef shark **31** *1834*
white-tipped sicklebill **21** *1216*, 1228

white-toothed shrew **12** *662*
white-whiskered puffbird **22** 1284
white-winged chough **25** 1470-1
white-winged crossbill **25** *1446*
white-winged guan **19** 1088
white-winged scoter **18** 1051
white-winged triller **23** 1357
white-winged trumpeter **19** *1104*, 1117
white-winged vampire bat **12** 708, 709, *711*
whitefin dolphin **10** 586
whitefish **31** 1824; **33** 1934
whitefly **41** 2438, 2450, *2452*
Whitehead's spider-hunter **24** *1416*, 1417
White's tree frog **26** *1501*, 1503; **30** 1792, 1795
whitethroat **24** 1394
whiting **33** *1951*
whooper swan **18** 1039, 1044
whooping crane **19** 1105, 1106, 1107
whydahs **25** *1454*, 1459, *1461*
wide-mouthed toads **30** 1798
wide-ribbed limpet **45** 2697; **46** 2701
wideawake **20** 1145
widow monkey **51** 3038
wigeon **18** 1044, 1047
wild boar **1** *12*; **6** 301, *305*; **7** *363*, 365-7, 370
wild boar, national parks **51** *3005*, 3006, 3013, 3052, 3060
wild cat **3** 138, 139; **51** 3013, 3018
wild cattle **8** 434, 461-80; **9** *481-2*; **10** *568*; **51** 3026, 3030
wild goat **9** 535; **10** *556*, 558-9, 570
wild rabbit **4** *214*
wild sheep **10** 561-70; **51** 3054
wildebeest *see* gnus
willow flycatcher **23** 1321
willow grouse **19** 1092, 1093
willow tit **24** *1402*, 1406
willow warbler **24** *1393-5*, 1398
Wilsonia **24** 1431
Wilson's bird of paradise **25** 1481
Wilson's phalarope **19** *1120*, 1131
Wilson's storm petrel **17** *968*, 976
wimple-piranha **32** 1908-9
window pane oyster **48** 2841-3
windscorpions **38** *2252-4*, *2260*
winged dragon **34** 1997
winged oyster **48** *2832*
wingless hexapods **39** *2327-36*
wingless insects **39** 2311, 2335-6
wingless stag beetle **42** 2502
winkles **45** 2694; **46** *2705*, 2707-8, 2712, 2714-5; **47** 2801
winter wren **23** 1377
wire-tailed manakin **23** 1331
wireworms **41** 2455, 2456
wisent **8** 468, *478-9*; **9** 482; **51** 3006, *3007*
wobbegong **31** *1826*, 1831-2, 1839
wolf **1** 14, 32, 36; **2** *110-11*, *112-13*, 114; **3** *128*, *131-2*
  classification **2** 117
  distribution **2** 115, 116
  national parks **51** 3006, 3012, 3014, 3036-7, *3056*
wolf herring **32** 1886, 1890; **33** *1940*
wolf spiders **38** 2258, 2263, *2266*, *2276*, 2277; **39** 2283
wolf-fishes **34** *2037*; **35** 2056, *2057*
Wolong Nature Reserve **51** 3002, *3058-9*
wolverine **1** *38*, 41, *46-7*, 56; **51** 3052, *3053*
  classification **1** 47
  distribution **1** 43
  territories **1** 44
woma python **28** 1633
wombats **11** 612, *616*, *633*, 634
wood...
  ants **43** 2529, *2563-4*
  bison **8** 469, 480; **9** 481
  cricket **40** 2376
  duck **18** *1048*, 1049, 1052
  fox **3** 126-7
  frog **30** 1778
  ibis **17** 1015
  mouse **5** 248, 259, *264-5*
  piddock **48** 2848
  pigeon **20** *1149*, *1154-5*, 1156, 1158-9; **51** 3650
  shrikes **23** 1357
  snakes **28** 1637, 1639
  stork **17** 1009, 1011, 1012, 1015
  tarpan **6** 347
  ticks **39** 2295
  turtle **26** 1539
  warblers **22** 1303; **24** 1398, 1431-3
  wasps **42** *2516*, *2519*
wood-boring beetles **41** 2456-7
wood-eating cockroach **40** 2390, 2391
wood-hoopoes **21** 1253; **22** *1270*, *1271-4*
wood-swallows **25** 1470, *1471*, 1482
woodchat shrike **23** *1366*, 1367
woodchuck **4** 227, 233
woodcock **19** 1126, 1130-1, 1135
woodcreepers **22** 1304, 1308, *1311*
  classification **22** 1303, 1310
  distribution **22** 1308
woodland cockroach **40** *2394*, 2395
woodland salamander **30** 1745, *1749-51*
woodlark **23** 1334, *1338*
woodlice **36** 2146; **37** 2182, *2188*, *2200*, 2201-2
woodpecker finch **24** *1424*, 1429
woodpeckers **16** *907*, 912; **22** *1282*, *1292-1300*
  classification **22** 1284, 1297
  distribution **22** 1282
  national parks **51** 3007, 3013, 3027
  nesting **22** *1296*
woodrat **5** *244-5*
woodworm beetles **41** 2457
woolly lemur **13** 742, 749
woolly monkeys **13** *762*, 764, 774, *779*; **14** 781-2
woolly opossum **11** 610, 615
woolly rhinoceros **7** 361
woolly spider monkey **13** 774
woolly-necked stork **17** 1012
worm eels **32** 1874, 1883
worm pipefish **34** 2000, 2002, 2004
worm shells **45** 2676-7, *2680*; **46** *2704*, 2712, *2717-18*
worm-lizards **27** 1564, *1615-16*; **29** 1708
  classification **26** 1510; **27** 1616
  distribution **27** 1606
  Jacobson's organ **27** 1562
worms **36** 2103
wrasses **34** 2011, *2012*, 2023-4, 2025
  classification **34** 2013, 2023
  cleaner stations **34** *2018-19*
  sleeping quarters **34** 2026-7
wreathed hornbill **51** 3030
wrens **22** 1302, 1303, *1304*, 1316-17; **24** *1376-9*, 1382
wrenthrush **24** 1431, 1433
wrinkle-faced bat **12** 708, 709
wrinkled nautilus **48** 2855, 2857
wrybill **19** 1125, 1126
wrynecks **22** *1279*, *1280*, *1292*, 1297, 1299
Wuchereria bancrofti **49** 2933
Wyulda squamicaudata **11** 625

Xantus' murrelet **20** 1148
Xantusia vigilis **27** 1570
Xantusiidae **27** 1570
Xenia **49** *2886*
Xenicidae **22** 1316
Xenicus gilviventria **22** 1316
xenodermin snake **28** 1643
Xenomystus nigri **32** 1869
Xenopeltidae **28** 1621, 1626
Xenopeltis unicolor **28** 1626
Xenophora **46** 2720, *2726*, 2727
Xenophoridae **46** 2720, 2724, 2727
Xenophthalmichthys **33** 1937, 1941
Xenopirostris **23** 1368
xenops **22** 1309, 1310
Xenops minutus **22** 1310
Xenopsylla cheopis **45** 2665, 2667
Xenopus laevis **30** 1769
Xenosauridae **27** 1609
xenosaurs **27** 1602, 1606, *1607*, 1609
Xenosaurus **27** 1609
Xestobium rufovillosum **41** 2456
Xiphias gladius **35** 2043
Xiphiidae **35** 2043
Xipholena punicea **23** 1322
Xiphophorus **33** 1978
  helleri **33** *1972*
Xiphosura **38** 2234, 2241
Xylocopa violacea **43** 2540, 2542
Xylophaga dorsalis **48** 2848
Xylophaginidae **48** 2848

Y

yaffle **22** 1296
yak **8** *462*, 463, *475-6*, 477, 480
  classification **8** 468
  distribution **8** 467
yapok opossum **11** 614, 615
Yarkand stag **7** 405
yellow anaconda **28** 1636
yellow armadillo **4** 197
yellow baboon **14** *806*
yellow bishop **25** 1460
yellow bittern **51** 3027
yellow butterflies **44** *2588*, 2633,

ABOVE The tropical, freshwater X-ray fish is almost totally transparent.

2636-8
'yellow eel' **32** 1874
yellow figbird **25** 1465
yellow goatfish **34** 2033
yellow golden mole **11** 655
yellow perch **34** 2014, 2015
yellow pocket gopher **4** 233
yellow wagtail **23** 1350, *1351*, 1352
yellow warbler **24** 1431, 1432
yellow-backed duiker **8** *436-7*, 440; **51** 3020
yellow-backed sunbird **24** 1417
yellow-bellied sapsucker **22** 1297, 1300
yellow-bellied sea snake **28** 1667, 1669
yellow-bellied toad **30** 1760, *1762*, *1771*
yellow-bellied turtle **26** 1538-9
yellow-bellied waxbill **25** 1453
yellow-billed blue magpie **25** 1494
yellow-billed hornbill **22** *1275*, 1278
yellow-billed loon **16** 954
yellow-billed magpie **25** 1491
yellow-billed oxpecker **25** *1462*, 1464
yellow-billed stork **16** *902-3*; **17** 1012, 1015
yellow-billed tropicbird **17** 980
yellow-breasted bowerbird **25** 1476
yellow-breasted flycatcher **24** 1398
yellow-breasted tit **51** 3050
yellow-browned warbler **51** 3056
yellow-chested apalis **24** 1394
yellow-crowned night heron **17** *996*
yellow-eyed penguin **16** *936*, 948, 949
yellow-footed marsupial mouse **11** *608*
yellow-footed rock wallaby **11** 637
yellow-fronted tinkerbird **22** 1288
yellow-handed titi **13** *762*
yellow-headed Amazon parrot **20** 1165, 1168
yellow-headed blackbird **24** *1438*
yellow-headed gecko **27** *1563*
yellow-headed rockfowl **24** 1392
yellow-headed vultures **18** 1062, 1064
yellow-shelled flat periwinkles **46** 2708, *2710-11*
yellow-shouldered bat **12** 705, 709
yellow-streaked greenbul **23** 1359
yellow-tailed woolly monkey **14** 781
yellow-throated longclaw **23** 1352, 1355
yellow-throated petronia **25** 1455
yellow-throated rock sparrow **25** 1455
yellow-tinted honeyeater **24** *1419*, 1420
yellow-winged bat **12** *690*
yellow-winged honeyeater **24** *1418*
yellowhammer **24** *1422*, 1429
Yellowstone National Park **51** 3002, 3004, *3040-1*
yellowtail parrotfish **34** 2026
Yoldia **48** 2837
arctica **48** 2834
limatula **48** 2834, *2835*
Yponomeuta **44** 2609
Yponomeutidae **44** 2609
Yponomeutoidea **44** 2609
yucca moth **44** 2595, 2600

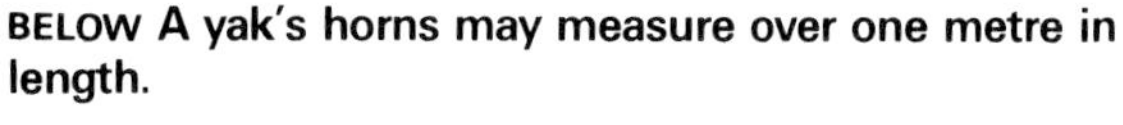
BELOW A yak's horns may measure over one metre in length.

ABOVE Although fairly tame, a Burchell's zebra will kick violently when cornered.

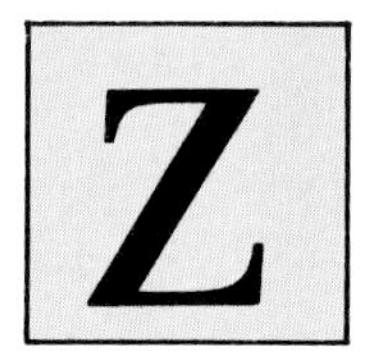

Z

Zabrus tenbriodes **42** 2461
Zacoleus idahoensis **48** 2824, 2849
Zaedyus pichiy **4** 197
Zaglossus bruijni **11** 606
Zaire, national park **51** *3001*, 3002, *3024*
Zalophus **3** 172
Zambezi bull shark **31** 1835
Zambezi lechwe **9** 512
Zambezi softshell turtle **26** 1553
Zanclea costata **47** 2798
Zanclus canescens **35** 2066-7
zander **34** 2014-15
Zanzara **45** *2644*
Zapata wren **23** 1377, 1379
Zapodidae **5** 254
zebra **5** 298, *299*; **6** *332-9*, *340-3*; **51** 3019, 3022, *3023*
zebra angelfish **34** 2024
zebra ark shell **48** *2832*
zebra danio **32** *1906*
zebra duiker **8** 437, 440; **51** 3020
zebra finch **25** 1449, 1452, 1453
zebra Lake Nyasa cichlid **35** 2049, *2051*
zebra moray **32** 1874, 1880
zebra tellin **48** 2847
zebra trout **33** *1930*, 1934
zebra-tailed lizard **27** 1579
zebrafish **34** *2005*, 2007, *2009*
Zebrasoma **35** 2065, 2067
Zebrina detrita **47** *2818*, 2819
zebu **8** 472, 474, 476-7
Zeidae **34** 1990
Zeiformes **34** 1990, *1996*
Zeledonia coronata **24** 1431
Zenaida macroura **20** 1156
Zenkerella insignis **4** 233
zeren **9** 525, 529
Zeugloptera **44** 2595, 2599
Zeugopterus punctatus **35** 2075
Zeus faber **34** 1990
zibet **2** *84*
zig-zag salamander **30** 1750
zig-zag heron **17** 1007
Zinjanthropus **15** 899
Ziphiidae **10** 593
Ziphius cavirostris **10** 593
Zoanthid polyps **49** *2897*
Zoarces viviparus **35** 2056
Zoarcidae **35** 2056
zokor **5** 248, 254
Zonitacea **47** 2817, 2818; **48** 2823-4
Zonites **48** 2824
Zonitidae **47** *2816*
Zonitoides **47** 2816
zooflagellates **50** 2976
Zoomastigophora **50** *2984*
Zoraptera **39** 2311; **41** 2432
zorilla **1** 39, 41, 42, 47
Zorotypidae **41** 2432
Zorotypus **41** 2432
zorro negro **3** 126-7
Zosteropidae **24** 1417
Zosterops **24** 1417
zulu boarfish **34** 1990
Zygaena filipendula **44** *2604*, 2609
Zygaenoidea **44** 2609
Zygogeomys trichopus **4** 233
Zygoptera **40** 2350, 2351
Zyras **42** 2472-3, 2477